Contents

KU-434-863

Birthweight

Mother's Age

Appendices

OFFI 3604410845 AL STATISTICS

WITHDRAWN

Series DH3 no. 28

Mortality statistics

Childhood, infant and perinatal

Review of the Registrar General on deaths in England and Wales, 1995

London: The Stationery Office

Information services

For general enquiries about official statistics, please contact the Office for National Statistics Public Enquiry Service on the following telephone numbers:

Social and Economic Statistics - 0171-533 6262/6363/6364
Business Statistics - 01633 812973

Alternatively write to Public Enquiry Service, Office for National Statistics, Zone DG/19, 1 Drummond Gate, London, SW1V 2QQ. Fax 0171-533 5719.

For more information about ONS's publications, electronic data dissemination or other information services, contact the Sales Office, Marketing and Customer Service Division, Office for National Statistics, Zone B1/06, 1 Drummond Gate, London, SW1V 2QQ. Tel 0171-533 5678 or fax 0171-533 5689.

Publications may also be obtained from The Stationery Office Publications Centre, P.O. Box 276, London, SW8 5DT. Tel 0171-873 9090 or fax 0171-873 8200.

Office for National Statistics

The Office for National Statistics (ONS) is the Government Agency responsible for compiling, analysing and disseminating many of the United Kingdom's economic, social and demographic statistics including the retail prices index, trade figures and labour market data as well as the periodic census of the population and health statistics. The head of ONS is also Registrar-General for England & Wales and the agency carries out all statutory registration of births, marriages and deaths.

ONS was formed in April 1996 from a merger of the Central Statistical Office and the Office of Population Censuses and Surveys. The Agency is independent of any other Government Department and is accountable to the Chancellor of the Exchequer.

 ## Government Statistical Service

ONS works in partnership with others in the Government Statistical Service (GSS) located throughout many different Government Departments. Together they provide a quality statistical service to a great many users, and this is reflected in the GSS Mission Statement:

"To provide Parliament, government and the wider community with the statistical information, analysis and advice needed to improve decision making, stimulate research and inform debate."

Each Department produces its own statistical publications, and the Office for National Statistics brings many of these statistics together in its compendia publications and databases. For further information on the source Departments, contact the ONS Public Enquiry Service on 0171-533 6262/6363.

© *Crown copyright 1997*
First published 1997

If you need to reproduce any contents from this publication, contact Copyright Enquiries, Marketing and Customer Services Division, Office for National Statistics, Zone B1/04, 1 Drummond Gate, London SW1V 2QQ. Tel 0171-533 5674 or fax 0171-533 5689.

ISBN 0 11 620933X

CANTERBURY CHRIST CHURCH COLLEGE	
360441084	
Cypher Group	20.1.99
618. 920 QRF	£30.00

Introduction

Mortality statistics: Childhood, infant and perinatal 1995 presents statistics relating to stillbirths, infant deaths and childhood deaths in England and Wales in 1995. Comparable statistics for 1975 to 1992 were published for each year in two separate volumes:

- *Mortality statistics: Perinatal & infant (social and biological factors)*
- *Mortality statistics: Childhood*

Statistics for 1993 and 1994 were published in a single volume:
- *Mortality statistics: Childhood, infant and perinatal 1993 & 1994.*

Statistics for years prior to 1975 appear in the *Registrar General's Statistical Review of England and Wales.*

For Scotland, comparable statistics appear in the *Annual Report of the Registrar General for Scotland*

For Northern Ireland, statistics appear in the *Annual Report of the Registrar General for Northern Ireland.*

1. Tables in this volume

Tables 1 to 6 relate to all stillbirths and infant and childhood deaths which occurred in 1995 and were registered in England and Wales.

Tables 7 to 25 relate to infant deaths which occurred in 1995, were registered in England and Wales, and which have been successfully linked to their corresponding birth records. This linkage of birth and infant death records has been conducted for each year since 1975, in order to obtain information on the social and biological factors of the baby's parents as registered on the birth record. Only a limited amount of information (some of which is confidential) relating to the parents of the deceased infant is obtainable from death registration; for example, occupation of parent (usually father). However a considerable amount of information (including confidential particulars) is given at birth registration, including age of parents, number of previous children born within marriage (parity), country of birth of parents, institution of birth and whether the baby was a singleton or multiple birth. This report presents data on all these factors and also includes information on cause of death, region of residence, and birthweight.

In the majority of the analyses children born outside marriage have been treated separately. One reason for this is that the mother's parity is not included in the information given at the registration of a birth outside marriage. In addition, the occupation data provided for births outside marriage are based on the mother's occupation unless the birth was registered jointly by the father and the mother (In 1995, 78 per cent of births outside marriage were registered jointly.) Thus for children born outside marriage and registered by the mother alone, only the occupation of the mother is recorded, and this information is not reliable enough to make any comparison with that obtained for children born within marriage.

Tables 26 to 33 also relate to infant deaths which have been successfully linked to their corresponding birth records, but here we are looking at the cohorts of babies who were born in 1994 and at their subsequent deaths. The mortality rates in these tables are therefore calculated by dividing the number of deaths of babies born in a given year by the true population at risk.

2. Notes and Definitions

Stillbirths and neonatal deaths - changes to cause of death coding in 1986

On 1 January 1986 new stillbirth and neonatal death certificates were introduced in England and Wales (specimen certificates are reproduced at Appendices A and B). These certificates follow the recommendations of the World Health Organisation made in the 9th Revision of the *International Classification of Diseases* (ICD9) whereby the causes of death are given separately in the following categories:

- a) Main diseases or conditions in fetus or infant
- b) Other diseases or conditions in fetus or infant
- c) Main maternal diseases or conditions affecting fetus or infant
- d) Other maternal diseases or conditions affecting fetus or infant
- e) Other relevant causes.

Whilst conditions arising in the mother which affected the fetus or infant could be mentioned on the old certificates, no provision was made for those cases in which the doctor thought that both maternal and fetal conditions contributed to the death. The new certificates overcome this problem. However, since equal weighting is given to main conditions in the fetus and in the mother, it is no longer possible to identify a single underlying cause of death for stillbirths and neonatal deaths. Therefore all tabulations which include cause had to be re-designed and now include the total number of mentioned conditions. It should be noted that a baby can have more than one main fetal condition and more than one main maternal condition, as well as 'other' causes.

Deaths included in this volume
The deaths recorded in this volume are those registered in England and Wales. Before 1972, deaths were assigned to the area of usual residence of the deceased if that was within England and Wales; if not, to the area of occurrence. From 1 January 1972, the death of a person whose usual residence is outside England and Wales is assigned to the country of residence. These deaths are included in the total figures for England and Wales but excluded from any subdivision of England and Wales.

Births included in this volume
The births recorded in this volume are those occurring in the relevant calendar year and subsequently registered in England and Wales. Before 1972 births were assigned to the area of the mother's usual residence if that was within England and Wales; if not, to the area of occurrence. However, from 1 January 1972 a birth to a mother whose usual residence is outside England and Wales is assigned to the country of residence. These births are included in the total figures for England and Wales but excluded from any subdivision of England and Wales.

Definition of stillbirth
On 1 October 1992 the legal definition of a stillbirth was altered from a baby born dead after 28 completed weeks gestation or more to one born dead after 24 completed weeks gestation or more.

Definitions of infant deaths

Early neonatal deaths	deaths at ages up to 6 completed days of life.
Perinatal deaths	stillbirths plus early neonatal deaths.
Late neonatal deaths	deaths at ages 7-27 completed days of life.
Postneonatal deaths	deaths at ages 28 days and over but under one year.
Infant deaths	deaths at ages under one year.

Causes of death
The classification of causes of death used in these tables is in accordance with the WHO's *International Classification of Diseases 1975,* 9th Revision (ICD9) which came into operation at the beginning of 1979.

Where more than one cause of death is mentioned on the medical certificate of a child dying after 28 days of life the choice of the assigned underlying cause is, in accordance with international procedure, determined in the main from the statement of the certifier. These procedures have been established by the World Health Organisation.

Deaths due to injury or poisoning are classified by the external cause of injury (E codes), and by the nature of injury code, which appear in the range 800-999 of ICD9 Chapter XVII. In the 1993/1994 volume, Tables 4 and 5 (stillbirths and neonatal deaths) listed only the nature of injury codes. Table 6 (postneonatal and childhood deaths) listed only external causes. The missing data appear in this volume in Appendix G.

Specimen medical certificates of cause of death for still-births, neonatal deaths (ages under 28 days) and postneonatal/childhood deaths (ages 28 days to 15 years) are reproduced as Appendices A to C. Specimen draft entries completed at the time of the registration of a still-birth or infant death appear as Appendices D and E respectively.

Amended causes of death
In some cases, more information on causes of death may become available at a later stage, so that the underlying cause of death may be subsequently amended. The Office for National Statistics (ONS) uses these confidential details of amended cause wherever possible in its statistics and tables. Users with access to individual records of deaths as shown in the public record may thus find some differences with published statistics.

At present there are two ways in which further details may be provided:

- by the use of Box B at the rear of the medical certificate of cause of death. When this box is ticked, the certifier is indicating that more information will be provided to ONS on request

- by coroners supplying further details of deaths where an inquest took place or a post-mortem without inquest was carried out.

Up until 1992, ONS (formerly OPCS) also sent out medical enquiries in cases for which insufficient details had been provided by the certifier for cause coding. As later described in Section 5 of this Introduction, these medical enquiries have been temporarily discontinued.

Accelerated registrations of deaths from injury or poisoning.
On 1 January 1978 certain provisions of the Criminal Law Act 1977, the Coroners (Amendment) Rules 1977 and the Registration of Births, Deaths and Marriages (Amendment) Regulations 1977 came into force. The two principal changes arising out of the legislation are (a) the abolition of the duty of a coroner's jury to name a person it finds guilty of causing a death and of a coroner to commit that person for trial and (b) in the case where an inquest is adjourned because a person has been charged with an offence in connection with the death or the police are investigating the circumstances surrounding the death, the introduction of provision for the death to be registered at the time of adjournment instead of, as previously, having to await the

outcome of the criminal proceedings. The result of such proceedings is notified by the coroner at a later date.

The legislation has a significant effect on the compilation of mortality statistics from injury or poisoning. All deaths assigned to these causes are coded in two ways, as recommended in the ICD 9th revision, to nature of injury codes and to external cause of injury (E) codes. It is not possible to assign the correct E code to some of these accelerated registration cases until results of proceedings are known.

Accordingly, the following procedures have been adopted. The E categories which are most affected by the legislation are those relating to motor vehicle incidents, homicides and open verdicts. All accelerated registrations relating to transport incidents are coded to the appropriate transport accident, as sufficient data are available on the coroner's certificate of adjournment. All other accelerated registrations are assigned to E988.8 (injury by other and unspecified means, undetermined whether accidentally or purposely inflicted) until results of proceedings are known, and the death can be reassigned to the correct E code.

When statistics were compiled for this volume, there were 33 infant or childhood deaths for 1995 assigned to code E988.8 still awaiting results of proceedings.

Standard regions

The composition of the standard regions of England and Wales in terms of counties (as constituted on 1 April 1974) is as follows:

North: Cleveland, Cumbria, Durham, Northumberland, Tyne and Wear

Yorkshire and Humberside: Humberside, North Yorkshire, South Yorkshire, West Yorkshire

East Midlands: Derbyshire, Leicestershire, Lincolnshire, Northamptonshire, Nottinghamshire

East Anglia: Cambridgeshire, Norfolk, Suffolk

South East: Bedfordshire, Berkshire, Buckinghamshire, East Sussex, Essex, Greater London, Hampshire, Hertfordshire, Isle of Wight, Kent, Oxfordshire, Surrey, West Sussex

South West: Avon, Cornwall and Isles of Scilly, Devon, Dorset, Gloucestershire, Somerset, Wiltshire

West Midlands: Hereford and Worcester, Shropshire, Staffordshire, Warwickshire, West Midlands

North West: Cheshire, Greater Manchester, Lancashire, Merseyside

Wales: Clwyd, Dyfed, Gwent, Gwynedd, Mid Glamorgan, Powys, South Glamorgan, West Glamorgan

Regional Health Authorities

The constitution of the regional health authorities of England and Wales, in terms of district health authorities, as at **1 April 1995** was as follows:

Northern: Tees, North Cumbria, South of Tyne, North Durham, South Durham, Northumberland, Newcastle & North Tyneside, Sunderland

Yorkshire: East Riding, Grimsby & Scunthorpe, North Yorkshire, Bradford, West Yorkshire, Leeds, Wakefield

Trent: North Derbyshire, South Derbyshire, Leicestershire, Lincolnshire, North Nottinghamshire, Nottingham, Barnsley, Doncaster, Rotherham, Sheffield

East Anglian: Cambridge, North West Anglia, Suffolk, East Norfolk, Bedfordshire, Huntingdon

North West Thames: East & North Hertfordshire, North West Hertfordshire, South West Hertfordshire, Barnet, Brent & Harrow, Hillingdon, Ealing, Hammersmith & Hounslow, Kensington, Chelsea & Westminster

North East Thames: South Essex, North Essex, Barking & Havering, Camden & Islington, E. London & the City, New River District, Redbridge & Waltham Forest

South East Thames: East Sussex, East Kent, West Kent, Bexley & Greenwich, Bromley, South East London

South West Thames: Western Surrey, Eastern Surrey, West Sussex, Croydon, Kingston & Richmond, Merton, Sutton & Wandsworth

Wessex: Dorset, Portsmouth & South East Hampshire, Southampton & South West Hampshire, North & Mid Hampshire, Wiltshire & Bath, Isle of Wight

Oxford: Berkshire, Buckinghamshire, Northamptonshire, Oxfordshire

South Western: Bristol, Cornwall & Isles of Scilly, Exeter & North Devon, Plymouth & Torbay, Gloucestershire, Somerset

West Midlands: Herefordshire, Worcester & District, Shropshire, North Staffordshire, South Staffordshire, Warwickshire, North Birmingham, South Birmingham, Coventry, Dudley, Sandwell, Solihull, Walsall, Wolverhampton, North Worcestershire

Mersey: South Cheshire, North Cheshire, Liverpool, St Helens & Knowsley, Sefton, Wirral

North Western: North West Lancashire, East Lancashire, South Lancashire, Bury & Rochdale, Manchester, Salford & Trafford, Stockport, Morecambe Bay, Wigan & Bolton, West Pennine

Wales: Clwyd, Dyfed, Gwent, Gwynedd, Mid Glamorgan, Powys, South Glamorgan, West Glamorgan

Method of linking deaths to corresponding birth records

A computer aided system enables the annual production of linked data. Linking is achieved by using the National Health Service (NHS) number of the dead child to identify the birth registration. Briefly, the system is as follows:

Draft entries of deaths (which are forms completed by the local registrar from information supplied during the interview with the informant) are sent to the NHS Central Register so that the Register can be updated. Drafts relating to children under 16 years of age are separated and the NHS number is entered (if not already present).

These entries are held on a Childhood Mortality computer file. The notifications on this file are then matched against the Production Deaths database. This database holds details of all deaths in England and Wales and provides the data for all the tables in this volume. When a match between entries on the two files is established, the NHS number on the Childhood Mortality record is copied to the corresponding record on the Production database. Any childhood death without an NHS number on the Production database is reported for further investigation.

The death records in the Production database, now enhanced with NHS numbers, are then compared against the Births database to establish links. A link is established using NHS number, date of birth and sex. All queries are resolved clerically.

Linkage is not possible in the case of children who were born abroad or for dead foundlings, as there is no birth registration available. Also linkage is not permissible in the case of an adopted child. These cases along with any others that failed to be linked are discussed in the next section.

Linkage of infant death records to their corresponding birth records enables production of two types of data file, one being the standard type of infant mortality data (deaths occurring in a calendar year), and the other a birth cohort with the data relating to deaths among children born in a calendar year. Most of the tabulations are of the standard type and present statistics for deaths occurring in 1995; tables 25 to 33, however, relate to deaths of infants born in 1994, as described at the beginning of this introduction.

For infant mortality, the two types of data files differ very little, as over half of the infant deaths occur in the first week of life and two thirds occur in the first month, with the result that almost all the deaths occur in the same year as the birth. The difference will be greater for postneonatal mortality where more children may die in the calendar year following their birth. There will, however, only be a difference in the mortality rates obtained from the two types of data if there is a large fluctuation in the number of births or a rapid change in the underlying mortality rates.

Analysis of unlinked cases

Between 1984 and 1995, the linkage rate for infant deaths has varied between 97.8 and 98.5 per cent; in 1995 the linkage rate was 98.3 per cent.

The unlinked cases can be split into two groups; those which cannot be linked (such as those born outside England and Wales, dead foundlings and adopted children) and others which theoretically should have been linked but for which no birth record could be found. The percentage of deaths in this second category is small (0.5 per cent in 1995).

Social class as defined by occupation

For the 1995 data, the 1990 Standard Occupational Classification has been used. The social class categories used are:

Social Class I	Professional occupations (for example, doctors and lawyers)
Social Class II	Managerial and technical occupations (for example, teachers and most managerial and senior administrative occupations)
Social Class IIIN	Non-manual skilled occupations (for example, clerks and shop assistants)
Social Class IIIM	Manual skilled occupations (for example, bricklayers and underground coalminers)
Social Class IV	Partly skilled occupations (for example, bus conductors and postmen)
Social Class V	Unskilled occupations (for example, porters and labourers)
Other	This includes residual groups, such as armed forces, persons with inadequately described occupations, persons who were unoccupied and persons with no stated occupation, who are not assigned to Social Classes I to V.

Births within/outside marriage

Generally speaking, a birth within marriage is that of a child born to parents who were lawfully married to one another either (a) at the date of the child's birth or (b) when the child was conceived even if they became divorced or the father died before the birth.

Some infants born outside marriage are deemed to have been born within marriage when the natural parents subsequently marry between the infant's birth and death. Birth registrations do not, however, identify children whose parents marry after the birth of the child. Consequently, all tabulations in this volume relate to the child's status at birth. This ensures that the numerators and denominators used to calculate rates are compatible.

Parity

Information on previous births is only collected for women having a birth within marriage. In this volume, parity is defined as the number of previous live or stillborn children by the present or any former husband, as stated at birth registration.

Area of residence

Tables referring to regional health authorities are based on the area of residence of the mother at the time of the child's birth. These data relate to the RHAs as they existed after the re-organisation of the health service which was implemented in April 1982. Infant deaths where the area of usual residence of the mother was outside England and Wales are included in the total figures for England and Wales but excluded from any subdivision of England Wales.

Information about the place of birth of the parents of children born in England and Wales has been recorded at birth registration since 1969, but data relating to the birthplace of parents have only been available for an infant mortality study of social factors since 1975 when routine linkage was started. It is important to remember, when interpreting these data, that birthplace does not necessarily indicate ethnic origin or race. For example, there are women born in India, whose fathers were there in the civil service, in the armed forces or in business and who later returned to Britain, and these women are now in the childbearing age-groups. Their children will be included in the groups shown as 'mother born in New Commonwealth' although they are not of Indian ethnic origin. Also there is an increasing number of young mothers who were born in Britain but whose parents are of New Commonwealth ethnic origin. In this volume these mothers are not identifiable among the groups of UK-born residents. For a discussion of this problem see the article 'New Commonwealth and Pakistani population estimates' in the HMSO publication *Population Trends 9* and 'Estimating the size of the ethnic minority populations in the 1980s' in the HMSO publication *Population Trends 44*.

Country of birth of mother

For tables which present data by country of birth of mother, the following collective names include:

United Kingdom	England, Wales, Scotland, Northern Ireland, Isle of Man and the Channel Islands
New Commonwealth East Africa	Kenya, Malawi, Tanzania, Uganda, Zambia
Rest of Africa	The Gambia, Ghana, Sierra Leone, Nigeria, Botswana, Losotho, Swaziland, Zimbabwe
Caribbean Commonwealth	Belize, Barbados, Jamaica, Trinidad & Tobago, other Commonwealth islands in the Caribbean, Guyana
Mediterranean Commonwealth	Gibraltar, Malta, Cyprus
Remainder of New Commonwealth	Maldives, Mauritius, Seychelles, British Indian Ocean Territory, Sri Lanka, Malaysia, Singapore, Hong Kong, other Commonwealth countries & islands in the Pacific, Commonwealth Islands & Territory in the South Atlantic & Antarctic
Remainder of Europe	all the countries of Europe excepting the United Kingdom, and including Turkey, the Commonwealth of Independent States, Estonia, Latvia, Lithuania, Georgia, Greenland, Madeira, the Faeroes, the Azores, and the Canary Islands, the Irish Republic, and the Mediterranean Commonwealth

Birthweight

Since 1975, district health authorities transfer to registrars in their area a list of all recent live-born babies and their birthweights for recording on the draft entry of birth. Registrars forward the draft entries to ONS for coding and keying into the mainframe computer. A similar system operates for stillbirths, although the initial source of the information is the medical certificate which is prepared by the certifying doctor or midwife and is passed, usually by the parent, to the registrar. Problems may arise if birthweight information reaches the registrars after the draft entries have been sent to ONS, if the mother lives in a health authority different from the one where she gave birth, or when the birthweights have been recorded in imperial weights. The level of birthweight recording improved consistently from 1975, and was nearly complete between 1983 and 1988. In 1989, however, ONS stopped investigating cases where the birthweight information was missing or incorrectly entered on the draft entry. Consequently the number of live birth computer records which lack birthweight information rose from 0.1 per cent in 1988 to 3.3 per cent in 1993. The number of stillbirth records which lack birthweight information rose from 0.5 per cent in 1988 to 7.2 per cent in 1993. During 1994, these investigations were re-introduced, reducing the figures to 2.5 per cent for live births and 3.9 per cent for stillbirths. In 1995, the figures were 0.3 per cent for live births and 2.1 per cent for stillbirths.

ONS cause groups for stillbirths and neonatal deaths
As mentioned earlier in this introduction, new stillbirth and neonatal death certificates were introduced on 1 January 1986, as a result of which it was no longer possible to identify a single underlying cause of death in these cases. This means that direct comparison between neonatal and postneonatal causes of death is not possible.

For this reason ONS, in conjunction with a team of experts in the field, has been developing a new method for classifying neonatal deaths and stillbirths. This allows the death to be assigned to a specific category, based on the likely timing of the insult leading to the death. A description of the classification was presented in the DH6 volume *Mortality Statistics: Childhood 1991*. A more comprehensive analysis was published in *Archives of Disease in Childhood 1994*, number 70. In brief, an algorithm has been prepared which directs any mention, in the case of neonatal deaths, and underlying cause, in the case of postneonatal deaths, to the first appropriate class of the following mutually exclusive categories:

Before the onset of labour
    1. Congenital anomalies
    2. Antepartum infections
    3. Conditions related to immaturity
In or shortly after labour
    4. Asphyxia, anoxia or trauma
Postnatal
    5. External conditions
    6. Infections
    7. Other specific conditions
    8. Sudden infant deaths
Unclassified
    9. Other conditions

A corresponding algorithm is used in the case of stillbirths.

The grouping of ICD9 codes into these nine categories for neonatal deaths appears as Appendix F. At present, causes of death appearing in line e of the stillbirth or neonatal death certificate (other relevant causes) are not taken into consideration by the algorithm. Development of the stillbirth algorithm has taken place since publication of the 1993 and 1994 data, so the 1995 figures are not directly comparable with earlier years.

Tables 8 to 13 and table 33 in this volume present statistics using this classification.

Symbols and conventions used
0.0, 0.00	less than 0.05, 0.005 respectively
-	nil
..	not available or not appropriate

Rates calculated from fewer than 20 deaths or stillbirths are printed in italics as a warning to the user that their reliabil-

ity as a measure may be affected by the small number of events.

3. Recent Developments in ONS Systems

For some time, ONS has been redeveloping its systems for collecting, processing and handling population, health and registration data, as well as procedures for providing outputs such as tables and extract listings. Changes affecting mortality data include:

- The progressive computerisation of registration, so that registrars in most local offices are now able to enter details on personal computers and then supply data to ONS on floppy disk. This means that information about most deaths can be handled more consistently and efficiently than before.

- The automation of cause of death coding, so that our procedures for assigning underlying cause of death are now automatic for almost all postneonatal deaths. As a result of this, ONS has brought all its coding rules into line with international practice.

- The use of a dynamic database to hold all deaths data, which is continually updated and amended as further information becomes available. Datasets for a particular period are extracted from the database at a time when there are no longer expected to be any significant changes to the data for that period.

4. Date of Extraction of Datasets

The dataset for 1995 deaths, from which tables in this volume were produced, was taken from the deaths database on 18 September 1996.

5. Major Changes since 1992

Occurrences v Registrations
Up to 1992, ONS publications gave numbers of death registrations during the period concerned, but from 1993 the figures in Monitors and Annual Reference Volumes represent occurrences, unless otherwise stated. This change will have little effect on annual totals but makes it easier to analyse seasonal variations in mortality.

Use of medical enquiries
Up until 1992, when the information provided by the certifying doctor was unclear or was not final, ONS sent a letter to the certifier asking for further information to help assign an underlying cause of death. In addition, a standard enquiry form was used for all neonatal deaths where the certifying doctor indicated that more information might become available. This procedure was discontinued in 1993 because we were unable to deal with these cases in a timely way. We intend to reintroduce it at the time of the implementation of ICD10, planned for 1998.

Absence of medical enquiries means that numbers of deaths assigned to certain less specific causes will tend to increase, while the numbers of deaths from more specific causes will be reduced. For most conditions, however, the effects are small. Further details appear in our DH2 publication, no. 21, *Mortality Statistics: Cause, 1993 & 1994.*

6. Trends in the data

Infant mortality rate

- Between 1994 and 1995, the infant mortality rate (as measured using death records which could be linked with the corresponding birth records) fell from 6.1 deaths per 1,000 live births to 6.0. There has been a steady fall in the rate since 1986, when there were 9.4 deaths per 1,000 live births. This steady improvement is reflected in both the neonatal and postneonatal rates, as shown graphically in Figure A.

Stillbirth rate

- On 1 October 1992 the legal definition of a stillbirth was altered from a baby born dead after 28 or more completed weeks gestation to one born dead after 24 or more completed weeks gestation. It is thus not possible to make a direct comparison between stillbirth rates before 1992 with those after 1992. If, however, we exclude the stillbirths of between 24 and 27 weeks gestation (of which there were 216 during the last 3 months of 1992, 906 during 1993, 891 during 1994, and 893 during 1995), then we have a consistent series of rates spanning the change in definition, which show that the stillbirth rate fell from 4.4 stillbirths per 1,000 live and stillbirths in 1994 to 4.2 in 1995. This compares with a figure of 4.4 in 1993 and 4.3 in 1992.

Causes of death - neonatal

- For the 2,698 neonatal deaths in 1995, as with previous years, the most frequently recorded infant conditions were prematurity (ICD9 765), congenital anomalies (ICD9 740-759), and respiratory conditions (ICD9 769-770): respectively 31 per cent, 18 per cent, and 19 per

cent of all main infant conditions mentioned. The figures are essentially unchanged from those in 1993.

Causes of death - postneonatal

- Sudden Infant Death Syndrome (SIDS, ICD9 798.0) was recorded as the underlying cause of 24 per cent of all postneonatal deaths in 1995. This compares with a figure of 27 per cent in both 1994 and 1993. Further statistics on sudden infant deaths appear in the ONS monitor DH3, *Sudden infant deaths.*

Causes of death - children

- As with previous years, injury and poisoning (ICD9 800-999) was the major cause of death for children aged 1-15 in 1995, accounting for a third of all boys' and a fifth of all girls' deaths in this age group.

Birthweight

- In 1995 57 per cent of babies who died in the first 7 days of life weighed under 1,500 grams at birth. By comparison, 46 per cent of stillbirths and only 1 per cent of all live births weighed under 1,500 grams at birth. In 1994, the figures were 61 per cent for deaths in the first 7 days, 45 per cent for stillbirths, and 1 per cent for live births. In 1993, the figures were 59 per cent, 45 per cent and 1 per cent respectively.

7. Further Information

Any enquiries relating to this publication should be made to:

Child Health Statistics,
Office for National Statistics,
Room B5/10,
1 Drummond Gate,
Pimlico,
London,
SW1V 2QQ.

Telephone 0171-533-5641

Figure A: Linked infant mortality rates, 1979-1995

Table 1 Live births, stillbirths, infant and childhood deaths under 15
England and Wales , 1980-95 **
Numbers and rates *

England and Wales

Year	Births		Deaths under 1				Childhood deaths			
	Live births	Still-births ***	Early neonatal	Neonatal	Post-neonatal	Infants	1-4 years	5-9 years	10-14 years	1-14 years
Numbers										
1980	656,234	4,773	4,042	5,023	2,876	7,899	1,186	866	919	2,971
1981	634,492	4,207	3,349	4,213	2,741	6,954	1,180	749	941	2,870
1982	625,931	3,939	3,148	3,925	2,850	6,775	1,137	644	899	2,680
1983	629,134	3,631	2,951	3,682	2,699	6,381	1,093	660	846	2,599
1984	636,818	3,643	2,811	3,530	2,456	5,986	1,064	608	803	2,475
1985	656,417	3,645	2,853	3,531	2,610	6,141	1,135	588	811	2,534
1986	661,018	3,549	2,823	3,489	2,824	6,313	1,064	573	652	2,289
1987	681,511	3,423	2,684	3,448	2,824	6,272	1,067	546	650	2,263
1988	693,577	3,382	2,701	3,421	2,849	6,270	1,095	606	620	2,321
1989	687,725	3,236	2,515	3,272	2,536	5,808	1,078	612	563	2,253
1990	706,140	3,256	2,498	3,221	2,343	5,564	1,027	553	568	2,148
1991	699,217	3,254	2,396	3,052	2,106	5,158	993	589	576	2,158
1992	689,656	2,944	2,294	2,955	1,584	4,539	874	516	521	1,911
1993	671,224	3,866	2,178	2,796	1,446	4,242	884	470	586	1,940
1994	664,256	3,816	2,142	2,749	1,371	4,120	796	465	535	1,796
1995	648,001	3,597	2,104	2,698	1,284	3,982	724	465	550	1,739

Year	**Rates ***	per 1,000 total births		per 1,000 live births			per 100,000 population of the same age			
1980		7.2	6.1	7.7	4.4	12.0	51	26	23	31
1981		6.6	5.2	6.6	4.3	11.0	50	23	24	30
1982		6.3	5.0	6.3	4.6	10.8	47	21	23	29
1983		5.7	4.7	5.9	4.3	10.1	44	23	22	28
1984		5.7	4.4	5.5	3.9	9.4	42	21	22	27
1985		5.5	4.3	5.4	4.0	9.4	45	20	23	28
1986		5.3	4.2	5.3	4.3	9.6	42	19	19	26
1987		5.0	3.9	5.1	4.1	9.2	42	18	20	25
1988		4.9	3.9	4.9	4.1	9.0	42	19	20	26
1989		4.7	3.6	4.8	3.7	8.4	40	19	19	26
1990		4.6	3.5	4.6	3.3	7.9	38	17	19	24
1991		4.6	3.4	4.4	3.0	7.4	36	18	19	24
1992		4.3	3.3	4.3	2.3	6.6	32	16	17	21
1993		5.7	3.2	4.2	2.2	6.3	32	14	18	21
1994		5.7	3.2	4.1	2.1	6.2	29	14	17	19
1995		5.5	3.2	4.2	2.0	6.1	26	14	17	19

*   Stillbirth and early neonatal rates per 1,000 live and stillbirths,
        Neonatal, Post-neonatal and infant mortality rates per 1,000 live births,
        Childhood mortality rates per 100,000 population of the same age
**   Including births and deaths to persons normally resident outside England and Wales
***   Excluding the 216 stillbirths of 24-27 weeks gestation which occurred between 1/10/92 and 31/12/92

Table 2 1995 Series DH3 no.28

Table 2 Live births, stillbirths and infant deaths
Country of occurrence
Constituent countries
Numbers and rates, 1995

United Kingdom

Country of occurrence	Births		Deaths under 1				Childhood deaths			
	Live births	Still-births	Early neonatal	Neonatal	Post-neonatal	Infants	1-4	5-9	10-14	1-14
Numbers										
United Kingdom	**731,912**	**4,141**	**2,392**	**3,070**	**1,456**	**4,526**	**817**	**538**	**638**	**1993**
England and Wales	648,001	3,597	2,104	2,698	1,284	3,982	724	465	550	1739
England**	613,064	3,403	2,000	2,553	1,186	3,739	669	427	508	1604
Wales**	34,486	175	98	133	70	203	39	20	25	84
Scotland	60,051	397	185	241	134	375	63	46	56	165
Northern Ireland	23,860	147	103	131	38	169	30	27	32	89
Rates*										
United Kindom		**5.6**	**3.2**	**4.2**	**2.0**	**6.2**	**26**	**14**	**17**	**19**
England and Wales		5.5	3.2	4.2	2.0	6.1	26	14	17	19
England**		5.5	3.2	4.2	1.9	6.1	26	13	17	18
Wales**		5.0	2.8	3.9	2.0	5.9	26	10	13	16
Scotland		6.6	3.1	4.0	2.2	6.2	24	14	17	18
Northern Ireland		6.1	4.3	5.5	1.6	7.1	29	20	24	24

*   Stillbirth and early neonatal rates per 1,000 live and stillbirths
    Neonatal, postneonatal and infant mortality rates per 1,000 live births
    Childhood mortality rates per 100,000 population of the same age
** Excluding non-residents

Table 3 Live births, stillbirths and infant deaths
Area of Residence
Numbers and rates, 1995

England and Wales
standard regions and
regional health authorities

Area	Numbers						Rates*				
	Births		Deaths								
	Live births	Stillbirths	Early neonatal	Neonatal	Post-neonatal	Infant	Stillbirth	Perinatal	Neonatal	Post-neonatal	Infant
England and Wales**	**648,001**	**3,597**	**2,104**	**2,698**	**1,284**	**3,982**	**5.5**	**8.7**	**4.2**	**2.0**	**6.1**
England	**613,064**	**3,403**	**2,000**	**2,553**	**1,186**	**3,739**	**5.5**	**8.8**	**4.2**	**1.9**	**6.1**
Wales	**34,486**	**175**	**98**	**133**	**70**	**203**	**5.0**	**7.9**	**3.9**	**2.0**	**5.9**
Standard Regions											
North	35,932	239	130	162	77	239	6.6	10.2	4.5	2.1	6.7
Yorkshire and Humberside	62,764	339	243	303	132	435	5.4	9.2	4.8	2.1	6.9
East Midlands	49,556	275	149	186	97	283	5.5	8.5	3.8	2.0	5.7
East Anglia	24,809	113	59	85	51	136	4.5	6.9	3.4	2.1	5.5
South East	239,588	1,357	725	931	426	1,357	5.6	8.6	3.9	1.8	5.7
Greater London	104,128	662	352	445	217	662	6.3	9.7	4.3	2.1	6.4
South West	54,355	249	157	201	88	289	4.6	7.4	3.7	1.6	5.3
West Midlands	67,091	400	285	353	122	475	5.9	10.1	5.3	1.8	7.1
North West	79,014	431	252	332	193	525	5.4	8.6	4.2	2.4	6.6
Regional Health Authorities											
Northern	34,096	230	122	154	73	227	6.7	10.3	4.5	2.1	6.7
Yorkshire	46,742	241	168	208	96	304	5.1	8.7	4.4	2.1	6.5
Trent	57,712	342	211	264	110	374	5.9	9.5	4.6	1.9	6.5
East Anglian	32,630	164	87	121	74	195	5.0	7.7	3.7	2.3	6.0
North West Thames	41,209	240	130	158	76	234	5.8	8.9	3.8	1.8	5.7
North East Thames	55,261	341	165	214	97	311	6.1	9.1	3.9	1.8	5.6
South East Thames	48,880	281	148	186	96	282	5.7	8.7	3.8	2.0	5.8
South West Thames	38,780	202	126	153	70	223	5.2	8.4	3.9	1.8	5.8
Wessex	37,490	176	114	150	68	218	4.7	7.7	4.0	1.8	5.8
Oxford	33,994	159	74	104	47	151	4.7	6.8	3.1	1.4	4.4
South Western	37,951	184	110	148	58	206	4.8	7.7	3.9	1.5	5.4
West Midlands	67,090	400	285	353	122	475	5.9	10.1	5.3	1.8	7.1
Mersey	28,643	141	80	113	62	175	4.9	7.7	3.9	2.2	6.1
North Western	52,586	302	180	227	137	364	5.7	9.1	4.3	2.6	6.9

*   Stillbirths and perinatal mortality rates per 1,000 live and stillbirths
     Neonatal, postneonatal,and infant mortality rates per 1,000 live births
** Including births and deaths to persons normally resident outside England and Wales.

Table 4 1995 Series DH3 no. 28

Table 4   Stillbirths and neonatal deaths
Main and other fetal/infant causes by sex
Numbers of mentions, 1995

England and Wales

ICD number	Cause of Death		Stillbirths		Deaths 0-6 Days		1 week		2 weeks		3 weeks		All neonatal deaths	
			Boys	Girls	Boys	Girls	Boy	Girls	Boys	Girls	Boys	Girls	Boys	Girls
All babies			1,911	1,686	1,206	898	184	129	105	67	57	52	1,552	1,146
All main fetal/infant mentions			1,097	970	1,462	1,058	230	162	140	79	66	68	1,898	1,367
All other fetal/infant mentions			350	327	1,037	770	217	134	112	73	63	49	1,429	1,026
001-139	**I Infectious and parasitic diseases**	**Main**	-	-	-	-	-	1	-	-	-	-	-	1
		Other	-	-	-	-	-	-	-	-	-	-	-	-
100-139	Other infectious and parasitic diseases and late effects of infectious and parasitic diseases	Main	-	-	-	-	-	1	-	-	-	-	-	1
		Other	-	-	-	-	-	-	-	-	-	-	-	-
110-118	Mycoses	Main	-	-	-	-	-	1	-	-	-	-	-	1
		Other	-	-	-	-	-	-	-	-	-	-	-	-
117	Other mycoses	Main	-	-	-	-	-	1	-	-	-	-	-	1
		Other	-	-	-	-	-	-	-	-	-	-	-	-
117.3	Aspergillosis	Main	-	-	-	-	-	1	-	-	-	-	-	1
		Other	-	-	-	-	-	-	-	-	-	-	-	-
140-239	**II Neoplasms**	**Main**	1	1	3	4	1	1	1	-	-	-	5	5
		Other	2	1	3	3	-	-	-	-	-	1	3	4
140-208	Malignant neoplasms	Main	-	-	1	-	1	1	-	-	-	-	2	1
		Other	-	-	-	1	-	-	-	-	-	1	-	2
150-159	Malignant neoplasm of digestive organs and peritoneum	Main	-	-	-	-	-	-	-	-	-	-	-	-
		Other	-	-	-	-	-	-	-	-	-	1	-	1
155	Malignant neoplasm of liver and intrahepatic bile ducts	Main	-	-	-	-	-	-	-	-	-	-	-	-
		Other	-	-	-	-	-	-	-	-	-	1	-	1
155.2	Liver, not specified as primary or secondary	Main	-	-	-	-	-	-	-	-	-	-	-	-
		Other	-	-	-	-	-	-	-	-	-	1	-	1
170-175	Malignant neoplasm of bone, connective tissue, skin and breast	Main	-	-	-	-	-	-	-	-	-	-	-	-
		Other	-	-	-	1	-	-	-	-	-	-	-	1
171	Malignant neoplasm of connective and other soft tissue	Main	-	-	-	-	-	-	-	-	-	-	-	-
		Other	-	-	-	1	-	-	-	-	-	-	-	1
171.9	Site unspecified	Main	-	-	-	-	-	-	-	-	-	-	-	-
		Other	-	-	-	1	-	-	-	-	-	-	-	1
190-199	Malignant neoplasm of other and unspecified sites	Main	-	-	1	-	-	-	-	-	-	-	1	-
		Other	-	-	-	-	-	-	-	-	-	-	-	-
191	Malignant neoplasm of brain	Main	-	-	1	-	-	-	-	-	-	-	1	-
		Other	-	-	-	-	-	-	-	-	-	-	-	-
191.0	Cerebrum, except lobes and ventricles	Main	-	-	1	-	-	-	-	-	-	-	1	-
		Other	-	-	-	-	-	-	-	-	-	-	-	-
200-208	Malignant neoplasm of lymphatic and haematopoietic tissue	Main	-	-	-	-	1	1	-	-	-	-	1	1
		Other	-	-	-	-	-	-	-	-	-	-	-	-
204-208	Leukaemia	Main	-	-	-	-	1	1	-	-	-	-	1	1
		Other	-	-	-	-	-	-	-	-	-	-	-	-
208	Leukaemia of unspecified cell type	Main	-	-	-	-	1	1	-	-	-	-	1	1
		Other	-	-	-	-	-	-	-	-	-	-	-	-
208.9	Unspecified	Main	-	-	-	-	1	1	-	-	-	-	1	1
		Other	-	-	-	-	-	-	-	-	-	-	-	-

Table 4 - *continued*

ICD number	Cause of Death		Stillbirths		Deaths 0-6 Days		1 week		2 weeks		3 weeks		All neonatal deaths	
			Boys	**Girls**	**Boys**	**Girls**	**Boys**	**Girls**	**Boys**	**Girls**	**Boys**	**Girls**	**Boys**	**Girls**
210-229	Benign neoplasms	Main	-	-	1	-	-	-	1	-	-	-	2	-
		Other	2	-	-	1	-	-	-	-	-	-	-	1
212	Benign neoplasm of respiratory and intrathoracic organs	Main	-	-	-	-	-	-	1	-	-	-	1	-
		Other	-	-	-	-	-	-	-	-	-	-	-	-
212.7	Heart	Main	-	-	-	-	-	-	1	-	-	-	1	-
		Other	-	-	-	-	-	-	-	-	-	-	-	-
228	Haemangioma and lymphangioma, any site	Main	-	-	1	-	-	-	-	-	-	-	1	-
		Other	2	-	-	1	-	-	-	-	-	-	-	1
228.1	Lymphangioma, any site	Main	-	-	1	-	-	-	-	-	-	-	1	-
		Other	2	-	-	1	-	-	-	-	-	-	-	1
235-239	Neoplasms of uncertain behaviour or unspecified nature	Main	1	1	1	4	-	-	-	-	-	-	1	4
		Other	-	1	3	1	-	-	-	-	-	-	3	1
235	Neoplasm of uncertain behaviour of digestive and respiratory systems	Main	-	-	-	-	-	-	-	-	-	-	-	-
		Other	-	-	1	-	-	-	-	-	-	-	1	-
235.8	Pleura, thymus and mediastinum	Main	-	-	-	-	-	-	-	-	-	-	-	-
		Other	-	-	1	-	-	-	-	-	-	-	1	-
238	Neoplasm of uncertain behaviour of other and unspecified sites and tissues	Main	1	1	-	2	-	-	-	-	-	-	-	2
		Other	-	1	-	-	-	-	-	-	-	-	-	-
238.0	Bone and articular cartilage	Main	-	1	-	2	-	-	-	-	-	-	-	2
		Other	-	1	-	-	-	-	-	-	-	-	-	-
238.9	Site unspecified	Main	1	-	-	-	-	-	-	-	-	-	-	-
		Other	-	-	-	-	-	-	-	-	-	-	-	-
239	Neoplasm of unspecified nature	Main	-	-	1	2	-	-	-	-	-	-	1	2
		Other	-	-	2	1	-	-	-	-	-	-	2	1
239.0	Digestive system	Main	-	-	-	-	-	-	-	-	-	-	-	-
		Other	-	-	1	-	-	-	-	-	-	-	1	-
239.2	Bone, soft tissue and skin	Main	-	-	-	1	-	-	-	-	-	-	-	1
		Other	-	-	-	-	-	-	-	-	-	-	-	-
239.6	Brain	Main	-	-	1	1	-	-	-	-	-	-	1	1
		Other	-	-	1	-	-	-	-	-	-	-	1	-
239.7	Endocrine glands, and other parts of nervous system	Main	-	-	-	-	-	-	-	-	-	-	-	-
		Other	-	-	-	1	-	-	-	-	-	-	-	1
240-279	**III Endocrine, nutritional and metabolic diseases and immunity disorders**	**Main**	2	2	4	5	1	2	-	1	1	-	6	8
		Other	-	2	7	4	3	1	-	-	1	-	11	5
250-259	Diseases of other endocrine glands	Main	1	-	-	1	-	-	-	-	-	-	-	1
		Other	-	1	1	-	-	-	-	-	-	-	1	-
251	Other disorders of pancreatic internal secretion	Main	-	-	-	1	-	-	-	-	-	-	-	1
		Other	-	-	-	-	-	-	-	-	-	-	-	-
251.2	Hypoglycaemia, unspecified	Main	-	-	-	1	-	-	-	-	-	-	-	1
		Other	-	-	-	-	-	-	-	-	-	-	-	-
253	Disorders of the pituitary gland and its hypothalamic control	Main	1	-	-	-	-	-	-	-	-	-	-	-
		Other	-	1	1	-	-	-	-	-	-	-	1	-
253.0	Acromegaly and gigantism	Main	1	-	-	-	-	-	-	-	-	-	-	-
		Other	-	1	1	-	-	-	-	-	-	-	1	-
270-279	Other metabolic disorders and immunity disorders	Main	1	2	4	4	1	2	-	1	1	-	6	7
		Other	-	1	6	4	3	1	-	-	1	-	10	5
270	Disorders of amino-acid transport and metabolism	Main	-	-	1	-	-	2	-	1	-	-	1	3
		Other	-	-	-	-	-	-	-	-	-	-	-	-

Table 4 1995 Series DH3 no. 28

Table 4 - *continued*

ICD number	Cause of Death		Stillbirths		Deaths 0-6 Days		1 week		2 weeks		3 weeks		All neonatal deaths	
			Boys	Girls	Boys	Girls	Boy	Girls	Boys	Girls	Boys	Girls	**Boys**	**Girls**
270.6	Disorders of urea cycle metabolism	Main	-	-	1	-	-	-	-	-	-	-	1	-
		Other	-	-	-	-	-	-	-	-	-	-	-	-
270.7	Other disturbances of straight-chain amino-acid metabolism	Main	-	-	-	-	-	2	-	1	-	-	-	3
		Other	-	-	-	-	-	-	-	-	-	-	-	-
271	Disorders of carbohydrate transport and metabolism	Main	-	-	-	-	-	-	-	-	-	-	-	-
		Other	-	-	-	-	1	-	-	-	-	-	1	-
271.1	Galactosaemia	Main	-	-	-	-	-	-	-	-	-	-	-	-
		Other	-	-	-	-	1	-	-	-	-	-	1	-
272	Disorders of lipoid metabolism	Main	-	-	-	-	-	-	-	-	-	-	-	-
		Other	-	1	-	-	-	-	-	-	-	-	-	-
272.4	Other and unspecified hyperlipidaemia	Main	-	-	-	-	-	-	-	-	-	-	-	-
		Other	-	1	-	-	-	-	-	-	-	-	-	-
276	Disorders of fluid, electrolyte and acid-base balance	Main	-	1	2	2	-	-	-	-	-	-	2	2
		Other	-	-	3	2	-	1	-	-	-	-	3	3
276.2	Acidosis	Main	-	-	-	1	-	-	-	-	-	-	-	1
		Other	-	-	2	-	-	-	-	-	-	-	2	-
276.4	Mixed acid-base balance disorder	Main	-	-	1	-	-	-	-	-	-	-	1	-
		Other	-	-	-	-	-	-	-	-	-	-	-	-
276.5	Volume depletion	Main	-	1	-	1	-	-	-	-	-	-	-	1
		Other	-	-	-	2	-	-	-	-	-	-	-	2
276.7	Hyperpotassaemia	Main	-	-	-	-	-	-	-	-	-	-	-	-
		Other	-	-	1	-	-	-	-	-	-	-	1	-
276.9	Electrolyte and fluid disorders, not elsewhere classified	Main	-	-	1	-	-	-	-	-	-	-	1	-
		Other	-	-	-	-	-	1	-	-	-	-	-	1
277	Other and unspecified disorders of metabolism	Main	1	-	1	2	1	-	-	-	1	-	3	2
		Other	-	-	2	1	1	-	-	-	1	-	4	1
277.0	Cystic fibrosis	Main	-	-	-	1	1	-	-	-	-	-	1	1
		Other	-	-	-	-	-	-	-	-	1	-	1	-
277.5	Mucopolysaccharidosis	Main	1	-	-	-	-	-	-	-	-	-	-	-
		Other	-	-	-	-	-	-	-	-	-	-	-	-
277.6	Other deficiencies of circulating enzymes	Main	-	-	1	-	-	-	-	-	-	-	1	-
		Other	-	-	-	-	-	-	-	-	-	-	-	-
277.8	Other	Main	-	-	-	-	-	-	-	-	-	-	-	-
		Other	-	-	1	-	-	-	-	-	-	-	1	-
277.9	Unspecified	Main	-	-	-	1	-	-	-	-	1	-	1	1
		Other	-	-	1	1	1	-	-	-	-	-	2	1
279	Disorders involving the immune mechanism	Main	-	1	-	-	-	-	-	-	-	-	-	-
		Other	-	-	1	1	1	-	-	-	-	-	2	1
279.1	Deficiency of cell-mediated immunity	Main	-	-	-	-	-	-	-	-	-	-	-	-
		Other	-	-	1	1	-	-	-	-	-	-	1	1
279.3	Unspecified immunity deficiency	Main	-	-	-	-	-	-	-	-	-	-	-	-
		Other	-	-	-	-	1	-	-	-	-	-	1	-
279.9	Unspecified	Main	-	1	-	-	-	-	-	-	-	-	-	-
		Other	-	-	-	-	-	-	-	-	-	-	-	-
280-289	**IV Diseases of blood and blood-forming organs**	**Main**	1	1	1	2	-	-	-	-	-	-	1	2
		Other	-	3	2	6	2	1	-	-	-	-	4	7
280-285	Anaemias	Main	1	-	1	1	-	-	-	-	-	-	1	1
		Other	-	1	-	5	-	-	-	-	-	-	-	5
285	Other and unspecified anaemias	Main	1	-	1	1	-	-	-	-	-	-	1	1
		Other	-	1	-	5	-	-	-	-	-	-	-	5
285.9	Anaemia unspecified	Main	1	-	1	1	-	-	-	-	-	-	1	1
		Other	-	1	-	5	-	-	-	-	-	-	-	5
286	Coagulation defects	Main	-	-	-	-	-	-	-	-	-	-	-	-
		Other	-	-	1	-	-	-	-	-	-	-	1	-
286.9	Other and unspecified coagulation defects	Main	-	-	-	-	-	-	-	-	-	-	-	-
		Other	-	-	1	-	-	-	-	-	-	-	1	-
287	Purpura and other haemorrhagic conditions	Main	-	1	-	1	-	-	-	-	-	-	-	1
		Other	-	2	1	1	2	1	-	-	-	-	3	2
287.5	Thrombocytopenia, unspecified	Main	-	1	-	1	-	-	-	-	-	-	-	1
		Other	-	2	1	1	2	1	-	-	-	-	3	2

Table 4 - *continued*

ICD number	Cause of Death		Stillbirths		Deaths								All neonatal deaths	
					0-6 Days		1 week		2 weeks		3 weeks			
			Boys	Girls	Boys	Girls	Boys	Girls	Boys	Girls	Boys	Girls	Boys	Girls
320-389	VI Diseases of the nervous system and sense organs	Main	1	-	6	11	4	7	11	2	3	1	24	21
		Other	1	-	2	4	1	1	3	-	-	1	6	6
320-359	Diseases of nervous system	Main	1	-	6	11	4	7	11	2	3	1	24	21
		Other	1	-	2	4	1	-	3	-	-	1	6	5
320-326	Inflammatory diseases of the central nervous system	Main	-	-	2	4	2	3	3	1	2	-	9	8
		Other	-	-	-	1	1	-	1	-	-	-	2	1
320-322	Meningitis	Main	-	-	2	4	2	3	3	1	2	-	9	8
		Other	-	-	-	1	1	-	-	-	-	-	1	1
320	Bacterial meningitis	Main	-	-	2	1	2	1	2	1	2	-	8	3
		Other	-	-	-	1	1	-	-	-	-	-	1	1
320.1	Pneumococcal meningitis	Main	-	-	1	-	-	-	-	-	-	-	1	-
		Other	-	-	-	-	-	-	-	-	-	-	-	-
320.2	Streptococcal meningitis	Main	-	-	-	1	2	1	1	-	2	-	5	2
		Other	-	-	-	1	1	-	-	-	-	-	1	1
320.3	Staphylococcal meningitis	Main	-	-	1	-	-	-	1	1	-	-	2	1
		Other	-	-	-	-	-	-	-	-	-	-	-	-
322	Meningitis of unspecified cause	Main	-	-	-	3	-	2	1	-	-	-	1	5
		Other	-	-	-	-	-	-	-	-	-	-	-	-
322.9	Meningitis, unspecified	Main	-	-	-	3	-	2	1	-	-	-	1	5
		Other	-	-	-	-	-	-	-	-	-	-	-	-
323	Encephalitis, myelitis and encephalomyelitis	Main	-	-	-	-	-	-	-	-	-	-	-	-
		Other	-	-	-	-	-	-	1	-	-	-	1	-
323.9	Unspecified cause	Main	-	-	-	-	-	-	-	-	-	-	-	-
		Other	-	-	-	-	-	-	1	-	-	-	1	-
330-337	Hereditary and degenerative diseases of the central nervous system	Main	-	-	2	-	-	-	2	-	-	-	4	-
		Other	-	-	-	-	-	-	1	-	-	1	1	1
331	Other cerebral degenerations	Main	-	-	-	-	-	-	-	-	-	-	-	-
		Other	-	-	-	-	-	-	-	-	-	1	-	1
331.4	Obstructive hydrocephalus	Main	-	-	-	-	-	-	-	-	-	-	-	-
		Other	-	-	-	-	-	-	-	-	-	1	-	1
332	Parkinson's disease	Main	-	-	1	-	-	-	-	-	-	-	1	-
		Other	-	-	-	-	-	-	-	-	-	-	-	-
332.0	Paralysis agitans	Main	-	-	1	-	-	-	-	-	-	-	1	-
		Other	-	-	-	-	-	-	-	-	-	-	-	-
335	Anterior horn cell disease	Main	-	-	1	-	-	-	2	-	-	-	3	-
		Other	-	-	-	-	-	-	1	-	-	-	1	-
335.0	Werdnig-Hoffmann disease	Main	-	-	1	-	-	-	2	-	-	-	3	-
		Other	-	-	-	-	-	-	-	-	-	-	-	-
335.2	Motor neurone disease	Main	-	-	-	-	-	-	-	-	-	-	-	-
		Other	-	-	-	-	-	-	1	-	-	-	1	-
340-349	Other disorders of the central nervous system	Main	1	-	1	5	-	1	5	1	-	-	6	7
		Other	1	-	2	1	-	-	1	-	-	-	3	1
343	Infantile cerebral palsy	Main	-	-	-	-	-	-	-	-	-	-	-	-
		Other	-	-	-	-	-	-	1	-	-	-	1	-
343.2	Quadriplegic	Main	-	-	-	-	-	-	-	-	-	-	-	-
		Other	-	-	-	-	-	-	1	-	-	-	1	-
345	Epilepsy	Main	1	-	-	1	-	-	-	1	-	-	-	2
		Other	-	-	-	1	-	-	-	-	-	-	-	1
345.0	Generalized nonconvulsive epilepsy	Main	1	-	-	1	-	-	-	-	-	-	-	1
		Other	-	-	-	-	-	-	-	-	-	-	-	-
345.3	Grand mal status	Main	-	-	-	-	-	-	-	-	-	-	-	-
		Other	-	-	-	1	-	-	-	-	-	-	-	1
345.9	Unspecified	Main	-	-	-	-	-	-	-	1	-	-	-	1
		Other	-	-	-	-	-	-	-	-	-	-	-	-
348	Other conditions of brain	Main	-	-	1	4	-	1	5	-	-	-	6	5
		Other	1	-	2	-	-	-	-	-	-	-	2	-

Table 4 1995 Series DH3 no. 28

Table 4 - *continued*

ICD number	Cause of Death		Stillbirths Boys	Stillbirths Girls	0-6 Days Boys	0-6 Days Girls	1 week Boy	1 week Girls	2 weeks Boys	2 weeks Girls	3 weeks Boys	3 weeks Girls	All neonatal deaths Boys	All neonatal deaths Girls
348.1	Anoxic brain damage	Main	-	-	-	1	-	-	-	-	-	-	-	1
		Other	-	-	-	-	-	-	-	-	-	-	-	-
348.3	Encephalopathy, unspecified	Main	-	-	-	3	-	-	2	-	-	-	2	3
		Other	-	-	-	-	-	-	-	-	-	-	-	-
348.5	Cerebral oedema	Main	-	-	-	-	-	-	1	-	-	-	1	-
		Other	-	-	-	-	-	-	-	-	-	-	-	-
348.8	Other	Main	-	-	-	-	-	-	1	-	-	-	1	-
		Other	1	-	1	-	-	-	-	-	-	-	1	-
348.9	Unspecified	Main	-	-	1	-	-	1	1	-	-	-	2	1
		Other	-	-	1	-	-	-	-	-	-	-	1	-
350-359	Diseases of the peripheral nervous system	Main	-	-	1	2	2	3	1	-	1	1	5	6
		Other	-	-	-	2	-	-	-	-	-	-	-	2
358	Myoneural disorders	Main	-	-	-	1	-	1	-	-	-	-	-	2
		Other	-	-	-	2	-	-	-	-	-	-	-	2
358.8	Other	Main	-	-	-	1	-	-	-	-	-	-	-	1
		Other	-	-	-	-	-	-	-	-	-	-	-	-
358.9	Unspecified	Main	-	-	-	-	-	1	-	-	-	-	-	1
		Other	-	-	-	2	-	-	-	-	-	-	-	2
359	Muscular dystrophies and other myopathies	Main	-	-	1	1	2	2	1	-	1	1	5	4
		Other	-	-	-	-	-	-	-	-	-	-	-	-
359.0	Congenital hereditary muscular dystrophy	Main	-	-	-	-	1	2	1	-	-	-	2	2
		Other	-	-	-	-	-	-	-	-	-	-	-	-
359.2	Myotonic disorders	Main	-	-	1	1	1	-	-	-	1	1	3	2
		Other	-	-	-	-	-	-	-	-	-	-	-	-
380-389	Diseases of the ear and mastoid process	Main	-	-	-	-	-	-	-	-	-	-	-	-
		Other	-	-	-	-	-	1	-	-	-	-	-	1
381-383	Otitis media and mastoiditis	Main	-	-	-	-	-	-	-	-	-	-	-	-
		Other	-	-	-	-	-	1	-	-	-	-	-	1
382	Suppurative and unspecified otitis media	Main	-	-	-	-	-	-	-	-	-	-	-	-
		Other	-	-	-	-	-	1	-	-	-	-	-	1
382.9	Unspecified otitis media	Main	-	-	-	-	-	-	-	-	-	-	-	-
		Other	-	-	-	-	-	1	-	-	-	-	-	1
390-459	**VII Diseases of the circulatory system**	**Main**	6	8	31	16	6	4	6	-	2	4	45	24
		Other	6	4	29	21	6	3	6	1	1	3	42	28
401	Essential hypertension	Main	-	-	-	-	-	-	-	-	-	-	-	-
		Other	-	2	-	-	-	-	-	-	-	-	-	-
401.9	Essential hypertension not specified as malignant or benign	Main	-	-	-	-	-	-	-	-	-	-	-	-
		Other	-	2	-	-	-	-	-	-	-	-	-	-
410-414	Ischaemic heart disease	Main	-	-	3	4	-	-	1	-	-	-	4	4
		Other	-	-	-	2	-	-	-	-	-	-	-	2
410	Acute myocardial infarction	Main	-	-	3	4	-	-	1	-	-	-	4	4
		Other	-	-	-	2	-	-	-	-	-	-	-	2
415-417	Diseases of pulmonary circulation	Main	-	-	11	9	2	1	1	-	-	2	14	12
		Other	-	-	9	6	1	-	2	-	-	1	12	7
416	Chronic pulmonary heart disease	Main	-	-	11	9	2	1	1	-	-	2	14	12
		Other	-	-	9	6	1	-	2	-	-	1	12	7
416.0	Primary pulmonary hypertension	Main	-	-	11	9	2	1	1	-	-	2	14	12
		Other	-	-	9	6	1	-	2	-	-	1	12	7
420-429	Other forms of heart disease	Main	5	8	11	1	3	-	2	-	2	2	18	3
		Other	6	2	5	6	-	1	2	-	-	2	7	9
420	Acute pericarditis	Main	-	-	-	-	-	-	-	-	-	-	-	-
		Other	-	-	-	1	-	-	-	-	-	-	-	1
420.9	Other and unspecified acute pericarditis	Main	-	-	-	-	-	-	-	-	-	-	-	-
		Other	-	-	-	1	-	-	-	-	-	-	-	1
421	Acute and subacute endocarditis	Main	-	-	-	-	-	-	-	-	-	1	-	1
		Other	-	-	-	-	-	-	-	-	-	-	-	-

Table 4 - *continued*

ICD number	Cause of Death		Stillbirths		Deaths 0-6 Days		1 week		2 weeks		3 weeks		All neonatal deaths	
			Boys	Girls	Boys	Girls	Boys	Girls	Boys	Girls	Boys	Girls	**Boys**	**Girls**
421.0	Acute and subacute bacterial endocarditis	Main	-	-	-	-	-	-	-	-	-	1	-	1
		Other	-	-	-	-	-	-	-	-	-	-	-	-
423	Other diseases of pericardium	Main	-	1	4	-	-	-	1	-	2	-	7	-
		Other	3	-	-	1	-	1	-	-	-	-	-	2
423.0	Haemopericardium	Main	-	-	2	-	-	-	-	-	-	-	2	-
		Other	-	-	-	-	-	-	-	-	-	-	-	-
423.9	Unspecified	Main	-	1	2	-	-	-	1	-	2	-	5	-
		Other	3	-	-	1	-	1	-	-	-	-	-	2
425	Cardiomyopathy	Main	1	-	4	-	2	-	-	-	-	-	6	-
		Other	-	-	1	3	-	-	-	-	-	-	1	3
425.1	Hypertrophic obstructive cardiomyopathy	Main	-	-	-	-	1	-	-	-	-	-	1	-
		Other	-	-	-	-	-	-	-	-	-	-	-	-
425.3	Endocardial fibroelastosis	Main	-	-	2	-	-	-	-	-	-	-	2	-
		Other	-	-	-	-	-	-	-	-	-	-	-	-
425.4	Other primary cardiomyopathies	Main	1	-	2	-	1		-	-	-	-	3	-
		Other	-	-	1	3	-	-	-	-	-	-	1	3
427	Cardiac dysrhythmias	Main	1	-	1	-	-	-	-	-	-	-	1	-
		Other	-	-	3	-	-	-	2	-	-	-	5	-
427.2	Paroxysmal tachycardia, unspecified	Main	-	-	1	-	-	-	-	-	-	-	1	-
		Other	-	-	-	-	-	-	-	-	-	-	-	-
427.8	Other	Main	1	-	-	-	-	-	-	-	-	-	-	-
		Other	-	-	2	-	-	-	1	-	-	-	3	-
427.9	Unspecified	Main	-	-	-	-	-	-	-	-	-	-	-	-
		Other	-	-	1	-	-	-	1	-	-	-	2	-
428	Heart failure	Main	-	-	1	-	-	-	1	-	-	-	2	-
		Other	-	-	-	-	-	-	-	-	-	-	-	-
428.0	Congestive heart failure	Main	-	-	1	-	-	-	1	-	-	-	2	-
		Other	-	-	-	-	-	-	-	-	-	-	-	-
429	Ill-defined descriptions and complications of heart disease	Main	3	7	1	1	1	-	-	-	-	1	2	2
		Other	3	2	1	1	-	-	-	-	-	2	1	3
429.0	Myocarditis, unspecified	Main	-	-	1	-	1	-	-	-	-	1	2	1
		Other	-	-	-	-	-	-	-	-	-	2	-	2
429.3	Cardiomegaly	Main	3	7	-	1	-	-	-	-	-	-	-	1
		Other	3	2	1	1	-	-	-	-	-	-		
430-438	Cerebrovascular disease	Main	-	-	2	1	-	3	2	-	-	-	4	4
		Other	-	-	2	-	1	-	-	-	-	-	3	-
434	Occlusion of cerebral arteries	Main	-	-	-	1	-	3	1	-	-	-	1	4
		Other	-	-	1	-	1	-	-	-	-	-	2	-
434.9	Unspecified	Main	-	-	-	1	-	3	1	-	-	-	1	4
		Other	-	-	1	-	1	-	-	-	-	-	2	-
437	Other and ill-defined cerebrovascular disease	Main	-	-	2	-	-	-	1	-	-	-	3	-
		Other	-	-	1	-	-	-	-	-	-	-	1	-
437.1	Other generalized ischaemic cerebrovascular disease	Main	-	-	2	-	-	-	1	-	-	-	3	-
		Other	-	-	1	-	-	-	-	-	-	-	1	-
440-459	Other diseases of the circulatory system	Main	1	-	4	1	1	-	-	-	-	-	5	1
		Other	-	-	13	7	4	2	2	1	1	-	20	10
440-448	Diseases of arteries, arterioles and capillaries	Main	-	-	-	1	1	-	-	-	-	-	1	1
		Other	-	-	-	-	1	-	1	-	1	-	3	-
443	Other peripheral vascular disease	Main	-	-	-	-	-	-	-	-	-	-	-	-
		Other	-	-	-	-	-	-	-	-	1	-	1	-
443.9	Unspecified	Main	-	-	-	-	-	-	-	-	-	-	-	-
		Other	-	-	-	-	-	-	-	-	1	-	1	-
444	Arterial embolism and thrombosis	Main	-	-	-	-	1	-	-	-	-	-	1	-
		Other	-	-	-	-	1	-	-	-	-	-	1	-
444.1	Of other aorta	Main	-	-	-	-	1	-	-	-	-	-	1	-
		Other	-	-	-	-	1	-	-	-	-	-	1	-
447	Other disorders of arteries and arterioles	Main	-	-	-	1	-	-	-	-	-	-	-	1
		Other	-	-	-	-	-	-	1	-	-	-	1	-

Table 4 1995 Series DH3 no. 28

Table 4 - *continued*

ICD number	Cause of Death		Stillbirths		Deaths 0-6 Days		1 week		2 weeks		3 weeks		All neonatal deaths	
			Boys	Girls	Boys	Girls	Boy	Girls	Boys	Girls	Boys	Girls	Boys	Girls
447.6	Arteritis, unspecified	Main	-	-	-	1	-	-	-	-	-	-	-	1
		Other	-	-	-	-	-	-	-	-	-	-	-	-
447.9	Unspecified	Main	-	-	-	-	-	-	-	-	-	-	-	-
		Other	-	-	-	-	-	-	1	-	-	-	1	-
458	Hypotension	Main	-	-	1	-	-	-	-	-	-	-	1	-
		Other	-	-	12	7	2	2	1	-	-	-	15	9
458.9	Unspecified	Main	-	-	1	-	-	-	-	-	-	-	1	-
		Other	-	-	12	7	2	2	1	-	-	-	15	9
459	Other disorders of circulatory system	Main	1	-	3	-	-	-	-	-	-	-	3	-
		Other	-	-	1	-	1	-	-	1	-	-	2	1
459.0	Haemorrhage, unspecified	Main	-	-	2	-	-	-	-	-	-	-	2	-
		Other	-	-	-	-	-	-	-	1	-	-	-	1
459.9	Unspecified	Main	1	-	1	-	-	-	-	-	-	-	1	-
		Other	-	-	1	-	1	-	-	-	-	-	2	-
460-519	**VIII Diseases of the respiratory system**	**Main**	**2**	**1**	**13**	**15**	**8**	**3**	**3**	**2**	**4**	**1**	**28**	**21**
		Other	**1**	**1**	**6**	**7**	**2**	**1**	**-**	**1**	**5**	**1**	**13**	**10**
460-465, 470-478	Diseases of upper respiratory tract	Main	-	-	-	-	-	-	-	-	-	-	-	-
		Other	-	-	-	-	1	-	-	-	-	-	1	-
465	Acute upper respiratory infections of multiple or unspecified site	Main	-	-	-	-	-	-	-	-	-	-	-	-
		Other	-	-	-	-	1	-	-	-	-	-	1	-
465.9	Unspecified site	Main	-	-	-	-	-	-	-	-	-	-	-	-
		Other	-	-	-	-	1	-	-	-	-	-	1	-
480-486	Pneumonia	Main	-	-	10	7	6	2	2	1	3	1	21	11
		Other	-	-	3	5	-	1	-	-	2	1	5	7
480	Viral pneumonia	Main	-	-	-	-	1	-	-	-	1	-	2	-
		Other	-	-	-	-	-	-	-	-	-	-	-	-
480.9	Viral pneumonia, unspecified	Main	-	-	-	-	1	-	-	-	1	-	2	-
		Other	-	-	-	-	-	-	-	-	-	-	-	-
481	Pneumococcal pneumonia	Main	-	-	-	-	1	-	-	-	-	-	1	-
		Other	-	-	-	-	-	1	-	-	-	-	-	1
482	Other bacterial pneumonia	Main	-	-	4	1	-	-	-	1	-	-	4	2
		Other	-	-	-	2	-	-	-	-	-	-	-	2
482.3	Pneumonia due to Streptococcus	Main	-	-	2	1	-	-	-	1	-	-	2	2
		Other	-	-	-	1	-	-	-	-	-	-	-	1
482.8	Pneumonia due to other specified bacteria	Main	-	-	1	-	-	-	-	-	-	-	1	-
		Other	-	-	-	1	-	-	-	-	-	-	-	1
482.9	Bacterial pneumonia, unspecified	Main	-	-	1	-	-	-	-	-	-	-	1	-
		Other	-	-	-	-	-	-	-	-	-	-	-	-
485	Bronchopneumonia, organism unspecified	Main	-	-	-	1	2	1	2	-	-	1	4	3
		Other	-	-	-	-	-	-	-	-	1	-	1	-
486	Pneumonia, organism unspecified	Main	-	-	6	5	2	1	-	-	2	-	10	6
		Other	-	-	3	3	-	-	-	-	1	1	4	4
510-519	Other diseases of respiratory system	Main	2	1	3	8	2	1	1	1	1	-	7	10
		Other	1	1	3	2	1	-	-	1	3	-	7	3
511	Pleurisy	Main	2	1	2	2	-	-	-	-	-	-	2	2
		Other	1	1	1	-	-	-	-	-	-	-	1	-
511.8	Other specified forms of effusion, except tuberculosis	Main	-	-	1	2	-	-	-	-	-	-	1	2
		Other	-	-	-	-	-	-	-	-	-	-	-	-
511.9	Unspecified pleural effusion	Main	2	1	1	-	-	-	-	-	-	-	1	-
		Other	1	1	1	-	-	-	-	-	-	-	1	-
514	Pulmonary congestion and hypostasis	Main	-	-	-	-	-	-	-	1	-	-	-	1
		Other	-	-	-	-	-	-	-	-	-	-	-	-
516	Other alveolar and parietoalveolar pneumopathy	Main	-	-	-	-	-	-	-	-	1	-	1	-
		Other	-	-	-	-	-	-	-	-	-	-	-	-
516.8	Other	Main	-	-	-	-	-	-	-	-	1	-	1	-
518	Other diseases of lung	Main	-	-	-	2	1	1	1	-	-	-	2	3
		Other	-	-	1	1	1	-	-	1	2	-	4	2

Table 4 - *continued*

ICD number	Cause of Death		Stillbirths		Deaths 0-6 Days		1 week		2 weeks		3 weeks		All neonatal deaths	
			Boys	Girls	Boys	Girls	Boys	Girls	Boys	Girls	Boys	Girls	**Boys**	**Girls**
518.8	Other diseases of lung, not elsewhere classified	Main	-	-	-	2	1	1	1	-	-	-	2	3
		Other	-	-	1	1	1	-	-	1	2	-	4	2
519	Other diseases of respiratory system	Main	-	-	1	4	1	-	-	-	-	-	2	4
		Other	-	-	1	1	-	-	-	-	1	-	2	1
519.1	Other diseases of trachea and bronchus, not elsewhere classified	Main	-	-	-	1	-	-	-	-	-	-	-	1
		Other	-	-	-	1	-	-	-	-	-	-	-	1
519.8	Other diseases of respiratory system, not elsewhere classified	Main	-	-	-	3	-	-	-	-	-	-	-	3
		Other	-	-	1	-	-	-	-	-	1	-	2	-
519.9	Unspecified	Main	-	-	1	-	1	-	-	-	-	-	2	-
		Other	-	-	-	-	-	-	-	-	-	-	-	-
520-579	**IX Diseases of the digestive system**	**Main**	-	1	2	5	3	-	2	3	2	2	9	10
		Other	-	1	2	4	2	-	-	2	1	2	5	8
520-529	Diseases of oral cavity, salivary glands and jaws	Main	-	-	-	1	-	-	-	-	-	-	-	1
		Other	-	-	-	1	-	-	-	-	-	-	-	1
524	Dentofacial anomalies, including malocclusion	Main	-	-	-	1	-	-	-	-	-	-	-	1
		Other	-	-	-	1	-	-	-	-	-	-	-	1
524.0	Major anomalies of jaw size	Main	-	-	-	1	-	-	-	-	-	-	-	1
		Other	-	-	-	1	-	-	-	-	-	-	-	1
530-537	Diseases of oesophagus, stomach and duodenum	Main	-	-	-	1	-	-	-	-	-	-	-	1
		Other	-	-	-	-	-	-	-	-	-	-	-	-
537	Other disorders of stomach and duodenum	Main	-	-	-	1	-	-	-	-	-	-	-	1
		Other	-	-	-	-	-	-	-	-	-	-	-	-
537.8	Other	Main	-	-	-	1	-	-	-	-	-	-	-	1
		Other	-	-	-	-	-	-	-	-	-	-	-	-
550-553	Hernia of abdominal cavity	Main	-	1	1	-	-	-	-	-	-	-	1	-
		Other	-	-	-	-	-	-	-	-	1	-	1	-
550	Inguinal hernia	Main	-	-	-	-	-	-	-	-	-	-	-	-
		Other	-	-	-	-	-	-	-	-	1	-	1	-
550.1	Inguinal hernia, with obstruction, without mention of gangrene	Main	-	-	-	-	-	-	-	-	-	-	-	-
		Other	-	-	-	-	-	-	-	-	1	-	1	-
553	Other hernia of abdominal cavity without mention of obstruction or gangrene	Main	-	1	1	-	-	-	-	-	-	-	1	-
		Other	-	-	-	-	-	-	-	-	-	-	-	-
553.1	Umbilical	Main	-	1	1	-	-	-	-	-	-	-	1	-
		Other	-	-	-	-	-	-	-	-	-	-	-	-
555-558	Noninfective enteritis and colitis	Main	-	-	-	-	1	-	1	-	-	-	2	-
		Other	-	-	-	-	1	-	-	-	-	-	1	-
557	Vascular insufficiency of intestine	Main	-	-	-	-	1	-	1	-	-	-	2	-
		Other	-	-	-	-	1	-	-	-	-	-	1	-
557.0	Acute	Main	-	-	-	-	1	-	1	-	-	-	2	-
		Other	-	-	-	-	1	-	-	-	-	-	1	-
560-569	Other diseases of intestine and peritoneum	Main	-	-	-	1	-	-	1	2	-	1	1	4
		Other	-	1	2	2	1	-	-	1	-	1	3	4
560	Intestinal obstruction without mention of hernia	Main	-	-	-	-	-	-	-	1	-	-	-	1
		Other	-	-	-	-	-	-	-	1	-	-	-	1
560.9	Unspecified intestinal obstruction	Main	-	-	-	-	-	-	-	1	-	-	-	1
		Other	-	-	-	-	-	-	-	1	-	-	-	1

Table 4 1995 Series DH3 no. 28

Table 4 - *continued*

ICD number	Cause of Death		Stillbirths Boys	Stillbirths Girls	0-6 Days Boys	0-6 Days Girls	1 week Boy	1 week Girls	2 weeks Boys	2 weeks Girls	3 weeks Boys	3 weeks Girls	All neonatal deaths Boys	All neonatal deaths Girls
564	Functional digestive disorders, not elsewhere classified	Main	-	-	-	-	-	-	-	1	-	-	-	1
		Other	-	-	-	-	-	-	-	-	-	-	-	-
564.8	Other functional disorders of intestine	Main	-	-	-	-	-	-	-	1	-	-	-	1
		Other	-	-	-	-	-	-	-	-	-	-	-	-
567-569	Disorders of peritoneum and intestines nec	Main	-	-	-	1	-	-	1	-	-	1	1	2
		Other	-	1	2	2	1	-	-	-	-	1	3	3
567	Peritonitis	Main	-	-	-	1	-	-	1	-	-	1	1	2
		Other	-	-	-	2	-	-	-	-	-	1	-	3
567.9	Unspecified	Main	-	-	-	1	-	-	1	-	-	1	1	2
		Other	-	-	-	2	-	-	-	-	-	1	-	3
568	Other disorders of peritoneum	Main	-	-	-	-	-	-	-	-	-	-	-	-
		Other	-	1	1	-	-	-	-	-	-	-	1	-
568.8	Other	Main	-	-	-	-	-	-	-	-	-	-	-	-
		Other	-	1	1	-	-	-	-	-	-	-	1	-
569	Other disorders of intestine	Main	-	-	-	-	-	-	-	-	-	-	-	-
		Other	-	-	1	-	1	-	-	-	-	-	2	-
569.4	Other disorders of rectum and anus	Main	-	-	-	-	-	-	-	-	-	-	-	-
		Other	-	-	-	-	1	-	-	-	-	-	1	-
569.8	Other	Main	-	-	-	-	-	-	-	-	-	-	-	-
		Other	-	-	1	-	-	-	-	-	-	-	1	-
570-579	Other diseases of digestive system	Main	-	-	1	2	2	-	-	1	2	1	5	4
		Other	-	-	-	1	-	-	-	1	-	1	-	3
572	Liver abscess and sequelae of chronic liver disease	Main	-	-	1	1	2	-	-	1	2	1	5	3
		Other	-	-	-	-	-	-	-	1	-	1	-	2
572.2	Hepatic coma	Main	-	-	-	-	1	-	-	-	-	-	1	-
		Other	-	-	-	-	-	-	-	-	-	-	-	-
572.4	Hepatorenal syndrome	Main	-	-	-	-	-	-	-	-	2	-	2	-
		Other	-	-	-	-	-	-	-	-	-	-	-	-
572.8	Other sequelae of chronic liver disease	Main	-	-	1	1	1	-	-	1	-	1	2	3
		Other	-	-	-	-	-	-	-	1	-	1	-	2
573	Other disorders of liver	Main	-	-	-	1	-	-	-	-	-	-	-	1
		Other	-	-	-	1	-	-	-	-	-	-	-	1
573.4	Hepatic infarction	Main	-	-	-	1	-	-	-	-	-	-	-	1
		Other	-	-	-	-	-	-	-	-	-	-	-	-
573.9	Unspecified	Main	-	-	-	-	-	-	-	-	-	-	-	-
		Other	-	-	-	1	-	-	-	-	-	-	-	1
580-629	**X Diseases of the genitourinary system**	**Main**	-	-	5	9	8	2	2	2	2	2	17	15
		Other	1	-	19	23	4	5	6	3	4	-	33	31
580-599	Diseases of urinary tract	Main	-	-	5	9	8	2	2	2	2	2	17	15
		Other	1	-	19	23	4	5	6	3	4	-	33	31
580-589	Nephritis and nephrotic syndrome and nephrosis	Main	-	-	5	9	7	2	2	1	2	2	16	14
		Other	-	-	18	22	4	5	6	3	3	-	31	30
581	Nephrotic syndrome	Main	-	-	-	-	-	-	-	-	-	-	-	-
		Other	-	-	1	-	-	-	-	-	-	-	1	-
581.9	Unspecified	Main	-	-	-	-	-	-	-	-	-	-	-	-
		Other	-	-	1	-	-	-	-	-	-	-	1	-
583	Nephritis and nephropathy, not specified as acute or chronic	Main	-	-	-	1	-	-	-	-	-	-	-	1
		Other	-	-	-	-	-	-	-	-	-	-	-	-
583.6	With lesion of renal cortical necrosis	Main	-	-	-	1	-	-	-	-	-	-	-	1
		Other	-	-	-	-	-	-	-	-	-	-	-	-
584-586	Renal failure	Main	-	-	5	8	7	2	2	1	2	2	16	13
		Other	-	-	17	22	4	5	6	3	3	-	30	30
584	Acute renal failure	Main	-	-	3	5	2	-	-	-	1	1	6	6
		Other	-	-	7	4	2	2	1	1	-	-	10	7
584.5	With lesion of tubular necrosis	Main	-	-	-	-	-	-	-	-	-	-	-	-
		Other	-	-	-	1	-	-	-	-	-	-	-	1
584.9	Unspecified	Main	-	-	3	5	2	-	-	-	1	1	6	6
		Other	-	-	7	3	2	2	1	1	-	-	10	6

Table 4 - *continued*

ICD number	Cause of Death		Stillbirths		Deaths 0-6 Days		1 week		2 weeks		3 weeks		All neonatal deaths	
			Boys	Girls	Boys	Girls	Boys	Girls	Boys	Girls	Boys	Girls	**Boys**	**Girls**
586	Renal failure, unspecified	Main	-	-	2	3	5	2	2	1	1	1	10	7
		Other	-	-	10	18	2	3	5	2	3	-	20	23
590-599	Other diseases of urinary system	Main	-	-	-	-	1	-	-	1	-	-	1	1
		Other	1	-	1	1	-	-	-	-	1	-	2	1
593	Other disorders of kidney and ureter	Main	-	-	-	-	1	-	-	1	-	-	1	1
		Other	1	-	-	1	-	-	-	-	-	-	-	1
593.8	Other	Main	-	-	-	-	-	-	-	1	-	-	-	1
		Other	1	-	-	1	-	-	-	-	-	-	-	1
593.9	Unspecified	Main	-	-	-	-	1	-	-	-	-	-	1	-
		Other	-	-	-	-	-	-	-	-	-	-	-	-
599	Other disorders of urethra and urinary tract	Main	-	-	-	-	-	-	-	-	-	-	-	-
		Other	-	-	1	-	-	-	-	-	1	-	2	-
599.6	Urinary obstruction, unspecified	Main	-	-	-	-	-	-	-	-	-	-	-	-
		Other	-	-	1	-	-	-	-	-	1	-	2	-
630-676	**XI Complications of pregnancy, childbirth and the puerperium**	**Main**	-	1	-	-	-	-	-	-	-	-	-	-
		Other	-	-	-	2	-	-	-	-	-	-	-	2
644	Early or threatened labour	Main	-	-	-	-	-	-	-	-	-	-	-	-
		Other	-	-	-	1	-	-	-	-	-	-	-	1
644.1	Early onset of delivery	Main	-	-	-	-	-	-	-	-	-	-	-	-
		Other	-	-	-	1	-	-	-	-	-	-	-	1
663	Umbilical cord complications	Main	-	1	-	-	-	-	-	-	-	-	-	-
		Other	-	-	-	-	-	-	-	-	-	-	-	-
663.3	Other and unspecified cord entanglement, without mention of compression	Main	-	1	-	-	-	-	-	-	-	-	-	-
		Other	-	-	-	-	-	-	-	-	-	-	-	-
669	Other complications of labour and delivery, not elsewhere classified	Main	-	-	-	-	-	-	-	-	-	-	-	-
		Other	-	-	-	1	-	-	-	-	-	-	-	1
669.7	Caesarean delivery, without mention of indication	Main	-	-	-	-	-	-	-	-	-	-	-	-
		Other	-	-	-	1	-	-	-	-	-	-	-	1
710-739	**XIII Diseases of the musculoskeletal system and connective tissue**	**Main**	1	2	2	1	-	-	-	-	-	-	2	1
		Other	-	1	2	3	-	-	-	-	1	-	3	3
718	Other derangement of joint	Main	-	-	-	-	-	-	-	-	-	-	-	-
		Other	-	-	-	1	-	-	-	-	-	-	-	1
718.8	Other joint derangement not elsewhere classified	Main	-	-	-	-	-	-	-	-	-	-	-	-
		Other	-	-	-	1	-	-	-	-	-	-	-	1
728	Disorders of muscle, ligament and fascia	Main	1	2	2	1	-	-	-	-	-	-	2	1
		Other	-	1	2	2	-	-	-	-	-	-	2	2
728.3	Other specific muscle disorders	Main	1	2	2	1	-	-	-	-	-	-	2	1
		Other	-	1	2	2	-	-	-	-	-	-	2	2
729	Other disorders of soft tissues	Main	-	-	-	-	-	-	-	-	-	-	-	-
		Other	-	-	-	-	-	-	-	-	1	-	1	-
729.4	Fasciitis, unspecified	Main	-	-	-	-	-	-	-	-	-	-	-	-
		Other	-	-	-	-	-	-	-	-	1	-	1	-
740-759	**XIV Congenital anomalies**	**Main**	153	129	260	197	41	40	22	19	7	18	330	274
		Other	68	83	201	150	25	20	24	22	17	15	267	207
740-742	All deformities of central nervous system	Main	33	53	26	27	2	2	4	1	-	1	32	31
		Other	11	14	10	13	1	-	2	1	-	1	13	15
740	Anencephalus and similar anomalies	Main	10	22	8	11	-	-	-	-	-	-	8	11
		Other	1	-	2	1	-	-	-	-	-	-	2	1
740.0	Anencephalus	Main	10	22	8	11	-	-	-	-	-	-	8	11
		Other	1	-	2	1	-	-	-	-	-	-	2	1
741,742.3	Spina bifida and hydrocephalus	Main	17	17	11	7	1	-	3	-	-	-	15	7
		Other	7	8	4	4	-	-	1	1	-	-	5	5

Table 4 1995 Series DH3 no. 28

Table 4 - *continued*

ICD number	Cause of Death		Stillbirths Boys	Girls	Deaths 0-6 Days Boys	Girls	1 week Boy	Girls	2 weeks Boys	Girls	3 weeks Boys	Girls	All neonatal deaths Boys	Girls
741	Spina bifida	Main	2	7	3	3	-	-	1	-	-	-	4	3
		Other	2	1	1	-	-	-	-	-	-	-	1	-
741.0	With hydrocephalus	Main	1	-	-	1	-	-	-	-	-	-	-	1
		Other	-	-	-	-	-	-	-	-	-	-	-	-
741.9	Without mention of hydrocephalus	Main	1	7	3	2	-	-	1	-	-	-	4	2
		Other	2	1	1	-	-	-	-	-	-	-	1	-
742	Other congenital anomalies of nervous system	Main	21	24	15	13	2	2	3	1	-	1	20	17
		Other	8	13	7	12	1	-	2	1	-	1	10	14
742.0	Encephalocele	Main	-	4	-	3	-	-	-	-	-	-	-	3
		Other	-	-	-	1	-	-	-	-	-	-	-	1
742.1	Microcephalus	Main	-	3	2	1	1	-	-	-	-	-	3	1
		Other	-	2	1	1	-	-	-	-	-	-	1	1
742.2	Reduction deformities of brain	Main	1	2	2	3	-	1	1	-	-	-	3	4
		Other	1	1	1	-	1	-	-	-	-	-	2	-
742.3	Congenital hydrocephalus	Main	16	10	8	5	1	-	2	-	-	-	11	5
		Other	5	7	3	4	-	-	1	1	-	-	4	5
742.4	Other specified anomalies of brain	Main	2	2	1	1	-	-	-	1	-	-	1	2
		Other	1	2	-	1	-	-	1	-	-	1	1	2
742.5	Other specified anomalies of spinal cord	Main	-	1	-	-	-	-	-	-	-	-	-	-
		Other	-	-	-	-	-	-	-	-	-	-	-	-
742.8	Other specified anomalies of nervous system	Main	-	-	1	-	-	1	-	-	-	-	1	1
		Other	-	-	-	1	-	-	-	-	-	-	-	1
742.9	Unspecified anomalies of brain, spinal cord and nervous system	Main	2	2	1	-	-	-	-	-	-	1	1	1
		Other	1	1	2	4	-	-	-	-	-	-	2	4
743	Congenital anomalies of eye	Main	-	-	-	-	-	-	-	-	-	-	-	-
		Other	-	1	1	-	-	-	-	-	-	-	1	-
743.9	Unspecified anomalies of eye	Main	-	-	-	-	-	-	-	-	-	-	-	-
		Other	-	1	1	-	-	-	-	-	-	-	1	-
744	Congenital anomalies of ear, face and neck	Main	-	-	4	-	-	-	-	-	-	-	4	-
		Other	-	2	1	-	-	-	-	-	-	-	1	-
744.3	Unspecified anomalies of ear	Main	-	-	3	-	-	-	-	-	-	-	3	-
		Other	-	1	1	-	-	-	-	-	-	-	1	-
744.9	Unspecified anomalies of face and neck	Main	-	-	1	-	-	-	-	-	-	-	1	-
		Other	-	1	-	-	-	-	-	-	-	-	-	-
745-747	Congenital anomalies of heart and circulatory system	Main	21	16	76	61	26	23	12	10	4	10	118	104
		Other	17	18	54	44	12	15	14	11	7	4	87	74
745	Bulbus cordis anomalies and anomalies of cardiac septal closure	Main	1	2	9	7	4	6	4	3	-	3	17	19
		Other	2	4	11	13	3	3	2	6	5	1	21	23
745.0	Common truncus	Main	-	1	2	1	-	1	-	-	-	-	2	2
		Other	-	-	-	1	-	1	-	-	-	-	-	2
745.1	Transposition of great vessels	Main	-	-	5	3	2	2	2	3	-	1	9	9
		Other	-	1	3	5	-	-	-	1	4	-	7	6
745.2	Tetralogy of Fallot	Main	1	-	-	2	-	2	-	-	-	1	-	5
		Other	-	-	3	2	-	2	1	-	-	-	4	4
745.3	Common ventricle	Main	-	-	1	-	-	-	-	-	-	-	1	-
		Other	-	-	-	-	-	-	-	-	-	-	-	-
745.4	Ventricular septal defect	Main	-	1	-	-	2	1	1	-	-	1	3	2
		Other	2	3	2	4	3	-	-	4	1	1	6	9
745.5	Ostium secundum type atrial septal defect	Main	-	-	1	-	-	-	1	-	-	-	2	-
		Other	-	-	2	-	-	-	-	1	-	-	2	1
745.6	Endocardial cushion defects	Main	-	-	-	1	-	-	-	-	-	-	-	1
		Other	-	-	1	1	-	-	1	-	-	-	2	1
746	Other congenital anomalies of heart	Main	16	12	53	44	18	13	6	6	3	4	80	67
		Other	13	12	22	19	5	8	7	4	-	1	34	32
746.0	Anomalies of pulmonary valve	Main	-	-	1	1	-	2	-	-	-	1	1	4
		Other	-	1	-	2	-	-	-	-	-	-	-	2
746.1	Tricuspid atresia and stenosis, congenital	Main	1	-	-	1	-	-	-	-	-	-	-	1
		Other	-	-	-	1	-	-	-	-	-	-	-	1
746.2	Ebstein's anomaly	Main	1	-	-	1	-	-	-	-	-	-	-	1
		Other	-	-	2	1	-	-	-	-	-	-	2	1
746.3	Congenital stenosis of aortic valve	Main	-	-	3	1	1	-	-	-	-	-	4	1
		Other	-	-	2	1	-	1	-	-	-	-	2	2

Table 4 - *continued*

ICD number	Cause of Death		Stillbirths Boys	Stillbirths Girls	0-6 Days Boys	0-6 Days Girls	1 week Boys	1 week Girls	2 weeks Boys	2 weeks Girls	3 weeks Boys	3 weeks Girls	All neonatal deaths Boys	All neonatal deaths Girls
746.4	Congenital insufficiency of aortic valve	Main	-	-	1	-	-	-	-	-	-	-	1	-
		Other	-	-	-	-	-	-	-	-	-	-	-	-
746.5	Congenital mitral stenosis	Main	-	-	-	-	1	-	-	-	-	-	1	-
		Other	-	-	1	-	-	-	-	-	-	-	1	-
746.7	Hypoplastic left heart syndrome	Main	2	1	9	11	6	2	-	2	-	-	15	15
		Other	1	-	-	-	-	-	-	-	-	1	-	1
746.8	Other specified anomalies of heart	Main	4	4	20	13	6	-	1	-	-	-	27	13
		Other	5	3	8	4	-	-	-	1	-	-	8	5
746.9	Unspecified anomalies of heart	Main	8	7	19	16	4	9	5	4	3	3	31	32
		Other	7	8	9	10	5	7	7	3	-	-	21	20
747	Other congenital anomalies of circulatory system	Main	4	2	14	10	4	4	2	1	1	3	21	18
		Other	2	2	21	12	4	4	5	1	2	2	32	19
747.0	Patent ductus arteriosus	Main	-	-	2	1	1	-	-	-	-	-	3	1
		Other	-	-	-	4	1	2	1	1	1	-	3	7
747.1	Coarctation of aorta	Main	1	-	2	1	2	4	1	-	-	3	5	8
		Other	-	-	4	2	2	1	3	-	1	1	10	4
747.2	Other anomalies of aorta	Main	-	-	3	2	-	-	-	-	-	-	3	2
		Other	-	-	1	-	-	-	-	-	-	-	1	-
747.3	Anomalies of pulmonary artery	Main	1	1	-	4	1	-	1	-	-	-	2	4
		Other	1	1	4	1	-	1	1	-	-	-	5	2
747.4	Anomalies of great veins	Main	-	-	1	-	-	-	-	-	1	-	2	-
		Other	-	-	2	3	-	-	-	-	-	1	2	4
747.5	Absence or hypoplasia of umbilical artery	Main	1	-	-	-	-	-	-	-	-	-	-	-
		Other	-	-	-	-	-	-	-	-				
747.6	Other anomalies of peripheral vascular system	Main	1	1	-	-	-	-	-	-	-	-	-	-
		Other	-	1	-	-	-	-	-	-	-	-	-	-
747.8	Other specified anomalies of circulatory system	Main	-	-	1	-	-	-	-	1	-	-	1	1
		Other	1	-	-	-	-	-	-	-	-	-	-	-
747.9	Unspecified anomalies of circulatory system	Main	-	-	5	2	-	-	-	-	-	-	5	2
		Other	-	-	10	2	1	-	-	-	-	-	11	2
748	Congenital anomalies of respiratory system	Main	1	2	71	41	6	2	2	1	1	2	80	46
		Other	1	1	30	27	3	-	2	1	-	-	35	28
748.0	Choanal atresia	Main	-	-	-	-	-	-	-	-	-	-	-	-
		Other	-	-	1	-	-	-	-	-	-	-	1	-
748.1	Other anomalies of nose	Main	-	-	-	-	-	-	-	-	-	-	-	-
		Other	-	-	-	1	-	-	-	-	-	-	-	1
748.3	Other anomalies of larynx, trachea and bronchus	Main	-	-	5	5	-	-	-	1	-	-	5	6
		Other	-	-	-	-	-	-	-	-	-	-	-	-
748.4	Congenital cystic lung	Main	-	2	1	2	1	-	-	-	-	-	2	2
		Other	-	-	-	2	-	-	-	-	-	-	-	2
748.5	Agenesis, hypoplasia and dysplasia of lung	Main	1	-	63	32	5	2	2	-	1	2	71	36
		Other	-	1	28	24	3	-	2	-	-	-	33	24
748.6	Other anomalies of lung	Main	-	-	1	1	-	-	-	-	-	-	1	1
		Other	1	-	1	-	-	-	-	1	-	-	1	1
748.9	Unspecified anomalies of respiratory system	Main	-	-	1	1	-	-	-	-	-	-	1	1
		Other	-	-	-	-	-	-	-	-	-	-	-	-
749-751	Cleft palate and lip; other congenital anomalies of upper alimentary tract and digestive system	Main	3	1	6	5	1	1	3	1	-	4	10	11
		Other	6	7	20	14	2	1	-	3	6	4	28	22
749	Cleft palate and cleft lip	Main	-	-	1	-	-	-	-	-	-	-	1	-
		Other	-	3	3	5	1	1	-	1	-	-	4	7
749.0	Cleft palate	Main	-	-	-	-	-	-	-	-	-	-	-	-
		Other	-	2	1	2	-	-	-	-	-	-	1	2
749.1	Cleft lip	Main	-	-	-	-	-	-	-	-	-	-	-	-
		Other	-	1	1	-	-	-	-	1	-	-	1	1
749.2	Cleft palate with cleft lip	Main	-	-	1	-	-	-	-	-	-	-	1	-
		Other	-	-	1	3	1	1	-	-	-	-	2	4
750	Other congenital anomalies of upper alimentary tract	Main	2	1	3	4	-	-	-	-	-	2	3	6
		Other	3	1	10	5	-	-	-	-	4	-	14	5
750.3	Tracheo-oesophageal fistula, oesophageal atresia and stenosis	Main	2	-	2	4	-	-	-	-	-	2	2	6
		Other	2	1	10	5	-	-	-	-	4	-	14	5

Table 4 1995 Series DH3 no. 28

Table 4 - *continued*

ICD number	Cause of Death		Stillbirths		Deaths 0-6 Days		1 week		2 weeks		3 weeks		All neonatal deaths	
			Boys	Girls	Boys	Girls	Boy	Girls	Boys	Girls	Boys	Girls	Boys	Girls
750.7	Other specified anomalies of stomach	Main	-	1	-	-	-	-	-	-	-	-	-	-
		Other	1	-	-	-	-	-	-	-	-	-	-	-
750.9	Unspecified anomalies of upper alimentary tract	Main	-	-	1	-	-	-	-	-	-	-	1	-
		Other	-	-	-	-	-	-	-	-	-	-	-	-
751	Other congenital anomalies of digestive system	Main	1	-	2	1	1	1	3	1	-	2	6	5
		Other	3	3	7	4	1	-	-	2	2	4	10	10
751.0	Meckel's diverticulum	Main	-	-	-	-	-	-	-	-	-	-	-	-
		Other	-	-	-	-	-	-	-	-	-	1	-	1
751.1	Atresia and stenosis of small intestine	Main	1	-	1	-	-	1	2	-	-	1	3	2
		Other	1	3	-	1	-	-	-	-	1	-	1	1
751.2	Atresia and stenosis of large intestine, rectum and analcanal	Main	-	-	-	-	-	-	-	-	-	1	-	1
		Other	1	-	4	3	-	-	-	-	1	-	5	3
751.4	Anomalies of intestinal fixation	Main	-	-	-	-	-	-	1	-	-	-	1	-
		Other	-	-	-	-	-	-	-	1	-	1	-	2
751.5	Other anomalies of intestine	Main	-	-	-	1	1	-	-	1	-	-	1	2
		Other	1	-	2	-	1	-	-	1	-	2	3	3
751.6	Anomalies of gallbladder, bile ducts and liver	Main	-	-	1	-	-	-	-	-	-	-	1	-
		Other	-	-	1	-	-	-	-	-	-	-	1	-
752	Congenital anomalies of genital organs	Main	-	-	1	-	-	-	-	-	-	-	1	-
		Other	-	-	3	1	-	-	-	-	-	-	3	1
752.5	Undescended testicle	Main	-	-	1	-	-	-	-	-	-	-	1	-
		Other	-	-	-	-	-	-	-	-	-	-	-	-
752.7	Indeterminate sex and pseudohermaphroditism	Main	-	-	-	-	-	-	-	-	-	-	-	-
		Other	-	-	1	1	-	-	-	-	-	-	1	1
752.9	Unspecified anomalies of genital organs	Main	-	-	-	-	-	-	-	-	-	-	-	-
		Other	-	-	2	-	-	-	-	-	-	-	2	-
753	Congenital anomalies of urinary system	Main	15	7	19	7	-	-	-	1	2	-	21	8
		Other	10	4	31	12	2	2	-	-	1	1	34	15
753.0	Renal agenesis and dysgenesis	Main	11	2	8	1	-	-	-	-	1	-	9	1
		Other	-	1	8	1	-	1	-	-	-	-	8	2
753.1	Cystic kidney disease	Main	2	2	6	4	-	-	-	-	-	-	6	4
		Other	2	-	7	4	-	1	-	-	-	-	7	5
753.2	Obstructive defects of renal pelvis and ureter	Main	1	2	-	-	-	-	-	1	-	-	-	1
		Other	3	2	6	2	1	-	-	-	-	-	7	2
753.3	Other specified anomalies of kidney	Main	-	-	-	1	-	-	-	-	-	-	-	1
		Other	1	-	-	-	-	-	-	-	-	-	-	-
753.8	Other specified anomalies of bladder and urethra	Main	-	-	-	-	-	-	-	-	-	-	-	-
		Other	1	-	-	-	-	-	-	-	-	-	-	-
753.9	Unspecified anomalies of urinary system	Main	1	1	5	1	-	-	-	-	1	-	6	1
		Other	3	1	10	5	1	-	-	-	1	1	12	6
754	Certain congenital musculoskeletal deformities	Main	1	-	-	-	-	-	-	-	-	-	-	-
		Other	2	2	4	2	-	-	-	1	1	-	5	3
754.2	Of spine	Main	-	-	-	-	-	-	-	-	-	-	-	-
		Other	-	1	-	-	-	-	-	-	-	-	-	-
754.3	Congenital dislocation of hip	Main	-	-	-	-	-	-	-	-	-	-	-	-
		Other	-	-	1	-	-	-	-	-	-	-	1	-
754.5	Varus deformities of feet	Main	-	-	-	-	-	-	-	-	-	-	-	-
		Other	-	-	2	1	-	-	-	-	1	-	3	1
754.7	Other deformities of feet	Main	1	-	1	-	-	-	-	-	-	-	1	-
		Other	2	1	1	1	-	-	-	1	-	-	1	2
755	Other congenital anomalies of limbs	Main	1	-	1	-	-	-	-	-	-	-	1	-
		Other	-	2	7	-	-	-	-	-	-	-	7	-
755.0	Polydactyly	Main	-	-	-	-	-	-	-	-	-	-	-	-
		Other	-	-	1	-	-	-	-	-	-	-	1	-
755.2	Reduction deformities of upper limb	Main	-	-	-	-	-	-	-	-	-	-	-	-
		Other	-	1	-	-	-	-	-	-	-	-	-	-
755.3	Reduction deformities of lower limb	Main	-	-	-	-	-	-	-	-	-	-	-	-
		Other	-	1	-	-	-	-	-	-	-	-	-	-
755.4	Reduction deformities, unspecified limb	Main	1	-	-	-	-	-	-	-	-	-	-	-
		Other	-	-	-	-	-	-	-	-	-	-	-	-
755.5	Other anomalies of upper limb, including shoulder girdle	Main	-	-	1	-	-	-	-	-	-	-	1	-
		Other	-	-	2	-	-	-	-	-	-	-	2	-
755.9	Unspecified anomalies of unspecified limb	Main	-	-	-	-	-	-	-	-	-	-	-	-
		Other	-	-	4	-	-	-	-	-	-	-	4	-

Table 4 - *continued*

ICD number	Cause of Death		Stillbirths		Deaths 0-6 Days		1 week		2 weeks		3 weeks		All neonatal deaths	
			Boys	Girls	Boys	Girls	Boys	Girls	Boys	Girls	Boys	Girls	Boys	Girls
756	Other congenital musculoskeletal anomalies	Main	9	6	35	17	1	3	-	1	-	-	36	21
		Other	10	12	14	16	2	-	3	2	1	3	20	21
756.0	Anomalies of skull and face bones	Main	-	1	1	-	-	-	-	-	-	-	1	-
		Other	1	-	-	1	-	-	-	-	-	-	-	1
756.1	Anomalies of spine	Main	-	1	-	-	-	-	-	-	-	-	-	-
		Other	-	3	2	-	-	-	-	-	-	-	2	-
756.3	Other anomalies of ribs and sternum	Main	-	-	-	-	-	-	-	-	-	-	-	-
		Other	-	-	1	-	-	-	-	-	-	-	1	-
756.4	Chondrodystrophy	Main	2	-	2	3	-	-	-	-	-	-	2	3
		Other	-	-	1	2	-	-	-	-	-	-	1	2
756.5	Osteodystrophies	Main	1	-	3	3	-	-	-	-	-	-	3	3
		Other	3	1	-	1	-	-	1	-	1	-	2	1
756.6	Anomalies of diaphragm	Main	2	2	23	11	-	3	-	-	-	-	23	14
		Other	1	-	3	6	1	-	1	1	-	2	5	9
756.7	Anomalies of abdominal wall	Main	4	2	6	-	1	-	-	1	-	-	7	1
		Other	5	8	6	6	1	-	1	1	-	1	8	8
756.8	Other specified anomalies of muscle, tendon, fascia and connective tissue	Main	-	-	-	-	-	-	-	-	-	-	-	-
		Other	-	-	1	-	-	-	-	-	-	-	1	-
757	Congenital anomalies of the integument	Main	-	-	2	-	-	-	-	-	-	-	2	-
		Other	-	-	-	-	-	-	-	-	-	-	-	-
757.1	Ichthyosis congenita	Main	-	-	1	-	-	-	-	-	-	-	1	-
		Other	-	-	-	-	-	-	-	-	-	-	-	-
757.9	Unspecified anomalies of the integument	Main	-	-	1	-	-	-	-	-	-	-	1	-
		Other	-	-	-	-	-	-	-	-	-	-	-	-
758	Chromosomal anomalies	Main	30	17	10	23	5	7	-	3	-	-	15	33
		Other	6	14	15	11	-	1	2	2	-	1	17	15
758.0	Down's syndrome	Main	7	6	1	4	-	1	-	-	-	-	1	5
		Other	3	5	6	5	-	-	-	-	-	-	6	5
758.1	Patau's syndrome	Main	4	1	3	7	3	-	-	1	-	-	6	8
		Other	-	1	1	2	-	-	-	-	-	-	1	2
758.2	Edwards's syndrome	Main	13	7	4	9	2	4	-	1	-	-	6	14
		Other	-	2	7	3	-	-	1	-	-	1	8	4
758.5	Other conditions due to autosomal anomalies	Main	1	-	-	-	-	-	-	-	-	-	-	-
		Other	-	-	-	-	-	-	-	-	-	-	-	-
758.6	Gonadal dysgenesis	Main	-	-	-	-	-	-	-	-	-	-	-	-
		Other	-	2	-	-	-	-	-	-	-	-	-	-
758.8	Other conditions due to sex chromosome anomalies	Main	1	1	1	-	-	-	-	-	-	-	1	-
		Other	-	-	1	-	-	-	-	-	-	-	1	-
758.9	Conditions due to anomaly of unspecified chromosome	Main	4	2	1	3	-	2	-	1	-	-	1	6
		Other	3	4	-	1	-	1	1	2	-	-	1	4
759	Other and unspecified congenital anomalies	Main	39	27	9	16	-	2	1	1	-	1	10	20
		Other	5	6	11	10	3	1	1	1	1	1	16	13
759.0	Anomalies of spleen	Main	-	-	-	-	-	-	-	-	-	-	-	-
		Other	-	-	-	-	-	-	-	1	-	-	-	1
759.4	Conjoined twins	Main	-	-	-	-	-	-	-	-	-	-	-	-
		Other	-	-	1	-	-	-	-	-	-	-	1	-
759.7	Multiple congenital anomalies, so described	Main	16	12	6	13	-	1	1	1	-	-	7	15
		Other	4	5	6	7	1	1	-	-	-	-	7	8
759.8	Other specified anomalies	Main	4	2	2	2	-	-	-	-	-	1	2	3
		Other	-	-	2	1	2	-	1	-	1	1	6	2
759.9	Congenital anomaly, unspecified	Main	19	13	1	1	-	1	-	-	-	-	1	2
		Other	1	1	2	2	-	-	-	-	-	-	2	2
760-779	XV Certain conditions originating in the perinatal period	Main	924	816	1,115	761	150	100	79	44	33	27	1,377	932
		Other	255	226	751	533	167	99	67	43	29	26	1,014	701
760	Fetus or newborn affected by maternal conditions which may be unrelated to present pregnancy	Main	2	2	-	-	-	-	-	-	-	-	-	-
		Other	2	5	-	1	-	1	-	-	-	-	-	2
760.0	Maternal hypertensive disorders	Main	2	2	-	-	-	-	-	-	-	-	-	-
		Other	2	3	-	1	-	1	-	-	-	-	-	2
760.1	Maternal renal and urinary tract diseases	Main	-	-	-	-	-	-	-	-	-	-	-	-
		Other	-	1	-	-	-	-	-	-	-	-	-	-

Table 4 1995 Series DH3 no. 28

Table 4 - *continued*

ICD number	Cause of Death		Stillbirths		Deaths 0-6 Days		1 week		2 weeks		3 weeks		All neonatal deaths	
			Boys	Girls	Boys	Girls	Boy	Girls	Boys	Girls	Boys	Girls	**Boys**	**Girls**
760.7	Noxious influences transmitted via placenta or breast milk	Main	-	-	-	-	-	-	-	-	-	-	-	-
		Other	-	1	-	-	-	-	-	-	-	-	-	-
761-763	Obstetric complications affecting fetus or newborn	Main	252	188	19	1	1	-	-	-	-	-	20	1
		Other	106	107	44	34	-	2	1	-	-	-	45	36
761	Fetus or newborn affected by maternal complications of pregnancy	Main	31	17	9	1	1	-	-	-	-	-	10	1
		Other	20	25	16	12	-	1	1	-	-	-	17	13
761.1	Premature rupture of membranes	Main	3	3	1	1	-	-	-	-	-	-	1	1
		Other	2	2	1	2	-	-	-	-	-	-	1	2
761.2	Oligohydramnios	Main	6	5	2	-	-	-	-	-	-	-	2	-
		Other	3	6	3	2	-	-	-	-	-	-	3	2
761.3	Polyhydramnios	Main	5	-	2	-	-	-	-	-	-	-	2	-
		Other	2	4	-	2	-	-	-	-	-	-	-	2
761.5	Multiple pregnancy	Main	13	8	4	-	1	-	-	-	-	-	5	-
		Other	13	13	12	6	-	1	1	-	-	-	13	7
761.7	Malpresentation before labour	Main	4	1	-	-	-	-	-	-	-	-	-	-
		Other	-	-	-	-	-	-	-	-	-	-	-	-
762	Fetus or newborn affected by complications of placenta, cord and membranes	Main	216	170	9	-	-	-	-	-	-	-	9	-
		Other	79	75	13	16	-	1	-	-	-	-	13	17
762.0	Placenta praevia	Main	-	-	-	-	-	-	-	-	-	-	-	-
		Other	2	-	-	-	-	-	-	-	-	-	-	-
762.1	Other forms of placental separation and haemorrhage	Main	79	74	4	-	-	-	-	-	-	-	4	-
		Other	17	20	3	4	-	-	-	-	-	-	3	4
762.2	Other and unspecified morphological and functional abnormalities of placenta	Main	31	33	1	-	-	-	-	-	-	-	1	-
		Other	13	13	1	1	-	-	-	-	-	-	1	1
762.3	Placental transfusion syndromes	Main	29	22	2	-	-	-	-	-	-	-	2	-
		Other	2	13	5	5	-	1	-	-	-	-	5	6
762.4	Prolapsed cord	Main	13	4	2	-	-	-	-	-	-	-	2	-
		Other	1	-	1	1	-	-	-	-	-	-	1	1
762.5	Other compression of umbilical cord	Main	50	34	-	-	-	-	-	-	-	-	-	-
		Other	35	23	-	1	-	-	-	-	-	-	-	1
762.6	Other and unspecified conditions of umbilical cord	Main	9	2	-	-	-	-	-	-	-	-	-	-
		Other	5	6	-	1	-	-	-	-	-	-	-	1
762.7	Chorioamnionitis	Main	5	1	-	-	-	-	-	-	-	-	-	-
		Other	4	-	3	3	-	-	-	-	-	-	3	3
763	Fetus or newborn affected by other complications of labour and delivery	Main	5	1	1	-	-	-	-	-	-	-	1	-
		Other	7	7	15	6	-	-	-	-	-	-	15	6
763.0	Breech delivery and extraction	Main	-	-	-	-	-	-	-	-	-	-	-	-
		Other	2	2	5	-	-	-	-	-	-	-	5	-
763.1	Other malpresentation, malposition and disproportion during labour and delivery	Main	2	-	-	-	-	-	-	-	-	-	-	-
		Other	4	3	3	1	-	-	-	-	-	-	3	1
763.2	Forceps delivery	Main	-	-	-	-	-	-	-	-	-	-	-	-
		Other	-	-	-	1	-	-	-	-	-	-	-	1
763.3	Delivery by vacuum extractor	Main	-	-	-	-	-	-	-	-	-	-	-	-
		Other	-	-	-	1	-	-	-	-	-	-	-	1
763.6	Precipitate delivery	Main	-	-	-	-	-	-	-	-	-	-	-	-
		Other	-	-	1	-	-	-	-	-	-	-	1	-
763.8	Other complications of labour and delivery	Main	3	1	1	-	-	-	-	-	-	-	1	-
		Other	1	2	6	3	-	-	-	-	-	-	6	3
764	Slow fetal growth and fetal malnutrition	Main	50	67	6	3	1	-	-	-	-	1	7	4
		Other	36	39	21	26	6	3	1	2	-	1	28	32
764.0	"Light-for-dates" without mention of fetal malnutrition	Main	-	3	-	-	-	-	-	-	-	-	-	-
		Other	6	3	2	-	-	-	-	-	-	-	2	-

Table 4 - *continued*

ICD number	Cause of Death		Stillbirths		Deaths 0-6 Days		1 week		2 weeks		3 weeks		All neonatal deaths	
			Boys	**Girls**	**Boys**	**Girls**	**Boys**	**Girls**	**Boys**	**Girls**	**Boys**	**Girls**	**Boys**	**Girls**
764.2	Fetal malnutrition without mention of	Main	-	-	-	-	-	-	-	-	-	1	-	1
		Other	-	-	-	-	-	-	-	-	-	-	-	-
764.9	Fetal growth retardation, unspecified	Main	50	64	6	3	1	-	-	-	-	-	7	3
		Other	30	36	19	26	6	3	1	2	-	1	26	32
765	Disorders relating to short gestation and unspecified low birthweight	Main	56	51	514	397	35	25	14	12	6	4	569	438
		Other	39	23	212	149	49	28	27	15	13	9	301	201
765.0	Extreme immaturity	Main	13	11	421	327	30	17	12	9	4	3	467	356
		Other	2	2	125	72	27	13	16	9	8	1	176	95
765.1	Other preterm infants	Main	43	40	93	70	5	8	2	3	2	1	102	82
		Other	37	21	87	77	22	15	11	6	5	8	125	106
766	Disorders relating to long gestation and high birthweight	Main	4	1	-	-	-	-	-	-	-	-	-	-
		Other	4	1	-	2	1	-	-	-	-	-	1	2
766.0	Exceptionally large baby	Main	-	-	-	-	-	-	-	-	-	-	-	-
		Other	-	-	-	1	-	-	-	-	-	-	-	1
766.1	Other "heavy-for-dates" infants	Main	1	1	-	-	-	-	-	-	-	-	-	-
		Other	2	-	-	-	-	-	-	-	-	-	-	-
766.2	Post-term infant, not 'heavy-for-dates'	Main	3	-	-	-	-	-	-	-	-	-	-	-
		Other	2	1	-	1	1	-	-	-	-	-	1	1
767	Birth trauma	Main	2	2	61	41	9	8	9	4	3	1	82	54
		Other	-	3	26	24	11	4	4	-	1	1	42	29
767.0	Subdural and cerebral haemorrhage	Main	2	2	61	41	9	8	9	4	3	1	82	54
		Other	-	2	21	22	9	4	4	-	1	1	35	27
767.4	Injury to spine and spinal cord	Main	-	-	-	-	-	-	-	-	-	-	-	-
		Other	-	-	-	1	-	-	-	-	-	-	-	1
767.8	Other	Main	-	-	-	-	-	-	-	-	-	-	-	-
		Other	-	-	-	-	2	-	-	-	-	-	2	-
767.9	Unspecified	Main	-	-	-	-	-	-	-	-	-	-	-	-
		Other	-	1	5	1	-	-	-	-	-	-	5	1
768-770	Hypoxia, birth asphyxia and other respiratory conditions	Main	307	264	384	221	67	31	31	13	9	7	491	272
		Other	22	15	315	203	61	27	20	11	10	4	406	245
768	Intrauterine hypoxia and birth asphyxia	Main	303	262	84	53	6	4	4	1	-	2	94	60
		Other	20	14	50	30	5	4	1	2	-	2	56	38
768.0	Fetal death from asphyxia or anoxia before onset of labour or at unspecified time	Main	283	245	-	-	-	-	-	-	-	-	-	-
		Other	20	14	-	-	-	-	-	-	-	-	-	-
768.1	Fetal death from asphyxia or anoxia during labour	Main	20	16	-	-	-	-	-	-	-	-	-	-
		Other	-	-	-	-	-	-	-	-	-	-	-	-
768.3	Fetal distress first noted during labour, in liveborn infant	Main	-	-	13	1	-	-	-	-	-	-	13	1
		Other	-	-	8	4	1	-	-	1	-	1	9	6
768.4	Fetal distress, unspecified, in liveborn infant	Main	-	-	13	11	2	1	-	1	-	2	15	15
		Other	-	-	20	10	3	3	-	-	-	-	23	13
768.5	Severe birth asphyxia	Main	-	-	28	23	2	3	3	-	-	-	33	26
		Other	-	-	6	8	-	1	1	1	-	1	7	11
768.9	Unspecified birth asphyxia in liveborn infant	Main	-	1	30	18	2	-	1	-	-	-	33	18
		Other	-	-	16	8	1	-	-	-	-	-	17	8
769	Respiratory distress syndrome	Main	-	-	127	75	29	11	11	3	2	1	169	90
		Other	-	-	124	85	20	10	9	5	5	2	158	102
770	Other respiratory conditions of fetus and newborn	Main	4	2	173	93	32	16	16	9	7	4	228	122
		Other	2	1	141	88	36	13	10	4	5	-	192	105
770.0	Congenital pneumonia	Main	-	-	4	3	-	-	-	-	1	-	5	3
		Other	1	-	4	1	-	-	-	-	-	-	4	1
770.1	Massive aspiration syndrome	Main	4	1	10	8	1	-	-	-	-	-	11	8
		Other	1	1	7	5	1	-	-	-	-	-	8	5
770.2	Interstitial emphysema and related conditions	Main	-	-	33	9	12	5	6	3	2	1	53	18
		Other	-	-	64	39	18	7	2	2	1	-	85	48
770.3	Pulmonary haemorrhage	Main	-	-	40	21	7	4	2	-	-	1	49	26
		Other	-	-	29	12	10	1	1	-	-	-	40	13

Table 4 1995 Series DH3 no. 28

Table 4 - *continued*

ICD number	Cause of Death		Stillbirths		Deaths								All neonatal deaths	
					0-6 Days		1 week		2 weeks		3 weeks			
			Boys	Girls	Boys	Girls	Boy	Girls	Boys	Girls	Boys	Girls	Boys	Girls
770.4	Primary atelectasis	Main	-	-	34	25	4	2	-	1	-	-	38	28
		Other	-	-	9	7	1	-	2	1	-	-	12	8
770.5	Other and unspecified atelectasis	Main	-	-	-	-	-	-	-	-	-	-	-	-
		Other	-	-	-	1	-	-	-	-	-	-	-	1
770.7	Chronic respiratory disease arising in the perinatal period	Main	-	-	1	-	1	1	-	2	2	-	4	3
		Other	-	-	-	-	2	1	1	-	4	-	7	1
770.8	Other respiratory problems after birth	Main	-	1	51	27	7	4	8	3	2	2	68	36
		Other	-	-	28	23	4	4	4	1	-	-	36	28
771	Infections specific to the perinatal period	Main	5	6	29	24	17	9	5	5	4	4	55	42
		Other	-	3	22	16	11	8	4	5	2	4	39	33
771.1	Congenital cytomegalovirus infection	Main	-	1	1	-	-	-	-	-	-	-	1	-
		Other	-	-	-	-	-	-	-	-	-	-	-	-
771.2	Other congenital infections	Main	-	-	2	1	1	1	-	-	1	1	4	3
		Other	-	-	-	-	1	-	-	-	-	-	1	-
771.7	Neonatal Candida infection	Main	-	-	-	-	-	-	-	-	-	-	-	-
		Other	-	-	-	-	-	1	-	-	-	-	-	1
771.8	Other infection specific to the perinatal period	Main	5	5	26	23	16	8	5	5	3	3	50	39
		Other	-	3	22	16	10	7	4	5	2	4	38	32
772	Fetal and neonatal haemorrhage	Main	4	5	41	34	5	5	2	1	2	-	50	40
		Other	1	1	59	31	17	13	3	4	1	2	80	50
772.0	Fetal blood loss	Main	3	4	5	4	-	-	-	-	-	-	5	4
		Other	-	-	6	2	1	-	-	1	-	-	7	3
772.1	Intraventricular haemorrhage	Main	1	1	33	25	4	5	2	1	2	-	41	31
		Other	-	-	48	25	15	13	3	3	1	2	67	43
772.2	Subarachnoid haemorrhage	Main	-	-	1	2	-	-	-	-	-	-	1	2
		Other	-	-	-	-	-	-	-	-	-	-	-	-
772.4	Gastrointestinal haemorrhage	Main	-	-	1	1	-	-	-	-	-	-	1	1
		Other	-	-	1	1	1	-	-	-	-	-	2	1
772.5	Adrenal haemorrhage	Main	-	-	-	1	-	-	-	-	-	-	-	1
		Other	-	-	-	-	-	-	-	-	-	-	-	-
772.6	Cutaneous haemorrhage	Main	-	-	-	-	-	-	-	-	-	-	-	-
		Other	1	1	4	3	-	-	-	-	-	-	4	3
772.8	Other	Main	-	-	-	1	1	-	-	-	-	-	1	1
		Other	-	-	-	-	-	-	-	-	-	-	-	-
772.9	Unspecified	Main	-	-	1	-	-	-	-	-	-	-	1	-
		Other	-	-	-	-	-	-	-	-	-	-	-	-
773	Haemolytic disease of fetus or newborn, due to isoimmunization	Main	3	2	-	1	-	-	-	-	-	-	-	1
		Other	2	-	2	2	-	-	-	-	-	-	2	2
773.0	Haemolytic disease due to Rh isoimmunization	Main	3	2	-	1	-	-	-	-	-	-	-	1
		Other	1	-	1	-	-	-	-	-	-	-	1	-
773.1	Haemolytic disease due to ABO isoimmunization	Main	-	-	-	-	-	-	-	-	-	-	-	-
		Other	-	-	-	1	-	-	-	-	-	-	-	1
773.2	Haemolytic disease due to other and unspecified isoimmunization	Main	-	-	-	-	-	-	-	-	-	-	-	-
		Other	1	-	1	1	-	-	-	-	-	-	1	1
774	Other perinatal jaundice	Main	-	-	1	-	-	-	-	-	-	1	1	1
		Other	-	-	-	1	-	-	-	-	-	-	-	1
774.4	Perinatal jaundice due to hepatocellular damage	Main	-	-	1	-	-	-	-	-	-	1	1	1
		Other	-	-	-	-	-	-	-	-	-	-	-	-
774.6	Unspecified fetal and neonatal jaundice	Main	-	-	-	-	-	-	-	-	-	-	-	-
		Other	-	-	-	1	-	-	-	-	-	-	-	1
775	Endocrine and metabolic disturbances specific to the fetus and newborn	Main	1	-	3	-	-	1	-	-	-	-	3	1
		Other	-	-	2	3	-	1	-	-	-	-	2	4
775.0	Syndrome of "infant of a diabetic mother"	Main	-	-	-	-	-	-	-	-	-	-	-	-
		Other	-	-	2	2	-	1	-	-	-	-	2	3
775.1	Neonatal diabetes mellitus	Main	1	-	-	-	-	-	-	-	-	-	-	-
		Other	-	-	-	-	-	-	-	-	-	-	-	-
775.8	Other transitory neonatal endocrine and metabolic disturbances	Main	-	-	3	-	-	-	-	-	-	-	3	-
		Other	-	-	-	1	-	-	-	-	-	-	-	1
775.9	Unspecified	Main	-	-	-	-	-	1	-	-	-	-	-	1
		Other	-	-	-	-	-	-	-	-	-	-	-	-

Table 4 - *continued*

ICD number	Cause of Death		Stillbirths Boys	Stillbirths Girls	0-6 Days Boys	0-6 Days Girls	1 week Boys	1 week Girls	2 weeks Boys	2 weeks Girls	3 weeks Boys	3 weeks Girls	All neonatal deaths Boys	All neonatal deaths Girls
776	Haematological disorders of fetus and newborn	Main	-	-	5	5	2	-	1	1	1	-	9	6
		Other	-	-	11	13	2	3	-	1	-	-	13	17
776.2	Disseminated intravascular coagulation in newborn	Main	-	-	5	4	2	-	-	1	1	-	8	5
		Other	-	-	10	11	2	2	-	-	-	-	12	13
776.3	Other transient neonatal disorders of coagulation	Main	-	-	-	1	-	-	1	-	-	-	1	1
		Other	-	-	1	2	-	1	-	1	-	-	1	4
777	Perinatal disorders of digestive system	Main	-	-	7	3	4	13	10	4	3	3	24	23
		Other	2	-	7	7	6	3	4	2	-	4	17	16
777.1	Other meconium obstruction	Main	-	-	-	-	-	-	-	-	-	-	-	-
		Other	2	-	-	-	-	-	-	-	-	-	-	-
777.5	Necrotizing enterocolitis in fetus or newborn	Main	-	-	6	2	4	10	8	4	3	2	21	18
		Other	-	-	2	3	4	3	3	1	-	3	9	10
777.6	Perinatal intestinal perforation	Main	-	-	1	1	-	3	2	-	-	1	3	5
		Other	-	-	3	4	2	-	1	1	-	1	6	6
777.8	Other	Main	-	-	-	-	-	-	-	-	-	-	-	-
		Other	-	-	2	-	-	-	-	-	-	-	2	-
778	Conditions involving the integument and temperature regulation of fetus and newborn	Main	27	15	14	8	-	-	-	1	-	-	14	9
		Other	8	6	9	6	-	-	-	1	-	-	9	7
778.0	Hydrops fetalis not due to isoimmunization	Main	26	15	13	8	-	-	-	1	-	-	13	9
		Other	6	5	6	4	-	-	-	1	-	-	6	5
778.3	Other hypothermia of newborn	Main	-	-	1	-	-	-	-	-	-	-	1	-
		Other	-	-	3	2	-	-	-	-	-	-	3	2
778.5	Other and unspecified oedema of newborn	Main	1	-	-	-	-	-	-	-	-	-	-	-
		Other	2	1	-	-	-	-	-	-	-	-	-	-
779	Other and ill-defined conditions originating in the perinatal period	Main	211	213	31	23	9	8	7	3	5	6	52	40
		Other	33	23	21	15	3	6	3	2	2	1	29	24
779.0	Convulsions in newborn	Main	-	-	3	-	-	1	-	-	1	-	4	1
		Other	-	-	4	1	1	-	1	-	-	-	6	1
779.6	Termination of pregnancy (fetus)	Main	12	18	2	3	-	-	-	-	-	-	2	3
		Other	5	4	-	1	-	-	-	-	-	-	-	1
779.8	Other	Main	6	7	26	20	9	7	7	3	4	6	46	36
		Other	3	-	17	13	2	6	2	2	2	1	23	22
779.9	Unspecified	Main	193	188	-	-	-	-	-	-	-	-	-	-
		Other	25	19	-	-	-	-	-	-	-	-	-	-
780-799	**XVI Signs, symptoms and ill-defined conditions**	**Main**	4	5	10	14	5	2	8	6	11	9	34	31
		Other	15	4	2	3	2	1	-	1	-	-	4	5
780-789	Symptoms	Main	2	2	2	4	-	-	1	-	1	-	4	4
		Other	10	2	2	1	1	1	-	1	-	-	3	3
780	General symptoms	Main	-	-	-	-	-	-	-	-	1	-	1	-
		Other	-	-	-	-	-	-	-	-	-	-	-	-
780.2	Syncope and collapse	Main	-	-	-	-	-	-	-	-	1	-	1	-
		Other	-	-	-	-	-	-	-	-	-	-	-	-
784	Symptoms involving head and neck	Main	-	-	-	-	-	-	-	-	-	-	-	-
		Other	1	-	-	-	-	-	-	-	-	-	-	-
784.2	Swelling, mass or lump in head and neck	Main	-	-	-	-	-	-	-	-	-	-	-	-
		Other	1	-	-	-	-	-	-	-	-	-	-	-
785	Symptoms involving cardiovascular system	Main	1	-	1	2	-	-	1	-	-	-	2	2
		Other	1	-	-	-	-	-	-	-	-	-	-	-
785.0	Tachycardia, unspecified	Main	1	-	-	-	-	-	-	-	-	-	-	-
		Other	-	-	-	-	-	-	-	-	-	-	-	-
785.4	Gangrene	Main	-	-	-	-	-	-	1	-	-	-	1	-
		Other	-	-	-	-	-	-	-	-	-	-	-	-
785.5	Shock without mention of trauma	Main	-	-	1	2	-	-	-	-	-	-	1	2
		Other	1	-	-	-	-	-	-	-	-	-	-	-
786	Symptoms involving respiratory system and other chest symptoms	Main	-	-	-	-	-	-	-	-	-	-	-	-
		Other	-	-	-	-	-	-	-	1	-	-	-	1
786.0	Dyspnoea and respiratory abnormalities	Main	-	-	-	-	-	-	-	-	-	-	-	-
		Other	-	-	-	-	-	-	-	1	-	-	-	1

Table 4 1995 Series DH3 no. 28

Table 4 - *continued*

ICD number	Cause of Death		Stillbirths		Deaths 0-6 Days		1 week		2 weeks		3 weeks		All neonatal deaths	
			Boys	Girls	Boys	Girls	Boy	Girls	Boys	Girls	Boys	Girls	Boys	Girls
787	Symptoms involving digestive system	Main	-	-	-	-	-	-	-	-	-	-	-	-
		Other	-	-	-	-	-	1	-	-	-	-	-	1
787.3	Flatulence, eructation and gas pain	Main	-	-	-	-	-	-	-	-	-	-	-	-
		Other	-	-	-	-	-	1	-	-	-	-	-	1
789	Other symptoms involving abdomen and pelvis	Main	1	2	1	2	-	-	-	-	-	-	1	2
		Other	8	2	2	1	1	-	-	-	-	-	3	1
789.0	Abdominal pain	Main	-	-	-	-	-	-	-	-	-	-	-	-
		Other	-	-	-	-	1	-	-	-	-	-	1	-
789.1	Hepatomegaly	Main	-	-	-	-	-	-	-	-	-	-	-	-
		Other	1	-	-	-	-	-	-	-	-	-	-	-
789.3	Abdominal or pelvic swelling, mass or lump	Main	-	-	-	-	-	-	-	-	-	-	-	-
		Other	-	-	1	-	-	-	-	-	-	-	1	-
789.5	Ascites	Main	1	2	1	2	-	-	-	-	-	-	1	2
		Other	7	2	1	1	-	-	-	-	-	-	1	1
790	Nonspecific findings on examination of blood	Main	-	-	-	-	1	-	-	1	-	-	1	1
		Other	-	-	-	-	-	-	-	-	-	-	-	-
790.7	Bacteraemia, unspecified	Main	-	-	-	-	1	-	-	1	-	-	1	1
		Other	-	-	-	-	-	-	-	-	-	-	-	-
793	Nonspecific abnormal findings on radiological and other examination of body structure	Main	2	1	-	-	-	-	-	-	-	-	-	-
		Other	4	2	-	-	-	-	-	-	-	-	-	-
793.9	Other	Main	2	1	-	-	-	-	-	-	-	-	-	-
		Other	4	2	-	-	-	-	-	-	-	-	-	-
795	Nonspecific abnormal histological and immunological findings	Main	-	1	-	-	-	-	-	-	-	-	-	-
		Other	-	-	-	-	-	-	-	-	-	-	-	-
795.2	Nonspecific abnormal findings on chromosomal analysis	Main	-	1	-	-	-	-	-	-	-	-	-	-
		Other	-	-	-	-	-	-	-	-	-	-	-	-
798	Sudden death, cause unknown	Main	-	-	4	9	3	1	7	5	9	9	23	24
		Other	-	-	-	2	1	-	-	-	-	-	1	2
798.0	Sudden infant death syndrome	Main	-	-	4	9	3	1	7	5	9	9	23	24
		Other	-	-	-	2	1	-	-	-	-	-	1	2
799	Other ill-defined and unknown causes of morbidity and mortality	Main	-	1	4	1	1	1	-	-	1	-	6	2
		Other	1	-	-	-	-	-	-	-	-	-	-	-
799.1	Respiratory failure	Main	-	-	-	-	-	-	-	-	1	-	1	-
		Other	-	-	-	-	-	-	-	-	-	-	-	-
799.3	Debility, unspecified	Main	-	-	-	1	-	-	-	-	-	-	-	1
		Other	-	-	-	-	-	-	-	-	-	-	-	-
799.8	Other ill-defined conditions	Main	-	-	-	-	1	-	-	-	-	-	1	-
		Other	-	-	-	-	-	-	-	-	-	-	-	-
799.9	Other unknown and unspecified cause	Main	-	1	4	-	-	1	-	-	-	-	4	1
		Other	1	-	-	-	-	-	-	-	-	-	-	-
800-999	**XVII Injury and poisoning**	**Main**	-	-	4	6	2	-	3	-	-	1	9	7
		Other	-	-	3	-	-	-	2	-	1	-	6	-
800-829	Fractures	Main	-	-	-	-	1	-	1	-	-	-	2	-
		Other	-	-	-	-	-	-	1	-	-	-	1	-
800-804	Fracture of skull	Main	-	-	-	-	1	-	1	-	-	-	2	-
		Other	-	-	-	-	-	-	1	-	-	-	1	-
803	Other and unqualified skull fractures	Main	-	-	-	-	1	-	1	-	-	-	2	-
		Other	-	-	-	-	-	-	1	-	-	-	1	-
850-854	Intracranial injury, excluding those with skull fracture	Main	-	-	-	2	1	-	2	-	-	-	3	2
		Other	-	-	-	-	-	-	-	-	-	-	-	-
851	Cerebral laceration and contusion	Main	-	-	-	-	1	-	-	-	-	-	1	-
		Other	-	-	-	-	-	-	-	-	-	-	-	-
852	Subarachnoid, subdural and extradural haemorrhage, following injury	Main	-	-	-	-	-	-	1	-	-	-	1	-
		Other	-	-	-	-	-	-	-	-	-	-	-	-

Table 4 - *continued*

ICD number	Cause of Death		Stillbirths		Deaths 0-6 Days		1 week		2 weeks		3 weeks		All neonatal deaths	
			Boys	Girls	Boys	Girls	Boys	Girls	Boys	Girls	Boys	Girls	**Boys**	**Girls**
853	Other and unspecified intracranial haemorrhage following injury	Main	-	-	-	-	-	-	1	-	-	-	1	-
		Other	-	-	-	-	-	-	-	-	-	-	-	-
854	Intracranial injury of other and unspecified nature	Main	-	-	-	2	-	-	-	-	-	-	-	2
		Other	-	-	-	-	-	-	-	-	-	-	-	-
860-869	Internal injury of chest, abdomen and pelvis	Main	-	-	-	2	-	-	-	-	-	-	-	2
		Other	-	-	-	-	-	-	-	-	-	-	-	-
864	Injury to liver	Main	-	-	-	1	-	-	-	-	-	-	-	1
		Other	-	-	-	-	-	-	-	-	-	-	-	-
868	Injury to other intraabdominal organs	Main	-	-	-	1	-	-	-	-	-	-	-	1
		Other	-	-	-	-	-	-	-	-	-	-	-	-
990-995	Other and unspecified effects of external causes	Main	-	-	3	1	-	-	-	-	-	1	3	2
		Other	-	-	1	-	-	-	-	-	1	-	2	-
994	Effects of other external causes	Main	-	-	2	1	-	-	-	-	-	1	2	2
		Other	-	-	1	-	-	-	-	-	1	-	2	-
994.7	Asphyxiation and strangulation	Main	-	-	1	1	-	-	-	-	-	1	1	2
		Other	-	-	-	-	-	-	-	-	1	-	1	-
994.9	Other	Main	-	-	1	-	-	-	-	-	-	-	1	-
		Other	-	-	1	-	-	-	-	-	-	-	1	-
995	Certain adverse effects not elsewhere classified	Main	-	-	1	-	-	-	-	-	-	-	1	-
		Other	-	-	-	-	-	-	-	-	-	-	-	-
995.5	Child maltreatment syndrome	Main	-	-	1	-	-	-	-	-	-	-	1	-
		Other	-	-	-	-	-	-	-	-	-	-	-	-
996-999	Complications of surgical and medical care not elslewhere classified	Main	-	-	1	1	-	-	-	-	-	-	1	1
		Other	-	-	2	-	-	-	1	-	-	-	3	-
996	Complications peculiar to certain specified procedures	Main	-	-	1	-	-	-	-	-	-	-	1	-
		Other	-	-	-	-	-	-	-	-	-	-	-	-
996.7	Other complications of internal prosthetic device, implant and graft	Main	-	-	1	-	-	-	-	-	-	-	1	-
		Other	-	-	-	-	-	-	-	-	-	-	-	-
998	Other complications of procedures, not elsewhere classified	Main	-	-	-	1	-	-	-	-	-	-	-	1
		Other	-	-	2	-	-	-	-	-	-	-	2	-
998.2	Accidental puncture or laceration during a procedure	Main	-	-	-	1	-	-	-	-	-	-	-	1
		Other	-	-	2	-	-	-	-	-	-	-	2	-
999	Complications of medical care, not elsewhere classified	Main	-	-	-	-	-	-	-	-	-	-	-	-
		Other	-	-	-	-	-	-	1	-	-	-	1	-
999.8	Other transfusion reaction	Main	-	-	-	-	-	-	-	-	-	-	-	-
		Other	-	-	-	-	-	-	1	-	-	-	1	-
E800-E999	**XVII External causes of injury and poisoning**	**Main**	1	3	6	12	1	-	3	-	1	3	**11**	**15**
		Other	1	-	8	7	3	2	4	-	3	-	**18**	**9**
E800-E848	Transport accidents	Main	-	1	-	-	-	-	-	-	-	-	-	-
		Other	-	-	-	1	-	-	-	-	-	-	-	1
E810-E819	Motor vehicle traffic accidents	Main	-	1	-	-	-	-	-	-	-	-	-	-
		Other	-	-	-	1	-	-	-	-	-	-	-	1
E819	Motor vehicle traffic accident of unspecified nature	Main	-	1	-	-	-	-	-	-	-	-	-	-
		Other	-	-	-	1	-	-	-	-	-	-	-	1

Table 4 1995 Series DH3 no. 28

Table 4 - *continued*

ICD number	Cause of Death		Stillbirths		Deaths 0-6 Days		1 week		2 weeks		3 weeks		All neonatal deaths	
			Boys	Girls	Boys	Girls	Boy	Girls	Boys	Girls	Boys	Girls	Boys	Girls
E870-E879	Misadventures during medical care, abnormal reactions, late complications	Main	1	2	3	8	1	-	2	-	1	2	7	10
		Other	1	-	7	6	2	2	3	-	3	-	15	8
E870-E876	Misadventures to patients during surgical and medical care	Main	1	2	-	-	-	-	-	-	-	-	-	-
		Other	1	-	1	-	-	-	-	-	-	-	1	-
E870	Accidental cut, puncture, perforation or haemorrhage during medical care	Main	1	2	-	-	-	-	-	-	-	-	-	-
		Other	1	-	1	-	-	-	-	-	-	-	1	-
E878,E879	Surgical and medical procedures as the cause of abnormal reaction of patient or later complication, without mention of misadventure at the time of procedure	Main	-	-	3	8	1	-	2	-	1	2	7	10
		Other	-	-	6	6	2	2	3	-	3	-	14	8
E878	Surgical operation and other surgical procedures as the cause of abnormal reaction of patient, or of later complication, without mention of misadventure at the time of operation	Main	-	-	3	8	1	-	2	-	1	2	7	10
		Other	-	-	6	6	2	2	3	-	2	-	13	8
E879	Other procedures, without mention of misadventure at the time of procedure, as the cause of abnormal reaction of patient, or of later complication	Main	-	-	-	-	-	-	-	-	-	-	-	-
		Other	-	-	-	-	-	-	-	-	1	-	1	-
E900-E929	Other accidents, including late effects	Main	-	-	2	-	-	-	-	-	-	1	2	1
		Other	-	-	1	-	-	-	-	-	-	-	1	-
E900-E909	Accidents due to natural and environmental factors	Main	-	-	2	-	-	-	-	-	-	-	2	-
		Other	-	-	1	-	-	-	-	-	-	-	1	-
E904	Hunger, thirst, exposure, neglect	Main	-	-	2	-	-	-	-	-	-	-	2	-
		Other	-	-	1	-	-	-	-	-	-	-	1	-
E913	Accidental mechanical suffocation	Main	-	-	-	-	-	-	-	-	-	1	-	1
		Other	-	-	-	-	-	-	-	-	-	-	-	-
E960-E969	Homicide and injury purposely inflicted by other persons	Main	-	-	-	-	-	-	1	-	-	-	1	-
		Other	-	-	-	-	1	-	1	-	-	-	2	-
E967	Child battering and other maltreatment	Main	-	-	-	-	-	-	-	-	-	-	-	-
		Other	-	-	-	-	1	-	1	-	-	-	2	-
E968	Assault by other and unspecified means	Main	-	-	-	-	-	-	1	-	-	-	1	-
		Other	-	-	-	-	-	-	-	-	-	-	-	-
E970-E999	Other violence	Main	-	-	1	4	-	-	-	-	-	-	1	4
		Other	-	-	-	-	-	-	-	-	-	-	-	-
E980-E989	Injury undetermined whether accidentally or purposely inflicted	Main	-	-	1	4	-	-	-	-	-	-	1	4
		Other	-	-	-	-	-	-	-	-	-	-	-	-

Table 4 - *continued*

ICD number	Cause of Death		Stillbirths		Deaths								All neonatal deaths	
					0-6 Days		1 week		2 weeks		3 weeks			
			Boys	**Girls**	Boys	Girls	Boys	Girls	Boys	Girls	Boys	Girls	**Boys**	**Girls**
E983	Hanging, strangulation or suffocation, undetermined whether accidentally or purposely inflicted	Main Other	- -	- -	1 -	- -	- -	- -	- -	- -	- -	- -	1 -	- -
E988	Injury by other and unspecified means, undetermined whether accidentally or purposely inflicted	Main Other	- -	- -	- -	4 -	- -	- -	- -	- -	- -	- -	- -	4 -
Other main fetal/infant conditions			-	-	-	-	-	-	-	-	-	-	-	-
Other other fetal/infant conditions			-	-	-	-	-	-	-	-	-	-	-	-

Table 5 1995 Series DH3 no. 28

Table 5 Stillbirths and neonatal deaths
Main and other maternal causes by sex
Numbers of mentions, 1995

England and Wales

ICD number	Cause of Death		Stillbirths		Deaths 0-6 Days		1 week		2 weeks		3 weeks		All neonatal deaths	
			Boys	Girls	Boys	Girls	Boys	Girls	Boys	Girls	Boys	Girls	Boys	Girls
	All babies		1,911	1,686	1,206	898	184	129	105	67	57	52	1,552	1,146
	All main maternal mentions		527	439	449	308	73	42	32	19	13	6	567	375
	All other maternal mentions		155	132	140	79	15	6	10	4	5	1	170	90
001-139	I Infectious and parasitic diseases	Main	2	9	8	5	1	1	-	-	1	-	10	6
		Other	3	3	4	1	-	-	-	-	-	-	4	1
010-018	Tuberculosis	Main	-	-	-	-	-	-	-	-	-	-	-	-
		Other	1	1	-	-	-	-	-	-	-	-	-	-
011	Pulmonary tuberculosis	Main	-	-	-	-	-	-	-	-	-	-	-	-
		Other	1	1	-	-	-	-	-	-	-	-	-	-
011.9	Unspecified	Main	-	-	-	-	-	-	-	-	-	-	-	-
		Other	1	1	-	-	-	-	-	-	-	-	-	-
020-041	Other bacterial diseases	Main	1	2	5	2	-	1	-	-	1	-	6	3
		Other	2	-	3	1	-	-	-	-	-	-	3	1
038	Septicaemia	Main	1	1	4	2	-	1	-	-	1	-	5	3
		Other	1	-	1	-	-	-	-	-	-	-	1	-
038.0	Streptococcal septicaemia	Main	-	1	2	-	-	-	-	-	1	-	3	-
		Other	-	-	-	-	-	-	-	-	-	-	-	-
038.4	Septicaemia due to other gram-negative organisms	Main	-	-	-	1	-	-	-	-	-	-	-	1
		Other	-	-	-	-	-	-	-	-	-	-	-	-
038.9	Unspecified septicaemia	Main	1	-	2	1	-	1	-	-	-	-	2	2
		Other	1	-	1	-	-	-	-	-	-	-	1	-
040	Other bacterial diseases	Main	-	-	-	-	-	-	-	-	-	-	-	-
		Other	-	-	-	1	-	-	-	-	-	-	-	1
040.8	Other bacterial diseases	Main	-	-	-	-	-	-	-	-	-	-	-	-
		Other	-	-	-	1	-	-	-	-	-	-	-	1
041	Bacterial infection in conditions classified elsewhere and of unspecified site	Main	-	1	1	-	-	-	-	-	-	-	1	-
		Other	1	-	2	-	-	-	-	-	-	-	2	-
041.0	Streptococcus	Main	-	1	1	-	-	-	-	-	-	-	1	-
		Other	1	-	2	-	-	-	-	-	-	-	2	-
045-079	Viral diseases	Main	1	4	-	-	1	-	-	-	-	-	1	-
		Other	-	2	-	-	-	-	-	-	-	-	-	-
050-057	Viral diseases accompanied by exanthem	Main	-	1	-	-	1	-	-	-	-	-	1	-
		Other	-	-	-	-	-	-	-	-	-	-	-	-
052	Chickenpox	Main	-	1	-	-	-	-	-	-	-	-	-	-
		Other	-	-	-	-	-	-	-	-	-	-	-	-
054	Herpes simplex	Main	-	-	-	-	1	-	-	-	-	-	1	-
		Other	-	-	-	-	-	-	-	-	-	-	-	-
054.9	Herpes simplex without mention of complication	Main	-	-	-	-	1	-	-	-	-	-	1	-
		Other	-	-	-	-	-	-	-	-	-	-	-	-
070-079	Other diseases due to viruses and Chlamydiae	Main	1	3	-	-	-	-	-	-	-	-	-	-
		Other	-	2	-	-	-	-	-	-	-	-	-	-
070	Viral hepatitis	Main	-	1	-	-	-	-	-	-	-	-	-	-
		Other	-	-	-	-	-	-	-	-	-	-	-	-
070.3	Viral hepatitis B without mention of hepatic coma	Main	-	1	-	-	-	-	-	-	-	-	-	-
		Other	-	-	-	-	-	-	-	-	-	-	-	-
078	Other diseases due to viruses and Chlamydiae	Main	-	1	-	-	-	-	-	-	-	-	-	-
		Other	-	-	-	-	-	-	-	-	-	-	-	-
078.5	Cytomegalic inclusion disease	Main	-	1	-	-	-	-	-	-	-	-	-	-
		Other	-	-	-	-	-	-	-	-	-	-	-	-
079	Viral infection in conditions classified elsewhere and of unspecified site	Main	1	1	-	-	-	-	-	-	-	-	-	-
		Other	-	2	-	-	-	-	-	-	-	-	-	-
079.0	Adenovirus	Main	1	-	-	-	-	-	-	-	-	-	-	-
		Other	-	-	-	-	-	-	-	-	-	-	-	-
079.8	Other	Main	-	-	-	-	-	-	-	-	-	-	-	-
		Other	-	1	-	-	-	-	-	-	-	-	-	-

Table 5 - *continued*

ICD number	Cause of Death		Stillbirths Boys	Stillbirths Girls	0-6 Days Boys	0-6 Days Girls	1 week Boys	1 week Girls	2 weeks Boys	2 weeks Girls	3 weeks Boys	3 weeks Girls	All neonatal deaths Boys	All neonatal deaths Girls
079.9	Unspecified	Main	-	1	-	-	-	-	-	-	-	-	-	-
		Other	-	1	-	-	-	-	-	-	-	-	-	-
100-139	Other infectious and parasitic diseases and late effects of infectious and parasitic diseases	Main	-	3	3	3	-	-	-	-	-	-	3	3
		Other	-	-	1	-	-	-	-	-	-	-	1	-
130-136	Other infectious and parasitic diseases	Main	-	3	3	3	-	-	-	-	-	-	3	3
		Other	-	-	1	-	-	-	-	-	-	-	1	-
136	Other and unspecified infectious and parasitic diseases	Main	-	3	3	3	-	-	-	-	-	-	3	3
		Other	-	-	1	-	-	-	-	-	-	-	1	-
136.9	Unspecified	Main	-	3	3	3	-	-	-	-	-	-	3	3
		Other	-	-	1	-	-	-	-	-	-	-	1	-
140-239	**II Neoplasms**	**Main**	1	-	-	1	-	-	-	-	-	-	-	1
		Other	-	2	-	-	-	-	-	-	-	-	-	-
140-208	Malignant neoplasms	Main	1	-	-	-	-	-	-	-	-	-	-	-
		Other	-	-	-	-	-	-	-	-	-	-	-	-
190-199	Malignant neoplasm of other and unspecified sites	Main	1	-	-	-	-	-	-	-	-	-	-	-
		Other	-	-	-	-	-	-	-	-	-	-	-	-
193	Malignant neoplasm of thyroid gland	Main	1	-	-	-	-	-	-	-	-	-	-	-
		Other	-	-	-	-	-	-	-	-	-	-	-	-
210-229	Benign neoplasms	Main	-	-	-	1	-	-	-	-	-	-	-	1
		Other	-	1	-	-	-	-	-	-	-	-	-	-
218	Uterine leiomyoma	Main	-	-	-	1	-	-	-	-	-	-	-	1
		Other	-	1	-	-	-	-	-	-	-	-	-	-
235-239	Neoplasms of uncertain behaviour or unspecified nature	Main	-	-	-	-	-	-	-	-	-	-	-	-
		Other	-	1	-	-	-	-	-	-	-	-	-	-
237	Neoplasm of uncertain behaviour of endocrine glands and nervous system	Main	-	-	-	-	-	-	-	-	-	-	-	-
		Other	-	1	-	-	-	-	-	-	-	-	-	-
237.7	Neurofibromatosis	Main	-	-	-	-	-	-	-	-	-	-	-	-
		Other	-	1	-	-	-	-	-	-	-	-	-	-
240-279	**III Endocrine, nutritional and metabolic diseases and immunity disorders**	**Main**	34	27	9	5	2	1	-	-	-	-	11	6
		Other	8	6	2	3	-	-	-	-	-	-	2	3
240-246	Disorders of thyroid gland	Main	-	2	-	-	-	-	-	-	-	-	-	-
		Other	-	1	1	1	-	-	-	-	-	-	1	1
242	Thyrotoxicosis with or without goitre	Main	-	-	-	-	-	-	-	-	-	-	-	-
		Other	-	1	1	1	-	-	-	-	-	-	1	1
242.9	Thyrotoxicosis without mention of goitre or other cause	Main	-	-	-	-	-	-	-	-	-	-	-	-
		Other	-	1	1	1	-	-	-	-	-	-	1	1
244	Acquired hypothyroidism	Main	-	2	-	-	-	-	-	-	-	-	-	-
		Other	-	-	-	-	-	-	-	-	-	-	-	-
244.9	Unspecified hypothyroidism	Main	-	2	-	-	-	-	-	-	-	-	-	-
		Other	-	-	-	-	-	-	-	-	-	-	-	-
250-259	Diseases of other endocrine glands	Main	33	23	8	5	2	1	-	-	-	-	10	6
		Other	7	3	1	2	-	-	-	-	-	-	1	2
250	Diabetes mellitus	Main	33	23	7	5	2	1	-	-	-	-	9	6
		Other	7	1	1	2	-	-	-	-	-	-	1	2

27

Table 5 1995 Series DH3 no. 28

Table 5 - *continued*

ICD number	Cause of Death		Stillbirths		Deaths 0-6 Days		1 week		2 weeks		3 weeks		All neonatal deaths	
			Boys	Girls	Boys	Girls	Boys	Girls	Boys	Girls	Boys	Girls	Boys	Girls
250.0	Diabetes mellitus without mention of complication	Main	32	22	7	5	2	1	-	-	-	-	9	6
		Other	4	1	1	2	-	-	-	-	-	-	1	2
250.1	Diabetes with ketoacidosis	Main	1	-	-	-	-	-	-	-	-	-	-	-
		Other	-	-	-	-	-	-	-	-	-	-	-	-
250.2	Diabetes with coma	Main	-	1	-	-	-	-	-	-	-	-	-	-
		Other	2	-	-	-	-	-	-	-	-	-	-	-
250.3	Diabetes with renal manifestations	Main	-	-	-	-	-	-	-	-	-	-	-	-
		Other	1	-	-	-	-	-	-	-	-	-	-	-
255	Disorders of adrenal glands	Main	-	-	-	-	-	-	-	-	-	-	-	-
		Other	-	2	-	-	-	-	-	-	-	-	-	-
255.0	Cushing's syndrome	Main	-	-	-	-	-	-	-	-	-	-	-	-
		Other	-	2	-	-	-	-	-	-	-	-	-	-
256	Ovarian dysfunction	Main	-	-	1	-	-	-	-	-	-	-	1	-
		Other	-	-	-	-	-	-	-	-	-	-	-	-
256.4	Polycystic ovaries	Main	-	-	1	-	-	-	-	-	-	-	1	-
		Other	-	-	-	-	-	-	-	-	-	-	-	-
270-279	Other metabolic disorders and immunity disorders	Main	1	2	1	-	-	-	-	-	-	-	1	-
		Other	1	2	-	-	-	-	-	-	-	-	-	-
271	Disorders of carbohydrate transport and metabolism	Main	-	1	-	-	-	-	-	-	-	-	-	-
		Other	1	1	-	-	-	-	-	-	-	-	-	-
271.3	Intestinal disaccharidase deficiencies and disaccharide malabsorption	Main	-	1	-	-	-	-	-	-	-	-	-	-
		Other	1	1	-	-	-	-	-	-	-	-	-	-
272	Disorders of lipid metabolism	Main	-	1	1	-	-	-	-	-	-	-	1	-
		Other	-	-	-	-	-	-	-	-	-	-	-	-
272.4	Other and unspecified hyperlipidaemia	Main	-	1	1	-	-	-	-	-	-	-	1	-
		Other	-	-	-	-	-	-	-	-	-	-	-	-
277	Other and unspecified disorders of metabolism	Main	1	-	-	-	-	-	-	-	-	-	-	-
		Other	-	-	-	-	-	-	-	-	-	-	-	-
277.8	Other	Main	1	-	-	-	-	-	-	-	-	-	-	-
		Other	-	-	-	-	-	-	-	-	-	-	-	-
278	Obesity and other hyperalimentation	Main	-	-	-	-	-	-	-	-	-	-	-	-
		Other	-	1	-	-	-	-	-	-	-	-	-	-
278.0	Obesity	Main	-	-	-	-	-	-	-	-	-	-	-	-
		Other	-	1	-	-	-	-	-	-	-	-	-	-
280-289	**IV Diseases of blood and blood-forming organs**	**Main**	4	5	4	-	1	-	1	-	-	-	6	-
		Other	3	1	-	-	-	-	-	-	-	-	-	-
280-285	Anaemias	Main	1	2	-	-	-	-	1	-	-	-	1	-
		Other	1	1	-	-	-	-	-	-	-	-	-	-
282	Hereditary haemolytic anaemias	Main	1	2	-	-	-	-	1	-	-	-	1	-
		Other	-	-	-	-	-	-	-	-	-	-	-	-
282.6	Sickle-cell anaemia	Main	1	2	-	-	-	-	1	-	-	-	1	-
		Other	-	-	-	-	-	-	-	-	-	-	-	-
285	Other and unspecified anaemias	Main	-	-	-	-	-	-	-	-	-	-	-	-
		Other	1	1	-	-	-	-	-	-	-	-	-	-
285.9	Anaemia unspecified	Main	-	-	-	-	-	-	-	-	-	-	-	-
		Other	1	1	-	-	-	-	-	-	-	-	-	-
286	Coagulation defects	Main	2	1	2	-	1	-	-	-	-	-	3	-
		Other	1	-	-	-	-	-	-	-	-	-	-	-
286.6	Defibrination syndrome	Main	2	1	1	-	1	-	-	-	-	-	2	-
		Other	-	-	-	-	-	-	-	-	-	-	-	-
286.9	Other and unspecified coagulation defects	Main	-	-	1	-	-	-	-	-	-	-	1	-
		Other	1	-	-	-	-	-	-	-	-	-	-	-
287	Purpura and other haemorrhagic conditions	Main	-	2	2	-	-	-	-	-	-	-	2	-
		Other	-	-	-	-	-	-	-	-	-	-	-	-
287.3	Primary thrombocytopenia	Main	-	2	-	-	-	-	-	-	-	-	-	-
		Other	-	-	-	-	-	-	-	-	-	-	-	-
287.5	Thrombocytopenia, unspecified	Main	-	-	2	-	-	-	-	-	-	-	2	-
		Other	-	-	-	-	-	-	-	-	-	-	-	-

Table 5 - *continued*

ICD number	Cause of Death		Stillbirths		Deaths 0-6 Days		1 week		2 weeks		3 weeks		All neonatal deaths	
			Boys	Girls	Boys	Girls	Boys	Girls	Boys	Girls	Boys	Girls	**Boys**	**Girls**
289	Other diseases of blood and blood-forming organs	Main	1	-	-	-	-	-	-	-	-	-	-	-
		Other	1	-	-	-	-	-	-	-	-	-	-	-
289.5	Other diseases of spleen	Main	1	-	-	-	-	-	-	-	-	-	-	-
		Other	-	-	-	-	-	-	-	-	-	-	-	-
289.8	Other	Main	-	-	-	-	-	-	-	-	-	-	-	-
		Other	1	-	-	-	-	-	-	-	-	-	-	-
290-319	**V Mental disorders**	**Main**	2	4	2	1	-	-	-	-	-	-	2	1
		Other	3	2	1	1	-	-	-	-	-	-	1	1
298	Other nonorganic psychoses	Main	-	-	1	1	-	-	-	-	-	-	1	1
		Other	1	-	-	-	-	-	-	-	-	-	-	-
298.9	Unspecified psychosis	Main	-	-	1	1	-	-	-	-	-	-	1	1
		Other	1	-	-	-	-	-	-	-	-	-	-	-
303	Alcohol dependence syndrome	Main	-	-	-	-	-	-	-	-	-	-	-	-
		Other	-	1	-	-	-	-	-	-	-	-	-	-
304	Drug dependence	Main	1	1	1	-	-	-	-	-	-	-	1	-
		Other	-	-	-	-	-	-	-	-	-	-	-	-
304.0	Morphine type	Main	-	1	1	-	-	-	-	-	-	-	1	-
		Other	-	-	-	-	-	-	-	-	-	-	-	-
304.3	Cannabis	Main	1	-	-	-	-	-	-	-	-	-	-	-
		Other	-	-	-	-	-	-	-	-	-	-	-	-
305	Nondependent abuse of drugs	Main	1	3	-	-	-	-	-	-	-	-	-	-
		Other	2	1	1	1	-	-	-	-	-	-	1	1
305.1	Tobacco	Main	-	1	-	-	-	-	-	-	-	-	-	-
		Other	1	1	1	-	-	-	-	-	-	-	1	-
305.5	Morphine type	Main	-	2	-	-	-	-	-	-	-	-	-	-
		Other	-	-	-	1	-	-	-	-	-	-	-	1
305.9	Other, mixed or unspecified	Main	1	-	-	-	-	-	-	-	-	-	-	-
		Other	1	-	-	-	-	-	-	-	-	-	-	-
320-389	**VI Diseases of the nervous system and sense organs**	**Main**	4	1	2	1	2	1	-	-	-	1	4	3
		Other	1	2	2	-	-	-	1	-	-	-	3	-
320-359	Diseases of nervous system	Main	4	1	2	1	2	1	-	-	-	1	4	3
		Other	-	2	2	-	-	-	1	-	-	-	3	-
320-326	Inflammatory diseases of the central nervous system	Main	-	-	-	-	-	1	-	-	-	-	-	1
		Other	-	-	-	-	-	-	-	-	-	-	-	-
320-322	Meningitis	Main	-	-	-	-	-	1	-	-	-	-	-	1
		Other	-	-	-	-	-	-	-	-	-	-	-	-
320	Bacterial meningitis	Main	-	-	-	-	-	1	-	-	-	-	-	1
		Other	-	-	-	-	-	-	-	-	-	-	-	-
320.2	Streptococcal meningitis	Main	-	-	-	-	-	1	-	-	-	-	-	1
		Other	-	-	-	-	-	-	-	-	-	-	-	-
330-337	Hereditary and degenerative diseases of the central nervous system	Main	1	-	-	-	-	-	-	-	-	-	-	-
		Other	-	1	-	-	-	-	-	-	-	-	-	-
331	Other cerebral degenerations	Main	1	-	-	-	-	-	-	-	-	-	-	-
		Other	-	-	-	-	-	-	-	-	-	-	-	-
331.4	Obstructive hydrocephalus	Main	1	-	-	-	-	-	-	-	-	-	-	-
		Other	-	-	-	-	-	-	-	-	-	-	-	-
335	Anterior horn cell disease	Main	-	-	-	-	-	-	-	-	-	-	-	-
		Other	-	1	-	-	-	-	-	-	-	-	-	-
335.1	Spinal muscular atrophy	Main	-	-	-	-	-	-	-	-	-	-	-	-
		Other	-	1	-	-	-	-	-	-	-	-	-	-
340-349	Other disorders of the central nervous system	Main	3	1	1	-	-	-	-	-	-	-	1	-
		Other	-	1	1	-	-	-	1	-	-	-	2	-
341	Other demyelinating diseases of central nervous system	Main	1	-	-	-	-	-	-	-	-	-	-	-
		Other	-	-	-	-	-	-	-	-	-	-	-	-

Table 5 1995 Series DH3 no. 28

Table 5 - *continued*

ICD number	Cause of Death		Stillbirths		Deaths 0-6 Days		1 week		2 weeks		3 weeks		All neonatal deaths	
			Boys	Girls	Boys	Girls	Boys	Girls	Boys	Girls	Boys	Girls	Boys	Girls
341.9	Unspecified	Main	1	-	-	-	-	-	-	-	-	-	-	-
		Other	-	-	-	-	-	-	-	-	-	-	-	-
345	Epilepsy	Main	2	1	1	-	-	-	-	-	-	-	1	-
		Other	-	1	1	-	-	-	1	-	-	-	2	-
345.3	Grand mal status	Main	1	-	-	-	-	-	-	-	-	-	-	-
		Other	-	-	-	-	-	-	1	-	-	-	1	-
345.9	Unspecified	Main	1	1	1	-	-	-	-	-	-	-	1	-
		Other	-	1	1	-	-	-	-	-	-	-	1	-
350-359	Diseases of the peripheral nervous system	Main	-	-	1	1	2	-	-	-	-	1	3	2
		Other	-	-	1	-	-	-	-	-	-	-	1	-
354	Mononeuritis of upper limb and mononeuritis multiplex	Main	-	-	-	-	-	-	-	-	-	-	-	-
		Other	-	-	1	-	-	-	-	-	-	-	1	-
354.0	Carpal tunnel syndrome	Main	-	-	-	-	-	-	-	-	-	-	-	-
		Other	-	-	1	-	-	-	-	-	-	-	1	-
359	Muscular dystrophies and other myopathies	Main	-	-	1	1	2	-	-	-	-	1	3	2
		Other	-	-	-	-	-	-	-	-	-	-	-	-
359.2	Myotonic disorders	Main	-	-	1	1	2	-	-	-	-	1	3	2
		Other	-	-	-	-	-	-	-	-	-	-	-	-
380-389	Diseases of the ear and mastoid process	Main	-	-	-	-	-	-	-	-	-	-	-	-
		Other	1	-	-	-	-	-	-	-	-	-	-	-
381-383	Otitis media and mastoiditis	Main	-	-	-	-	-	-	-	-	-	-	-	-
		Other	1	-	-	-	-	-	-	-	-	-	-	-
382	Suppurative and unspecified otitis media	Main	-	-	-	-	-	-	-	-	-	-	-	-
		Other	1	-	-	-	-	-	-	-	-	-	-	-
382.9	Unspecified otitis media	Main	-	-	-	-	-	-	-	-	-	-	-	-
		Other	1	-	-	-	-	-	-	-	-	-	-	-
390-459	**VII Diseases of the circulatory system**	**Main**	**32**	**41**	**9**	**5**	**4**	**2**	**-**	**-**	**-**	**-**	**13**	**7**
		Other	**17**	**10**	**1**	**1**	**-**	**-**	**-**	**-**	**1**	**-**	**2**	**1**
393-398	Chronic rheumatic heart disease	Main	1	1	-	-	-	-	-	-	-	-	-	-
		Other	-	-	-	-	-	-	-	-	-	-	-	-
394	Diseases of mitral valve	Main	-	1	-	-	-	-	-	-	-	-	-	-
		Other	-	-	-	-	-	-	-	-	-	-	-	-
394.0	Mitral stenosis	Main	-	1	-	-	-	-	-	-	-	-	-	-
		Other	-	-	-	-	-	-	-	-	-	-	-	-
395	Diseases of aortic valve	Main	1	-	-	-	-	-	-	-	-	-	-	-
		Other	-	-	-	-	-	-	-	-	-	-	-	-
395.9	Other and unspecified	Main	1	-	-	-	-	-	-	-	-	-	-	-
		Other	-	-	-	-	-	-	-	-	-	-	-	-
401	Essential hypertension	Main	27	36	5	2	3	-	-	-	-	-	8	2
		Other	15	7	1	1	-	-	-	-	-	-	1	1
401.9	Essential hypertension not specified as malignant or benign	Main	27	36	5	2	3	-	-	-	-	-	8	2
		Other	15	7	1	1	-	-	-	-	-	-	1	1
403	Hypertensive renal disease	Main	-	-	-	-	-	-	-	-	-	-	-	-
		Other	-	2	-	-	-	-	-	-	-	-	-	-
403.9	Hypertensive renal disease not specified as as malignant or benign	Main	-	-	-	-	-	-	-	-	-	-	-	-
		Other	-	2	-	-	-	-	-	-	-	-	-	-
415-417	Diseases of pulmonary circulation	Main	-	-	-	-	-	-	-	-	-	-	-	-
		Other	1	1	-	-	-	-	-	-	-	-	-	-
415	Acute pulmonary heart disease	Main	-	-	-	-	-	-	-	-	-	-	-	-
		Other	1	1	-	-	-	-	-	-	-	-	-	-
415.1	Pulmonary embolism	Main	-	-	-	-	-	-	-	-	-	-	-	-
		Other	1	1	-	-	-	-	-	-	-	-	-	-
420-429	Other forms of heart disease	Main	1	1	-	-	-	-	-	-	-	-	-	-
		Other	-	-	-	-	-	-	-	-	-	-	-	-
425	Cardiomyopathy	Main	1	-	-	-	-	-	-	-	-	-	-	-
		Other	-	-	-	-	-	-	-	-	-	-	-	-

Table 5 - *continued*

ICD number	Cause of Death		Stillbirths		Deaths 0-6 Days		1 week		2 weeks		3 weeks		All neonatal deaths	
			Boys	Girls	Boys	Girls	Boys	Girls	Boys	Girls	Boys	Girls	Boys	Girls
425.1	Hypertrophic obstructive cardiomyopathy	Main	1	-	-	-	-	-	-	-	-	-	-	-
		Other	-	-	-	-	-	-	-	-	-	-	-	-
427	Cardiac dysrhythmias	Main	-	1	-	-	-	-	-	-	-	-	-	-
		Other	-	-	-	-	-	-	-	-	-	-	-	-
427.5	Cardiac arrest	Main	-	1	-	-	-	-	-	-	-	-	-	-
		Other	-	-	-	-	-	-	-	-	-	-	-	-
430-438	Cerebrovascular disease	Main	1	3	2	1	-	1	-	-	-	-	2	2
		Other	-	-	-	-	-	-	-	-	1	-	1	-
430	Subarachoid haemorrhage	Main	-	1	-	-	-	-	-	-	-	-	-	-
		Other	-	-	-	-	-	-	-	-	-	-	-	-
431,432	Intracerebral and other intracranial haemorrhage	Main	1	1	2	1	-	1	-	-	-	-	2	2
		Other	-	-	-	-	-	-	-	-	1	-	1	-
431	Intracerebral haemorrhage	Main	1	1	2	1	-	1	-	-	-	-	2	2
		Other	-	-	-	-	-	-	-	-	1	-	1	-
437	Other and ill-defined cerebrovascular disease	Main	-	1	-	-	-	-	-	-	-	-	-	-
		Other	-	-	-	-	-	-	-	-	-	-	-	-
437.3	Cerebral aneurysm, nonruptured	Main	-	1	-	-	-	-	-	-	-	-	-	-
		Other	-	-	-	-	-	-	-	-	-	-	-	-
440-459	Other diseases of the circulatory system	Main	2	-	2	2	1	1	-	-	-	-	3	3
		Other	1	-	-	-	-	-	-	-	-	-	-	-
440-448	Diseases of arteries, arterioles and capillaries	Main	1	-	-	-	-	-	-	-	-	-	-	-
		Other	-	-	-	-	-	-	-	-	-	-	-	-
443	Other peripheral vascular disease	Main	1	-	-	-	-	-	-	-	-	-	-	-
		Other	-	-	-	-	-	-	-	-	-	-	-	-
443.0	Raynaud's syndrome	Main	1	-	-	-	-	-	-	-	-	-	-	-
		Other	-	-	-	-	-	-	-	-	-	-	-	-
453	Other venous embolism and thrombosis	Main	-	-	-	1	1	-	-	-	-	-	1	1
		Other	1	-	-	-	-	-	-	-	-	-	-	-
453.9	Of unspecified site	Main	-	-	-	1	1	-	-	-	-	-	1	1
		Other	1	-	-	-	-	-	-	-	-	-	-	2
458	Hypotension	Main	1	-	-	1	-	1	-	-	-	-	-	2
		Other	-	-	-	-	-	-	-	-	-	-	-	-
458.9	Unspecified	Main	1	-	-	1	-	1	-	-	-	-	-	2
		Other	-	-	-	-	-	-	-	-	-	-	-	-
459	Other disorders of circulatory system	Main	-	-	2	-	-	-	-	-	-	-	2	-
		Other	-	-	-	-	-	-	-	-	-	-	-	-
459.0	Haemorrhage, unspecified	Main	-	-	2	-	-	-	-	-	-	-	2	-
		Other	-	-	-	-	-	-	-	-	-	-	-	-
460-519	**VIII Diseases of the respiratory system**	**Main**	3	2	1	1	-	-	-	-	-	-	1	1
		Other	1	2	-	1	-	-	-	-	-	-	-	1
460-465, 470-478	Diseases of upper respiratory tract	Main	1	-	-	-	-	-	-	-	-	-	-	-
		Other	-	1	-	-	-	-	-	-	-	-	-	-
460	Acute nasopharyngitis (common cold)	Main	1	-	-	-	-	-	-	-	-	-	-	-
		Other	-	-	-	-	-	-	-	-	-	-	-	-
465	Acute upper respiratory infections of multiple or unspecified site	Main	-	-	-	-	-	-	-	-	-	-	-	-
		Other	-	1	-	-	-	-	-	-	-	-	-	-
465.9	Unspecified site	Main	-	-	-	-	-	-	-	-	-	-	-	-
		Other	-	1	-	-	-	-	-	-	-	-	-	-
487	Influenza	Main	1	-	-	-	-	-	-	-	-	-	-	-
		Other	-	1	-	-	-	-	-	-	-	-	-	-
510-519	Other diseases of respiratory system	Main	1	2	1	1	-	-	-	-	-	-	1	1
		Other	1	-	-	1	-	-	-	-	-	-	-	1
512	Pneumothorax	Main	-	-	1	1	-	-	-	-	-	-	1	1
		Other	-	-	-	1	-	-	-	-	-	-	-	1
519	Other diseases of respiratory system	Main	1	2	-	-	-	-	-	-	-	-	-	-
		Other	1	-	-	-	-	-	-	-	-	-	-	-
519.8	Other diseases of respiratory system, not elsewhere classified	Main	1	2	-	-	-	-	-	-	-	-	-	-
		Other	1	-	-	-	-	-	-	-	-	-	-	-

Table 5 1995 Series DH3 no. 28

Table 5 - *continued*

ICD number	Cause of Death		Stillbirths		Deaths 0-6 Days		1 week		2 weeks		3 weeks		All neonatal deaths	
			Boys	Girls	Boys	Girls	Boys	Girls	Boys	Girls	Boys	Girls	Boys	Girls
520-579	**IX Diseases of the digestive system**	Main	1	4	4	1	1	-	-	-	1	-	6	1
		Other	-	1	-	-	-	-	-	-	1	-	1	-
540-543	Appendicitis	Main	-	1	-	-	-	-	-	-	-	-	-	-
		Other	-	-	-	-	-	-	-	-	-	-	-	-
540	Acute appendicitis	Main	-	1	-	-	-	-	-	-	-	-	-	-
		Other	-	-	-	-	-	-	-	-	-	-	-	-
540.0	With generalized peritonitis	Main	-	1	-	-	-	-	-	-	-	-	-	-
		Other	-	-	-	-	-	-	-	-	-	-	-	-
555-558	Noninfective enteritis and colitis	Main	-	1	2	-	1	-	-	-	1	-	4	-
		Other	-	-	-	-	-	-	-	-	1	-	1	-
555	Regional enteritis	Main	-	-	-	-	1	-	-	-	1	-	2	-
		Other	-	-	-	-	-	-	-	-	-	-	-	-
555.9	Unspecified site	Main	-	-	-	-	1	-	-	-	1	-	2	-
		Other	-	-	-	-	-	-	-	-	-	-	-	-
557	Vascular insuffiency of intestine	Main	-	-	2	-	-	-	-	-	-	-	2	-
		Other	-	-	-	-	-	-	-	-	1	-	1	-
557.0	Acute	Main	-	-	1	-	-	-	-	-	-	-	1	-
		Other	-	-	-	-	-	-	-	-	-	-	-	-
557.9	Unspecified	Main	-	-	1	-	-	-	-	-	-	-	1	-
		Other	-	-	-	-	-	-	-	-	1	-	1	-
558	Other noninfective gastroenteritis and colitis	Main	-	1	-	-	-	-	-	-	-	-	-	-
		Other	-	-	-	-	-	-	-	-	-	-	-	-
560-569	Other diseases of intestine and peritoneum	Main	-	-	-	1	-	-	-	-	-	-	-	1
		Other	-	-	-	-	-	-	-	-	-	-	-	-
560	Intestinal obstruction without mention of hernia	Main	-	-	-	1	-	-	-	-	-	-	-	1
		Other	-	-	-	-	-	-	-	-	-	-	-	-
560.2	Volvulus	Main	-	-	-	1	-	-	-	-	-	-	-	1
		Other	-	-	-	-	-	-	-	-	-	-	-	-
570-579	Other diseases of digestive system	Main	1	2	2	-	-	-	-	-	-	-	2	-
		Other	-	1	-	-	-	-	-	-	-	-	-	-
571	Chronic liver disease and cirrhosis	Main	-	1	-	-	-	-	-	-	-	-	-	-
		Other	-	-	-	-	-	-	-	-	-	-	-	-
571.4	Chronic hepatitis	Main	-	1	-	-	-	-	-	-	-	-	-	-
		Other	-	-	-	-	-	-	-	-	-	-	-	-
572	Liver abscess and sequelae of chronic liver disease	Main	-	-	-	-	-	-	-	-	-	-	-	-
		Other	-	1	-	-	-	-	-	-	-	-	-	-
572.8	Other sequelae of chronic liver disease	Main	-	-	-	-	-	-	-	-	-	-	-	-
		Other	-	1	-	-	-	-	-	-	-	-	-	-
573	Other disorders of liver	Main	1	-	2	-	-	-	-	-	-	-	2	-
		Other	-	-	-	-	-	-	-	-	-	-	-	-
573.3	Hepatitis unspecified	Main	1	-	-	-	-	-	-	-	-	-	-	-
		Other	-	-	-	-	-	-	-	-	-	-	-	-
573.9	Unspecified	Main	-	-	2	-	-	-	-	-	-	-	2	-
		Other	-	-	-	-	-	-	-	-	-	-	-	-
577	Diseases of pancreas	Main	-	1	-	-	-	-	-	-	-	-	-	-
		Other	-	-	-	-	-	-	-	-	-	-	-	-
577.0	Acute pancreatitis	Main	-	1	-	-	-	-	-	-	-	-	-	-
		Other	-	-	-	-	-	-	-	-	-	-	-	-
580-629	**X Diseases of the genitourinary system**	Main	3	1	5	3	1	1	-	-	-	-	6	4
		Other	2	-	2	3	2	-	-	1	-	-	4	4
580-599	Diseases of urinary tract	Main	1	1	4	2	1	-	-	-	-	-	5	2
		Other	2	-	1	1	2	-	-	1	-	-	3	2
580-589	Nephritis and nephrotic syndrome and nephrosis	Main	1	-	1	1	1	-	-	-	-	-	2	1
		Other	1	-	1	1	-	-	-	-	-	-	1	1
581	Nephrotic syndrome	Main	1	-	-	-	1	-	-	-	-	-	1	-
		Other	-	-	-	-	-	-	-	-	-	-	-	-

Table 5 - *continued*

ICD number	Cause of Death		Stillbirths		Deaths 0-6 Days		1 week		2 weeks		3 weeks		All neonatal deaths	
			Boys	Girls	Boys	Girls	Boys	Girls	Boys	Girls	Boys	Girls	Boys	Girls
581.9	Unspecified	Main	1	-	-	-	1	-	-	-	-	-	1	-
		Other	-	-	-	-	-	-	-	-	-	-	-	-
583	Nephritis and nephropathy, not specified as acute or chronic	Main	-	-	-	-	-	-	-	-	-	-	-	-
		Other	1	-	-	-	-	-	-	-	-	-	-	-
583.9	With unspecified pathological lesion in kidney	Main	-	-	-	-	-	-	-	-	-	-	-	-
		Other	1	-	-	-	-	-	-	-	-	-	-	-
584-586	Renal failure	Main	-	-	1	1	-	-	-	-	-	-	1	1
		Other	-	-	1	1	-	-	-	-	-	-	1	1
586	Renal failure, unspecified	Main	-	-	1	1	-	-	-	-	-	-	1	1
		Other	-	-	1	1	-	-	-	-	-	-	1	1
590-599	Other diseases of urinary system	Main	-	1	3	1	-	-	-	-	-	-	3	1
		Other	1	-	-	-	2	-	-	1	-	-	2	1
593	Other disorders of kidney and ureter	Main	-	1	1	-	-	-	-	-	-	-	1	-
		Other	1	-	-	-	-	-	-	-	-	-	-	-
593.9	Unspecified	Main	-	1	1	-	-	-	-	-	-	-	1	-
		Other	1	-	-	-	-	-	-	-	-	-	-	-
599	Other disorders of urethra and urinary tract	Main	-	-	2	1	-	-	-	-	-	-	2	1
		Other	-	-	-	-	2	-	-	1	-	-	2	1
599.0	Urinary tract infection, site not specified	Main	-	-	2	1	-	-	-	-	-	-	2	1
		Other	-	-	-	-	2	-	-	1	-	-	2	1
615	Inflammatory diseases of uterus, except cervix	Main	1	-	-	-	-	-	-	-	-	-	-	-
		Other	-	-	-	-	-	-	-	-	-	-	-	-
615.9	Unspecified	Main	1	-	-	-	-	-	-	-	-	-	-	-
		Other	-	-	-	-	-	-	-	-	-	-	-	-
616	Inflammatory disease of cervix, vagina and vulva	Main	-	-	-	-	-	1	-	-	-	-	-	1
		Other	-	-	-	1	-	-	-	-	-	-	-	1
616.1	Vaginitis and vulvovaginitis	Main	-	-	-	-	-	1	-	-	-	-	-	1
		Other	-	-	-	1	-	-	-	-	-	-	-	1
620	Noninflammatory disorders of ovary, fallopian tube and broad ligament	Main	-	-	-	1	-	-	-	-	-	-	-	1
		Other	-	-	-	-	-	-	-	-	-	-	-	-
620.2	Other and unspecified ovarian cyst	Main	-	-	-	1	-	-	-	-	-	-	-	1
		Other	-	-	-	-	-	-	-	-	-	-	-	-
623	Noninflammatory disorders of vagina	Main	1	-	1	-	-	-	-	-	-	-	1	-
		Other	-	-	1	1	-	-	-	-	-	-	1	1
623.5	Leukorrhoea, not specified as infective	Main	-	-	-	-	-	-	-	-	-	-	-	-
		Other	-	-	1	-	-	-	-	-	-	-	1	-
623.8	Other	Main	1	-	1	-	-	-	-	-	-	-	1	-
		Other	-	-	-	1	-	-	-	-	-	-	-	1
630-676	**XI Complications of pregnancy, childbirth and the puerperium**	**Main**	428	329	398	281	60	35	31	17	11	4	500	337
		Other	106	93	117	64	12	6	8	3	3	1	140	74
633	Ectopic pregnancy	Main	-	-	-	1	-	-	-	-	-	-	-	1
		Other	-	-	-	-	-	-	-	-	-	-	-	-
633.8	Other ectopic pregnancy	Main	-	-	-	1	-	-	-	-	-	-	-	1
		Other	-	-	-	-	-	-	-	-	-	-	-	-
634	Spontaneous abortion	Main	-	-	2	-	-	-	-	-	-	-	2	-
		Other	1	-	-	-	-	1	-	-	-	-	-	1
634.9	Without mention of complication	Main	-	-	2	-	-	-	-	-	-	-	2	-
		Other	1	-	-	-	-	1	-	-	-	-	-	1
635	Legally induced abortion	Main	-	1	1	1	-	-	-	-	-	-	1	1
		Other	1	-	-	-	-	-	-	-	-	-	-	-
635.9	Without mention of complication	Main	-	1	1	1	-	-	-	-	-	-	1	1
		Other	1	-	-	-	-	-	-	-	-	-	-	-
637	Unspecified abortion	Main	-	-	-	1	-	-	-	-	-	-	-	1
		Other	-	-	-	1	-	-	-	-	-	-	-	1
637.9	Without mention of complication	Main	-	-	-	1	-	-	-	-	-	-	-	1
		Other	-	-	-	1	-	-	-	-	-	-	-	1

Table 5 1995 Series DH3 no. 28

Table 5 - *continued*

ICD number	Cause of Death		Stillbirths		Deaths 0-6 Days		1 week		2 weeks		3 weeks		All neonatal deaths	
			Boys	Girls	Boys	Girls	Boys	Girls	Boys	Girls	Boys	Girls	Boys	Girls
641	Antepartum haemorrhage, abruptio placentae, and placenta praevia	Main	215	128	79	61	12	3	5	-	1	-	97	64
		Other	17	15	15	7	-	-	3	1	-	-	18	8
641.1	Haemorrhage from placenta praevia	Main	5	4	4	2	1	-	-	-	-	-	5	2
		Other	3	2	3	1	-	-	1	-	-	-	4	1
641.2	Premature separation of placenta	Main	162	100	37	27	3	1	4	-	1	-	45	28
		Other	7	7	4	1	-	-	-	1	-	-	4	2
641.9	Unspecified antepartum haemorrhage	Main	48	24	38	32	8	2	1	-	-	-	47	34
		Other	7	6	8	5	-	-	2	-	-	-	10	5
642	Hypertension complicating pregnancy, childbirth and the puerperium	Main	68	80	38	32	12	10	4	1	2	1	56	44
		Other	28	18	5	5	2	-	-	-	-	-	7	5
642.4	Mild or unspecified pre-eclampsia	Main	32	47	18	18	7	5	1	1	2	-	28	24
		Other	15	12	1	4	2	-	-	-	-	-	3	4
642.5	Severe pre-eclampsia	Main	1	8	6	2	1	2	-	-	-	-	7	4
		Other	1	-	1	-	-	-	-	-	-	-	1	-
642.6	Eclampsia	Main	2	3	1	-	1	-	-	-	-	-	2	-
		Other	-	-	-	-	-	-	-	-	-	-	-	-
642.9	Unspecified hypertension complicating pregnancy, childbirth and the puerperium	Main	33	22	13	12	3	3	3	-	-	1	19	16
		Other	12	6	3	1	-	-	-	-	-	-	3	1
644	Early or threatened labour	Main	9	5	98	71	16	12	7	7	3	1	124	91
		Other	2	2	28	5	2	2	2	-	-	-	32	7
644.1	Early onset of delivery	Main	9	5	98	71	16	12	7	7	3	1	124	91
		Other	2	2	28	5	2	2	2	-	-	-	32	7
645	Prolonged pregnancy	Main	1	-	-	-	-	-	-	-	-	-	-	-
		Other	-	1	-	-	-	-	-	-	-	-	-	-
646	Other complications of pregnancy, not elsewhere classified	Main	5	11	5	1	1	-	-	-	-	-	6	1
		Other	1	-	1	1	-	-	-	-	-	-	1	1
646.2	Unspecified renal disease in pregnancy, without mention of hypertension	Main	2	5	-	-	1	-	-	-	-	-	1	-
		Other	1	-	1	-	-	-	-	-	-	-	1	-
646.6	Infections of genitourinary tract in pregnancy	Main	3	5	2	1	-	-	-	-	-	-	2	1
		Other	-	-	-	1	-	-	-	-	-	-	-	1
646.7	Liver disorders in pregnancy	Main	-	1	3	-	-	-	-	-	-	-	3	-
		Other	-	-	-	-	-	-	-	-	-	-	-	-
647	Infective and parasitic conditions in the mother classifiable elsewhere but complicating pregnancy, children and the puerperium	Main	3	1	1	1	-	-	-	-	-	-	1	1
		Other	-	-	2	1	-	-	-	-	-	-	2	1
647.8	Other specified infective and parasitic diseases	Main	1	-	-	1	-	-	-	-	-	-	-	1
		Other	-	-	1	-	-	-	-	-	-	-	1	-
647.9	Unspecified infection or infestation	Main	2	1	1	-	-	-	-	-	-	-	1	-
		Other	-	-	1	1	-	-	-	-	-	-	1	1
648	Other current conditions in the mother classifiable elsewhere but complicating pregnancy, children and the puerperium	Main	20	10	4	-	-	-	-	-	-	-	4	-
		Other	2	-	-	1	-	-	-	-	-	-	-	1
648.0	Diabetes mellitus	Main	18	7	4	-	-	-	-	-	-	-	4	-
		Other	1	-	-	1	-	-	-	-	-	-	-	1
648.2	Anaemia	Main	-	1	-	-	-	-	-	-	-	-	-	-
		Other	-	-	-	-	-	-	-	-	-	-	-	-
648.9	Other	Main	2	2	-	-	-	-	-	-	-	-	-	-
		Other	1	-	-	-	-	-	-	-	-	-	-	-
651	Multiple gestation	Main	14	14	21	14	4	4	5	1	-	2	30	21
		Other	9	9	13	10	-	2	-	-	-	-	13	13
651.0	Twin pregnancy	Main	11	12	17	9	1	3	3	1	-	2	21	15
		Other	7	9	8	4	-	1	-	1	-	-	8	6
0651.1	Triplet pregnancy	Main	1	-	2	3	-	-	2	-	-	-	4	3
		Other	2	-	2	2	-	-	-	-	-	-	2	2

34

Table 5 - *continued*

ICD number	Cause of Death		Stillbirths		Deaths 0-6 Days		1 week		2 weeks		3 weeks		All neonatal deaths	
			Boys	Girls	Boys	Girls	Boys	Girls	Boys	Girls	Boys	Girls	Boys	Girls
651.2	Quadruplet pregnancy	Main	-	-	-	1	-	-	-	-	-	-	-	1
		Other	-	-	-	3	-	1	-	-	-	-	-	4
651.9	Unspecified	Main	2	2	2	1	3	1	-	-	-	-	5	2
		Other	-	-	3	1	-	-	-	-	-	-	3	1
652	Malposition and malpresentation of fetus	Main	-	1	4	4	-	1	1	2	-	-	5	7
		Other	2	3	1	-	-	-	-	-	-	-	1	-
652.2	Breech presentation without mention of version	Main	-	1	1	3	-	-	1	1	-	-	2	4
		Other	2	1	1	-	-	-	-	-	-	-	1	-
652.3	Transverse or oblique presentation	Main	-	-	-	-	-	-	-	-	-	-	-	-
		Other	-	1	-	-	-	-	-	-	-	-	-	-
652.8	Other	Main	-	-	3	1	-	1	-	1	-	-	3	3
		Other	-	1	-	-	-	-	-	-	-	-	-	-
654	Abnormality of organs and soft tissues of pelvis	Main	2	2	11	3	2	-	1	-	-	-	14	3
		Other	1	2	1	4	-	-	-	-	-	-	1	4
654.0	Congenital abnormalities of uterus	Main	1	-	1	-	1	-	-	-	-	-	2	-
		Other	1	-	1	-	-	-	-	-	-	-	1	-
654.2	Uterine scar from previous surgery	Main	-	-	-	-	-	-	-	-	-	-	-	-
		Other	-	-	-	2	-	-	-	-	-	-	-	2
654.5	Cervical incompetence	Main	1	1	10	3	-	-	1	-	-	-	11	3
		Other	-	1	-	2	-	-	-	-	-	-	-	2
655	Known or suspected fetal abnormality affecting management of mother	Main	-	1	1	-	-	-	-	-	-	-	1	-
		Other	-	-	-	-	-	-	-	-	-	-	-	-
655.4	Suspected damage to fetus from other disease in the mother	Main	-	1	1	-	-	-	-	-	-	-	1	-
		Other	-	-	-	-	-	-	-	-	-	-	-	-
656	Other fetal and placental problems affecting management of mother	Main	28	20	10	7	1	-	1	-	-	-	12	7
		Other	11	4	5	3	1	-	-	1	1	-	7	4
656.0	Fetal-maternal haemorrhage	Main	-	-	-	-	-	-	-	-	-	-	-	-
		Other	-	-	1	-	-	-	-	-	-	-	1	-
656.1	Rhesus isoimmunization	Main	4	1	2	1	-	-	-	-	-	-	2	1
		Other	2	3	-	-	-	-	-	-	-	-	-	-
656.2	Isoimmunization from other and unspecified blood-group incompatibility	Main	2	4	-	2	-	-	-	-	-	-	-	2
		Other	-	-	-	-	-	-	-	-	-	-	-	-
656.3	Fetal distress	Main	2	-	1	-	-	-	-	-	-	-	1	-
		Other	2	-	3	1	1	-	-	-	1	-	5	1
656.5	Poor fetal growth	Main	17	10	6	4	1	-	1	-	-	-	8	4
		Other	3	-	-	2	-	-	-	-	-	-	-	2
656.7	Other placental conditions	Main	3	5	1	-	-	-	-	-	-	-	1	-
		Other	4	1	1	-	-	-	-	1	-	-	1	1
657	Polyhydramnios	Main	4	2	7	6	1	2	-	-	-	-	8	8
		Other	5	8	1	2	1	-	-	-	1	-	3	2
658	Other problems associated with amniotic cavity and membranes	Main	22	21	93	56	6	3	3	3	5	-	107	62
		Other	14	8	18	15	1	-	1	-	-	-	20	15
658.0	Oligohydramnios	Main	3	2	26	13	1	-	1	-	-	-	28	13
		Other	6	1	5	1	-	-	-	-	-	-	5	1
658.1	Premature rupture of membranes	Main	7	9	17	17	-	1	-	-	2	-	19	18
		Other	3	5	4	4	-	-	-	-	-	-	4	4
658.2	Delayed delivery after spontaneous or unspecified rupture of membranes	Main	8	6	28	15	3	2	2	1	1	-	34	18
		Other	5	1	6	5	1	-	-	-	-	-	7	5
658.4	Infection of amniotic cavity	Main	2	4	14	8	2	-	-	2	2	-	18	10
		Other	-	1	2	3	-	-	-	-	-	-	2	3
658.8	Other	Main	2	-	8	3	-	-	-	-	-	-	8	3
		Other	-	-	1	2	-	-	1	-	-	-	2	2
659	Other indications for care or intervention related to labour and delivery and nec	Main	6	6	2	2	-	-	-	-	-	-	2	2
		Other	3	7	2	-	-	-	-	-	-	-	2	-

Table 5 1995 Series DH3 no. 28

Table 5 - *continued*

ICD number	Cause of Death		Stillbirths		Deaths 0-6 Days		1 week		2 weeks		3 weeks		All neonatal deaths	
			Boys	Girls	Boys	Girls	Boys	Girls	Boys	Girls	Boys	Girls	Boys	Girls
659.0	Failed mechanical induction	Main	3	3	1	-	-	-	-	-	-	-	1	-
		Other	2	5	-	-	-	-	-	-	-	-	-	-
659.2	Maternal pyrexia during labour, unspecified	Main	3	3	1	2	-	-	-	-	-	-	1	2
		Other	1	2	2	-	-	-	-	-	-	-	2	-
660	Obstructed labour	Main	-	-	-	-	1		-	-	-	-	1	-
		Other	1	1	1	-	-	-	-	-	-	-	1	-
660.1	Obstruction by bony pelvis	Main	-	-	-	-	-	-	-	-	-	-	-	-
		Other	-	-	1	-	-	-	-	-	-	-	1	-
660.4	Shoulder dystocia	Main	-	-	-	-	-	-	-	-	-	-	-	-
		Other	1	1	-	-	-	-	-	-	-	-	-	-
660.5	Locked twins	Main	-	-	-	-	1		-	-	-	-	1	-
		Other	-	-	-	-	-	-	-	-	-	-	-	-
662	Long labour	Main	-	1	1	-	-	-	-	-	-	-	1	-
		Other	-	-	-	-	-	-	-	-	-	-	-	-
662.1	Prolonged labour, unspecified	Main	-	1	-	-	-	-	-	-	-	-	-	-
		Other	-	-	-	-	-	-	-	-	-	-	-	-
662.3	Delayed delivery of second twin, triplet, etc.	Main	-	-	1	-	-	-	-	-	-	-	1	-
		Other	-	-	-	-	-	-	-	-	-	-	-	-
663	Umbilical cord complications	Main	27	18	6	5	-	-	2	1	-	-	8	6
		Other	6	8	-	3	-	-	-	-	-	-	-	3
663.0	Prolapse of cord	Main	5	3	2	3	-	-	2	1	-	-	4	4
		Other	2	-	-	1	-	-	-	-	-	-	-	1
663.2	Other and unspecified cord entanglement, with compression	Main	18	9	-	-	-	-	-	-	-	-	-	-
		Other	4	5	-	-	-	-	-	-	-	-	-	-
663.3	Other and unspecified cord entanglement, without mention of compression	Main	3	3	-	-	-	-	-	-	-	-	-	-
		Other	-	2	-	-	-	-	-	-	-	-	-	-
663.5	Vasa praevia	Main	-	-	4	2	-	-	-	-	-	-	4	2
		Other	-	-	-	2	-	-	-	-	-	-	-	2
663.8	Other	Main	1	3	-	-	-	-	-	-	-	-	-	-
		Other	-	1	-	-	-	-	-	-	-	-	-	-
665	Other obstetrical trauma	Main	4	6	5	7	1	-	-	-	-	-	6	7
		Other	-	1	-	-	-	-	-	-	-	-	-	-
665.1	Rupture of uterus during and after labour	Main	4	6	5	7	1	-	-	-	-	-	6	7
		Other	-	1	-	-	-	-	-	-	-	-	-	-
666	Postpartum haemorrhage	Main	-	-	-	-	-	-	-	-	-	-	-	-
		Other	-	-	1	-	-	-	-	-	-	-	1	-
666.1	Other immediate postpartum haemorrhage	Main	-	-	-	-	-	-	-	-	-	-	-	-
		Other	-	-	1	-	-	-	-	-	-	-	1	-
669	Other complications of labour and delivery, not elsewhere classified	Main	-	-	9	8	3	-	2	2	-	-	14	10
		Other	2	6	23	6	5	1	2	-	1	1	31	8
669.5	Forceps or ventouse delivery without mention of indication	Main	-	-	-	-	-	-	-	-	-	-	-	-
		Other	1	3	1	-	-	-	-	-	-	-	1	-
669.7	Caesarean delivery, without mention of indication	Main	-	-	9	8	3	-	2	2	-	-	14	10
		Other	1	2	22	6	5	1	2	-	1	1	30	8
669.9	Unspecified	Main	-	-	-	-	-	-	-	-	-	-	-	-
		Other	-	1	-	-	-	-	-	-	-	-	-	-
673	Obstetrical pulmonary embolism	Main	-	1	-	-	-	-	-	-	-	-	-	-
		Other	-	-	-	-	-	-	-	-	-	-	-	-
673.1	Amniotic fluid embolism	Main	-	1	-	-	-	-	-	-	-	-	-	-
		Other	-	-	-	-	-	-	-	-	-	-	-	-
710-739	**XIII Diseases of the musculoskeletal system and connective tissue**	**Main**	1	3	2	2	-	-	-	1	-	-	2	3
		Other	-	1	1	-	-	-	-	-	-	-	1	-
710	Diffuse diseases of connective tissue	Main	1	3	2	2	-	-	-	1	-	-	2	3
		Other	-	1	1	-	-	-	-	-	-	-	1	-
710.0	Systemic lupus erythematosus	Main	1	3	1	2	-	-	-	1	-	-	1	3
		Other	-	1	1	-	-	-	-	-	-	-	1	-
710.1	Systemic sclerosis	Main	-	-	1	-	-	-	-	-	-	-	1	-
		Other	-	-	-	-	-	-	-	-	-	-	-	-

Table 5 - *continued*

ICD number	Cause of Death		Stillbirths		Deaths 0-6 Days		1 week		2 weeks		3 weeks		All neonatal deaths	
			Boys	Girls	Boys	Girls	Boys	Girls	Boys	Girls	Boys	Girls	Boys	Girls
740-759	XIV Congenital anomalies	Main	1	1	1	-	1	-	-	-	-	1	2	1
		Other	1	2	3	2	-	-	-	-	-	-	3	2
740-742	All deformities of central nervous system	Main	-	-	-	-	-	-	-	-	-	-	-	-
		Other	-	-	1	-	-	-	-	-	-	-	1	-
741,742.3	Spina bifida and hydrocephalus	Main	-	-	-	-	-	-	-	-	-	-	-	-
		Other	-	-	1	-	-	-	-	-	-	-	1	-
741	Spina bifida	Main	-	-	-	-	-	-	-	-	-	-	-	-
		Other	-	-	1	-	-	-	-	-	-	-	1	-
741.9	Without mention of hydrocephalus	Main	-	-	-	-	-	-	-	-	-	-	-	-
		Other	-	-	1	-	-	-	-	-	-	-	1	-
745-747	Congenital anomalies of heart and circulatory system	Main	-	-	-	-	-	-	-	-	-	1	-	1
		Other	-	1	-	2	-	-	-	-	-	-	-	2
746	Other congenital anomalies of heart	Main	-	-	-	-	-	-	-	-	-	-	-	-
		Other	-	-	-	2	-	-	-	-	-	-	-	2
746.1	Tricuspid atresia and stenosis, congenital	Main	-	-	-	-	-	-	-	-	-	-	-	-
		Other	-	-	-	1	-	-	-	-	-	-	-	1
746.9	Unspecified anomalies of heart	Main	-	-	-	-	-	-	-	-	-	-	-	-
		Other	-	-	-	1	-	-	-	-	-	-	-	1
747	Other congenital anomalies of circulatory system	Main	-	-	-	-	-	-	-	-	-	1	-	1
		Other	-	1	-	-	-	-	-	-	-	-	-	-
747.1	Coarctation of aorta	Main	-	-	-	-	-	-	-	-	-	-	-	-
		Other	-	1	-	-	-	-	-	-	-	-	-	-
747.6	Other anomalies of peripheral vascular system	Main	-	-	-	-	-	-	-	-	-	1	-	1
		Other	-	-	-	-	-	-	-	-	-	-	-	-
752	Congenital anomalies of genital organs	Main	-	1	-	-	-	-	-	-	-	-	-	-
		Other	-	-	1	-	-	-	-	-	-	-	1	-
752.3	Other anomalies of uterus	Main	-	1	-	-	-	-	-	-	-	-	-	-
		Other	-	-	-	-	-	-	-	-	-	-	-	-
752.4	Anomalies of cervix, vagina and external female genitalia	Main	-	-	-	-	-	-	-	-	-	-	-	-
		Other	-	-	1	-	-	-	-	-	-	-	1	-
753	Congenital anomalies of urinary system	Main	1	-	1	-	1	-	-	-	-	-	2	-
		Other	-	1	1	-	-	-	-	-	-	-	1	-
753.0	Renal agenesis and dysgenesis	Main	1	-	-	-	-	-	-	-	-	-	-	-
		Other	-	-	-	-	-	-	-	-	-	-	-	-
753.1	Cystic kidney disease	Main	-	-	1	-	1	-	-	-	-	-	2	-
		Other	-	1	1	-	-	-	-	-	-	-	1	-
758	Chromosomal anomalies	Main	-	-	-	-	-	-	-	-	-	-	-	-
		Other	1	-	-	-	-	-	-	-	-	-	-	-
758.6	Gonadal dysgenesis	Main	-	-	-	-	-	-	-	-	-	-	-	-
		Other	1	-	-	-	-	-	-	-	-	-	-	-
760-779	XV Certain conditions originating in the perinatal period	Main	7	4	3	-	-	1	-	-	-	-	3	1
		Other	2	3	4	-	1	-	-	-	-	-	5	-
760	Fetus or newborn affected by maternal conditions which may be unrelated to present pregnancy	Main	1	-	-	-	-	-	-	-	-	-	-	-
		Other	-	-	-	-	-	-	-	-	-	-	-	-
760.5	Maternal injury	Main	1	-	-	-	-	-	-	-	-	-	-	-
		Other	-	-	-	-	-	-	-	-	-	-	-	-
761-763	Obstetric complications affecting fetus or newborn	Main	3	1	1	-	-	1	-	-	-	-	1	1
		Other	-	-	-	-	1	-	-	-	-	-	1	-
761	Fetus or newborn affected by maternal complications of pregnancy	Main	2	-	1	-	-	-	-	-	-	-	1	-
		Other	-	-	-	-	1	-	-	-	-	-	1	-
761.3	Polyhydramnios	Main	-	-	1	-	-	-	-	-	-	-	1	-
		Other	-	-	-	-	-	-	-	-	-	-	-	-

Table 5 1995 Series DH3 no. 28

Table 5 - *continued*

ICD number	Cause of Death		Stillbirths Boys	Stillbirths Girls	0-6 Days Boys	0-6 Days Girls	1 week Boys	1 week Girls	2 weeks Boys	2 weeks Girls	3 weeks Boys	3 weeks Girls	All neonatal deaths Boys	All neonatal deaths Girls
761.5	Multiple pregnancy	Main	1	-	-	-	-	-	-	-	-	-	-	-
		Other	-	-	-	-	1	-	-	-	-	-	1	-
761.6	Maternal death	Main	1	-	-	-	-	-	-	-	-	-	-	-
		Other	-	-	-	-	-	-	-	-	-	-	-	-
762	Fetus or newborn affected by complications of placenta, cord and membranes	Main	1	1	-	-	-	1	-	-	-	-	-	1
		Other	-	-	-	-	-	-	-	-	-	-	-	-
762.1	Other forms of placental separation and haemorrhage	Main	1	1	-	-	-	1	-	-	-	-	-	1
		Other	-	-	-	-	-	-	-	-	-	-	-	-
764	Slow fetal growth and fetal malnutrition	Main	1	3	1	-	-	-	-	-	-	-	1	-
		Other	1	3	3	-	-	-	-	-	-	-	3	-
764.9	Fetal growth retardation, unspecified	Main	1	3	1	-	-	-	-	-	-	-	1	-
		Other	1	3	3	-	-	-	-	-	-	-	3	-
768-770	Hypoxia, birth asphyxia and other respiratory conditions	Main	-	-	1	-	-	-	-	-	-	-	1	-
		Other	-	-	1	-	-	-	-	-	-	-	1	-
769	Respiratory distress syndrome	Main	-	-	1	-	-	-	-	-	-	-	1	-
		Other	-	-	-	-	-	-	-	-	-	-	-	-
770	Other respiratory conditions of fetus and newborn	Main	-	-	-	-	-	-	-	-	-	-	-	-
		Other	-	-	1	-	-	-	-	-	-	-	1	-
770.8	Other respiratory problems after birth	Main	-	-	-	-	-	-	-	-	-	-	-	-
		Other	-	-	1	-	-	-	-	-	-	-	1	-
773	Haemolytic disease of fetus or newborn, due to isoimmunization	Main	2	-	-	-	-	-	-	-	-	-	-	-
		Other	-	-	-	-	-	-	-	-	-	-	-	-
773.0	Haemolytic disease due to Rh isoimmunization	Main	2	-	-	-	-	-	-	-	-	-	-	-
		Other	-	-	-	-	-	-	-	-	-	-	-	-
779	Other and ill-defined conditions originating in the perinatal period	Main	-	-	-	-	-	-	-	-	-	-	-	-
		Other	1	-	-	-	-	-	-	-	-	-	-	-
779.6	Termination of pregnancy (fetus)	Main	-	-	-	-	-	-	-	-	-	-	-	-
		Other	1	-	-	-	-	-	-	-	-	-	-	-
780-799	**XVI Signs, symptoms and ill-defined conditions**	**Main**	1	4	1	2	-	-	-	-	-	-	1	2
		Other	1	1	-	1	-	-	-	-	-	-	-	1
780-789	Symptoms	Main	-	2	1	2	-	-	-	-	-	-	1	2
		Other	-	-	-	-	-	-	-	-	-	-	-	-
780	General symptoms	Main	-	-	1	-	-	-	-	-	-	-	1	-
		Other	-	-	-	-	-	-	-	-	-	-	-	-
780.3	Convulsions	Main	-	-	1	-	-	-	-	-	-	-	1	-
		Other	-	-	-	-	-	-	-	-	-	-	-	-
783	Symptoms concerning nutrition, metabolism development	Main	-	1	-	-	-	-	-	-	-	-	-	-
		Other	-	-	-	-	-	-	-	-	-	-	-	-
783.4	Lack of expected normal physiological development	Main	-	1	-	-	-	-	-	-	-	-	-	-
		Other	-	-	-	-	-	-	-	-	-	-	-	-
786	Symptoms involving respiratory system and other chest symptoms	Main	-	-	-	2	-	-	-	-	-	-	-	2
		Other	-	-	-	-	-	-	-	-	-	-	-	-
786.3	Haemoptysis	Main	-	-	-	2	-	-	-	-	-	-	-	2
		Other	-	-	-	-	-	-	-	-	-	-	-	-
787	Symptoms involving digestive system	Main	-	1	-	-	-	-	-	-	-	-	-	-
		Other	-	-	-	-	-	-	-	-	-	-	-	-
787.0	Nausea and vomiting	Main	-	1	-	-	-	-	-	-	-	-	-	-
		Other	-	-	-	-	-	-	-	-	-	-	-	-
790	Nonspecific findings on examination of blood	Main	-	1	-	-	-	-	-	-	-	-	-	-
		Other	1	-	-	-	-	-	-	-	-	-	-	-

Table 5 - *continued*

ICD number	Cause of Death		Stillbirths Boys	Stillbirths Girls	0-6 Days Boys	0-6 Days Girls	1 week Boys	1 week Girls	2 weeks Boys	2 weeks Girls	3 weeks Boys	3 weeks Girls	All neonatal deaths Boys	All neonatal deaths Girls
790.2	Abnormal glucose tolerance test	Main	-	1	-	-	-	-	-	-	-	-	-	-
		Other	-	-	-	-	-	-	-	-	-	-	-	-
790.9	Other	Main	-	-	-	-	-	-	-	-	-	-	-	-
		Other	1	-	-	-	-	-	-	-	-	-	-	-
791	Nonspecific findings on examination of urine	Main	-	-	-	-	-	-	-	-	-	-	-	-
		Other	-	1	-	-	-	-	-	-	-	-	-	-
791.5	Glycosuria	Main	-	-	-	-	-	-	-	-	-	-	-	-
		Other	-	1	-	-	-	-	-	-	-	-	-	-
795	Nonspecific abnormal histological and immunological findings	Main	1	-	-	-	-	-	-	-	-	-	-	-
		Other	-	-	-	-	-	-	-	-	-	-	-	-
795.7	Other nonspecific immunological findings	Main	1	-	-	-	-	-	-	-	-	-	-	-
		Other	-	-	-	-	-	-	-	-	-	-	-	-
799	Other ill-defined and unknown causes of morbidity and mortality	Main	-	1	-	-	-	-	-	-	-	-	-	-
		Other	-	-	-	1	-	-	-	-	-	-	-	1
799.1	Respiratory failure	Main	-	-	-	-	-	-	-	-	-	-	-	-
		Other	-	-	-	1	-	-	-	-	-	-	-	1
799.8	Other ill-defined conditions	Main	-	1	-	-	-	-	-	-	-	-	-	-
		Other	-	-	-	-	-	-	-	-	-	-	-	-
800-999	**XVII Injury and poisoning**	**Main**	2	2	-	-	-	-	-	-	-	-	-	-
		Other	4	1	1	-	-	-	1	-	-	-	2	-
800-829	Fractures	Main	-	-	-	-	-	-	-	-	-	-	-	-
		Other	-	-	-	-	-	-	1	-	-	-	1	-
805-809	Fracture of neck and trunk	Main	-	-	-	-	-	-	-	-	-	-	-	-
		Other	-	-	-	-	-	-	1	-	-	-	1	-
808	Fracture of pelvis	Main	-	-	-	-	-	-	-	-	-	-	-	-
		Other	-	-	-	-	-	-	1	-	-	-	1	-
860-869	Internal injury of chest, abdomen and pelvis	Main	-	-	-	-	-	-	-	-	-	-	-	-
		Other	1	-	-	-	-	-	-	-	-	-	-	-
868	Injury to other intraabdominal organs	Main	-	-	-	-	-	-	-	-	-	-	-	-
		Other	1	-	-	-	-	-	-	-	-	-	-	-
960-979	Poisoning by drugs, medicaments and biological substances	Main	2	2	-	-	-	-	-	-	-	-	-	-
		Other	3	1	1	-	-	-	-	-	-	-	1	-
962	Poisoning by hormones and synthetic substitutes	Main	-	-	-	-	-	-	-	-	-	-	-	-
		Other	-	-	1	-	-	-	-	-	-	-	1	-
962.0	Adrenal cortical steroids	Main	-	-	-	-	-	-	-	-	-	-	-	-
		Other	-	-	1	-	-	-	-	-	-	-	1	-
964	Poisoning by agents primarily affecting blood constituents	Main	1	1	-	-	-	-	-	-	-	-	-	-
		Other	1	1	-	-	-	-	-	-	-	-	-	-
964.2	Anticoagulants	Main	1	1	-	-	-	-	-	-	-	-	-	-
		Other	1	1	-	-	-	-	-	-	-	-	-	-
972	Poisoning by agents primarily affecting the cardiovascular system	Main	-	-	-	-	-	-	-	-	-	-	-	-
		Other	1	-	-	-	-	-	-	-	-	-	-	-
972.6	Other antihypertensive agents	Main	-	-	-	-	-	-	-	-	-	-	-	-
		Other	1	-	-	-	-	-	-	-	-	-	-	-
977	Poisoning by other and unspecified drugs and medicaments	Main	1	1	-	-	-	-	-	-	-	-	-	-
		Other	1	-	-	-	-	-	-	-	-	-	-	-
977.9	Unspecified drug or medicament	Main	1	1	-	-	-	-	-	-	-	-	-	-
		Other	1	-	-	-	-	-	-	-	-	-	-	-

Table 5 1995 Series DH3 no. 28

Table 5 - *continued*

ICD number	Cause of Death		Stillbirths		Deaths 0-6 Days		1 week		2 weeks		3 weeks		All neonatal deaths	
			Boys	Girls	Boys	Girls	Boys	Girls	Boys	Girls	Boys	Girls	Boys	Girls
E800-E999	**XVII External causes of injury and poisoning**	**Main**	1	2	-	-	-	-	-	-	-	-	-	-
		Other	3	2	1	1	-	-	-	-	-	-	1	1
E800-E848	Transport accidents	Main	1	-	-	-	-	-	-	-	-	-	-	-
		Other	1	-	-	-	-	-	-	-	-	-	-	-
E810-E819	Motor vehicle traffic accidents	Main	1	-	-	-	-	-	-	-	-	-	-	-
		Other	1	-	-	-	-	-	-	-	-	-	-	-
E819	Motor vehicle traffic accident of unspecified nature	Main	1	-	-	-	-	-	-	-	-	-	-	-
		Other	1	-	-	-	-	-	-	-	-	-	-	-
E870-E879	Misadventures during medical care, abnormal reactions, late complications	Main	-	2	-	-	-	-	-	-	-	-	-	-
		Other	-	2	1	1	-	-	-	-	-	-	1	1
E878,E879	Surgical and medical procedures as the cause of abnormal reaction of patient or later complication, without mention of misadventure at the time of procedure	Main	-	2	-	-	-	-	-	-	-	-	-	-
		Other	-	2	1	1	-	-	-	-	-	-	1	1
E878	Surgical operation and other surgical procedures as the cause of abnormal reaction of patient, or of later complication, without mention of misadventure at the time of operation	Main	-	1	-	-	-	-	-	-	-	-	-	-
		Other	-	2	1	1	-	-	-	-	-	-	1	1
E879	Other procedures, without mention of misadventure at the time of procedure, as the cause of abnormal reaction of patient, or of later complication	Main	-	1	-	-	-	-	-	-	-	-	-	-
		Other	-	-	-	-	-	-	-	-	-	-	-	-
E880-E888	Accidental falls	Main	-	-	-	-	-	-	-	-	-	-	-	-
		Other	1	-	-	-	-	-	-	-	-	-	-	-
E888	Other and unspecified fall	Main	-	-	-	-	-	-	-	-	-	-	-	-
		Other	1	-	-	-	-	-	-	-	-	-	-	-
E900-E929	Other accidents, including late effects	Main	-	-	-	-	-	-	-	-	-	-	-	-
		Other	1	-	-	-	-	-	-	-	-	-	-	-
E916-E928	Other accidents	Main	-	-	-	-	-	-	-	-	-	-	-	-
		Other	1	-	-	-	-	-	-	-	-	-	-	-
E928	Other and unspecified environmental and accidental causes	Main	-	-	-	-	-	-	-	-	-	-	-	-
		Other	1	-	-	-	-	-	-	-	-	-	-	-
Other main maternal conditions			-	-	-	-	-	-	-	-	-	-	-	-
Other other maternal conditions			-	-	-	1	-	-	-	-	-	-	-	1

Table 6 Postneonatal and childhood deaths
Underlying cause of death by sex
Numbers, 1995

England and Wales

ICD number	Cause of Death	Age at death All ages 28 days to 15 years		Months 1-5		6-11		1-11		Years 1-4		5-9		10-14		1-15	
		Boys	Girls	Boys	Girls	Boys	Girls	Boys	Girls	Boys	Girls	Boys	Girls	Boys	Girls	Boys	Girls
	All causes	**1,868**	**1,323**	**570**	**384**	**198**	**132**	**768**	**516**	**391**	**333**	**269**	**196**	**340**	**210**	**1,100**	**807**
001-139	**I Infectious and parasitic diseases**	**152**	**112**	**38**	**32**	**30**	**14**	**68**	**46**	**49**	**40**	**13**	**12**	**15**	**7**	**84**	**66**
001-009	Intestinal infectious diseases	13	15	10	9	3	2	13	11	-	3	-	-	-	1	-	4
003	Other salmonella infections	1	2	1	1	-	1	1	2	-	-	-	-	-	-	-	-
003.1	Salmonella septicaemia	1	2	1	1	-	1	1	2	-	-	-	-	-	-	-	-
008	Intestinal infections due to other organisms	1	3	1	-	-	1	1	1	-	2	-	-	-	-	-	2
008.8	Other organism, not elsewhere classified	1	3	1	-	-	1	1	1	-	2	-	-	-	-	-	2
009	Ill-defined intestinal infections	11	10	8	8	3	-	11	8	-	1	-	-	-	1	-	2
009.0	Infectious colitis, enteritis and gastroenteritis	10	10	7	8	3	-	10	8	-	1	-	-	-	1	-	2
009.1	Colitis, enteritis and gastroenteritis of persumed infectious origin	1	-	1	-	-	-	1	-								
010-018	Tuberculosis	4	-	-	-	-	-	-	-	1	-	2	-	1	-	4	-
011	Pulmonary tuberculosis	3	-	-	-	-	-	-	-	1	-	1	-	1	-	3	-
011.6	Tuberculous pneumonia (any form)	2	-	-	-	-	-	-	-	-	-	1	-	1	-	2	-
011.9	Unspecified	1	-	-	-	-	-	-	-	1	-	-	-	-	-	1	-
017	Tuberculosis of other organs	1	-	-	-	-	-	-	-	-	-	1	-	-	-	1	-
017.0	Skin and subcutaneous cellular tissue	1	-	-	-	-	-	-	-	-	-	1	-	-	-	1	-
020-041	Other bacterial diseases	102	73	25	16	19	8	44	24	40	32	6	8	8	4	58	49
033	Whooping cough	1	-	1	-	-	-	1	-	-	-	-	-	-	-	-	-
033.9	Whooping cough, unspecified organism	1	-	1	-	-	-	1	-	-	-	-	-	-	-	-	-
036	Meningococcal infection	70	46	10	3	12	6	22	9	33	24	6	5	5	3	48	37
036.0	Meningococcal meningitis	6	5	-	-	2	-	2	-	3	3	1	-	-	1	4	5
036.2	Meningococcaemia	60	37	9	2	10	6	19	8	27	21	5	3	5	2	41	29
036.3	Waterhouse-Friderichsen syndrome, meningococcal	3	2	1	1	-	-	1	1	2	-	-	-	-	-	2	1
036.9	Unspecified	1	2	-	-	-	-	-	-	1	-	-	2	-	-	1	2
038	Septicaemia	29	21	13	12	6	1	19	13	7	5	-	2	3	1	10	8
038.0	Streptococcal septicaemia	4	5	3	2	-	-	3	2	1	1	-	1	-	1	1	3
038.1	Staphylococcal septicaemia	-	2	-	1	-	-	-	1	-	1	-	-	-	-	-	1
038.2	Pneumococcal septicaemia	-	1	-	-	-	-	-	-	-	-	-	1	-	-	-	1
038.4	Septicaemia due to other gram-negative organisms	8	4	4	4	1	-	5	4	3	-	-	-	-	-	3	-
038.9	Unspecified septicaemia	17	9	6	5	5	1	11	6	3	3	-	-	3	-	6	3
041	Bacterial infection in conditions classified elsewhere and of unspecified site	2	6	1	1	1	1	2	2	-	3	-	1	-	-	-	4
041.0	Streptococcus	-	2	-	-	-	1	-	1	-	1	-	-	-	-	-	1
041.5	Haemophilus influenzae (H. influenzae)	-	1	-	-	-	-	-	-	-	1	-	-	-	-	-	1
041.7	Pseudomonas	-	2	-	-	-	-	-	-	-	-	-	1	-	1	-	2
041.8	Other	-	1	-	1	-	-	-	1	-	-	-	-	-	-	-	-
041.9	Bacterial infection, unspecified	2	-	1	-	1	-	2	-	-	-	-	-	-	-	-	-
042-044	HIV infection	4	-	-	-	1	-	1	-	1	-	-	-	2	-	3	-
042	Human immunodeficiency virus infection with specified conditions	3	-	-	-	1	-	1	-	-	-	-	-	2	-	2	-
042.1	Causing other specified infections	2	-	-	-	1	-	1	-	-	-	-	-	1	-	1	-

Table 6 1995 Series DH3 no. 28

Table 6 - *continued*

ICD number	Cause of Death	All ages 28 days to 15 years		Months 1-5		6-11		1-11		Years 1-4		5-9		10-14		1-15	
		Boys	Girls	Boys	Girls	Boys	Girls	Boys	Girls	Boys	Girls	Boys	Girls	Boys	Girls	Boys	Girls
042.9	Acquired immunodeficiency syndrome, unspecified	1	-	-	-	-	-	-	-	-	-	-	-	1	-	1	-
044	Other human immunodeficiency virus infection	1	-	-	-	-	-	-	-	1	-	-	-	-	-	1	-
044.9	Human immunodeficiency virus infection, unspecified	1	-	-	-	-	-	-	-	1	-	-	-	-	-	1	-
045-079	Viral diseases	15	16	1	2	4	4	5	6	3	4	3	3	3	1	10	10
045-049	Poliomyelitis and other non-arthropod-borne viral diseases of central nervous system	6	4	-	-	-	1	-	1	3	1	-	2	2	-	6	3
046	Slow virus infection of central nervous system	3	-	-	-	-	-	-	-	-	-	-	-	2	-	3	-
046.2	Subacute sclerosing panencephalitis	3	-	-	-	-	-	-	-	-	-	-	-	2	-	3	-
048	Other enterovirus diseases of central nerous system	1	-	-	-	-	-	-	-	1	-	-	-	-	-	1	-
049	Other non-arthropod-borne viral diseases of central nervous system	2	4	-	-	-	-	-	1	2	1	-	2	-	-	2	3
049.9	Unspecified	2	4	-	-	-	1	-	1	2	1	-	2	-	-	2	3
050-057	Viral diseases accompanied by exanthem	4	1	-	1	1	-	1	1	-	-	2	-	1	-	3	-
052	Chickenpox	1	1	-	1	1	-	1	1	-	-	-	-	-	-	-	-
053	Herpes zoster	1	-	-	-	-	-	-	-	-	-	1	-	-	-	1	-
053.9	Herpes zoster without mention of complication	1	-	-	-	-	-	-	-	-	-	1	-	-	-	1	-
054	Herpes simplex	2	-	-	-	-	-	-	-	-	-	1	-	1	-	2	-
054.3	Herpetic meningoencephalitis	2	-	-	-	-	-	-	-	-	-	1	-	1	-	2	-
070-079	Other diseases due to viruses and Chlamydiae	5	11	1	1	3	3	4	4	-	3	1	1	-	1	1	7
070	Viral hepatitis	-	1	-	-	-	-	-	-	-	1	-	-	-	-	-	1
070.9	Unspecified viral hepatitis without mention of hepatic coma	-	1	-	-	-	-	-	-	-	1	-	-	-	-	-	1
075	Infectious mononucleosis	-	1	-	-	-	-	-	-	-	-	-	-	-	-	-	1
078	Other diseases due to viruses and Chlamydiae	3	4	1	1	1	2	2	3	-	1	1	-	-	-	1	1
078.5	Cytomegalic inclusion disease	2	4	-	1	1	2	1	3	-	1	1	-	-	-	1	1
078.8	Other	1	-	1	-	-	-	1	-	-	-	-	-	-	-	-	-
079	Viral infection in conditions classified elsewhere and of unspecified site	2	5	-	-	2	1	2	1	-	1	-	1	-	1	-	4
079.9	Unspecified	2	5	-	-	2	1	2	1	-	1	-	1	-	1	-	4
100-139	Other infectious and parasitic diseases and late effects of infectious and parasitic diseases	14	8	2	5	3	-	5	5	4	1	2	1	1	1	9	3
110-118	Mycoses	10	4	1	3	1	-	2	3	3	-	2	-	1	1	8	1
112	Candidiasis	2	3	1	3	-	-	1	3	1	-	-	-	-	-	1	-
112.5	Disseminated	1	2	-	2	-	-	-	2	1	-	-	-	-	-	1	-
112.9	Of unspecified site	1	1	1	1	-	-	1	1	-	-	-	-	-	-	-	-
117	Other mycoses	8	1	-	-	1	-	1	-	2	-	2	-	1	1	7	1
117.3	Aspergillosis	6	-	-	-	-	-	-	-	1	-	2	-	1	-	6	-
117.9	Other and unspecified	2	1	-	-	1	-	1	-	1	-	-	-	-	1	1	1

Table 6 - *continued*

ICD number	Cause of Death	All ages 28 days to 15 years		Months 1-5		6-11		1-11		Years 1-4		5-9		10-14		1-15	
		Boys	Girls	Boys	Girls	Boys	Girls	Boys	Girls	Boys	Girls	Boys	Girls	Boys	Girls	Boys	Girls
130-136	Other infectious and parasitic diseases	4	4	1	2	2	-	3	2	1	1	-	1	-	-	1	2
130	Toxoplasmosis	1	-	-	-	-	-	-	-	1	-	-	-	-	-	1	-
135	Sarcoidosis	-	1	-	1	-	-	-	1	-	-	-	-	-	-	-	-
136	Other and unspecified infectious and parasitic diseases	3	3	1	1	2	-	3	1	-	1	-	1	-	-	-	2
136.3	Pneumocystosis	3	2	1	1	2	-	3	1	-	-	-	1	-	-	-	1
136.9	Unspecified	-	1	-	-	-	-	-	-	-	1	-	-	-	-	-	1
140-239	**II Neoplasms**	**204**	**164**	**2**	**5**	**6**	**4**	**8**	**9**	**48**	**39**	**72**	**48**	**63**	**52**	**196**	**155**
140-208	Malignant neoplasms	186	140	1	2	4	3	5	5	44	30	68	44	57	47	181	135
140-149	Malignant neoplasm of lip, oral cavity and pharynx	3	1	-	-	-	-	-	-	-	-	2	-	1	1	3	1
143	Malignant neoplasm of gum	1	-	-	-	-	-	-	-	-	-	-	-	1	-	1	-
143.9	Gum, unspecified	1	-	-	-	-	-	-	-	-	-	-	-	1	-	1	-
147	Malignant neoplasm of nasopharynx	2	1	-	-	-	-	-	-	-	-	2	-	-	1	2	1
147.9	Nasopharynx, unspecified	2	1	-	-	-	-	-	-	-	-	2	-	-	1	2	1
150-159	Malignant neoplasm of digestive organs and peritoneum	4	6	-	-	-	1	-	1	1	3	-	-	2	1	4	5
153	Malignant neoplasm of colon	1	-	-	-	-	-	-	-	-	-	-	-	-	-	1	-
153.9	Colon, unspecified	1	-	-	-	-	-	-	-	-	-	-	-	-	-	1	-
155	Malignant neoplasm of liver and intrahepatic bile ducts	3	5	-	-	-	1	-	1	1	3	-	-	2	1	3	4
155.0	Liver, primary	2	2	-	-	-	-	-	-	1	2	-	-	1	-	2	2
155.2	Liver, not specified as primary or secondary	1	3	-	-	-	1	-	1	-	1	-	-	1	1	1	2
157	Malignant neoplasm of pancreas	-	1	-	-	-	-	-	-	-	-	-	-	-	-	-	1
157.9	Part unspecified	-	1	-	-	-	-	-	-	-	-	-	-	-	-	-	1
160-165	Malignant neoplasm of respiratory and intrathoracic organs	1	-	-	-	-	-	-	-	-	-	-	-	1	-	1	-
162	Malignant neoplasm of trachea, bronchus and lung	1	-	-	-	-	-	-	-	-	-	-	-	1	-	1	-
162.9	Bronchus and lung, unspecified	1	-	-	-	-	-	-	-	-	-	-	-	1	-	1	-
170-175	Malignant neoplasm of bone, connective tissue, skin and breast	18	20	-	-	-	-	-	-	4	4	4	6	9	7	18	20
170	Malignant neoplasm of bone and articular cartilage	9	5	-	-	-	-	-	-	1	-	1	1	6	3	9	5
170.2	Vertebral column, excluding sacrum and coccyx	2	-	-	-	-	-	-	-	1	-	-	-	1	-	2	-
170.3	Ribs, sternum and clavicle	1	-	-	-	-	-	-	-	-	-	-	-	1	-	1	-
170.7	Lower limb, long bones	1	1	-	-	-	-	-	-	-	-	-	1	1	-	1	1
170.9	Site unspecified	5	4	-	-	-	-	-	-	-	-	1	-	3	3	5	4
171	Malignant neoplasm of connective and other soft tissue	9	13	-	-	-	-	-	-	3	4	3	5	3	3	9	13
171.3	Lower limb, including hip	-	1	-	-	-	-	-	-	-	-	-	-	-	1	-	1
171.6	Pelvis	-	3	-	-	-	-	-	-	-	1	-	1	-	1	-	3
171.9	Site unspecified	9	9	-	-	-	-	-	-	3	3	3	4	3	1	9	9
173	Other malignant neoplasm of skin	-	2	-	-	-	-	-	-	-	-	-	-	-	1	-	2

Table 6 1995 Series DH3 no. 28

Table 6 - *continued*

ICD number	Cause of Death	All ages 28 days to 15 years		Months 1-5		6-11		1-11		Years 1-4		5-9		10-14		1-15	
		Boys	Girls	Boys	Girls	Boys	Girls	Boys	Girls	Boys	Girls	Boys	Girls	Boys	Girls	Boys	Girls
173.4	Scalp and skin of neck	-	1	-	-	-	-	-	-	-	-	-	-	-	-	-	1
173.9	Site unspecified	-	1	-	-	-	-	-	-	-	-	-	-	-	1	-	1
179-189	Malignant neoplasm of genitourinary organs	4	5	-	-	-	-	-	-	2	1	1	3	1	1	4	5
189	Malignant neoplasm of kidney and other and specified urinary organs	4	5	-	-	-	-	-	-	2	1	1	3	1	1	4	5
189.0	Kidney, except pelvis	4	5	-	-	-	-	-	-	2	1	1	3	1	1	4	5
190-199	Malignant neoplasm of other and unspecified sites	65	52	-	-	2	1	2	1	21	12	21	21	20	15	63	51
190	Malignant neoplasm of eye	1	-	-	-	-	-	-	-	-	-	-	-	1	-	1	-
190.6	Choroid	1	-	-	-	-	-	-	-	-	-	-	-	1	-	1	-
191	Malignant neoplasm of brain	33	38	-	-	2	1	2	1	9	8	10	15	12	13	31	37
191.0	Cerebrum, except lobes and ventricles	3	1	-	-	-	-	-	-	2	-	-	1	1	-	3	1
191.1	Frontal lobe	1	-	-	-	-	-	-	-	-	-	-	-	1	-	1	-
191.5	Ventricle	1	-	-	-	-	-	-	-	1	-	-	-	-	-	1	-
191.6	Cerebellum	6	5	-	-	1	-	1	-	2	3	1	1	2	1	5	5
191.7	Brain stem	12	19	-	-	1	-	1	-	2	2	7	12	2	5	11	19
191.9	Brain, unspecified	10	13	-	-	-	1	-	1	2	3	2	1	6	7	10	12
192	Malignant neoplasm of other and unspecified parts of nervous system	3	-	-	-	-	-	-	-	-	-	1	-	2	-	3	-
192.2	Spinal cord	3	-	-	-	-	-	-	-	-	-	1	-	2	-	3	-
194	Malignant neoplasm of other endocrine glands and related structures	26	12	-	-	-	-	-	-	12	4	10	6	3	1	26	12
194.0	Suprarenal gland	24	12	-	-	-	-	-	-	11	4	10	6	3	1	24	12
194.4	Pineal gland	2	-	-	-	-	-	-	-	1	-	-	-	-	-	2	-
199	Malignant neoplasm without specification of site	2	2	-	-	-	-	-	-	-	-	-	-	2	1	2	2
199.0	Disseminated	1	1	-	-	-	-	-	-	-	-	-	-	1	-	1	1
199.1	Other	1	1	-	-	-	-	-	-	-	-	-	-	1	1	1	1
200-208	Malignant neoplasm of lymphatic and haematopoietic tissue	91	56	1	2	2	1	3	3	16	10	40	14	23	22	88	53
200	Lymphosarcoma and reticulosarcoma	4	1	-	-	-	-	-	-	1	-	3	-	-	1	4	1
200.1	Lymphosarcoma	1	1	-	-	-	-	-	-	1	-	-	-	-	1	1	1
200.2	Burkitt's tumour	3	-	-	-	-	-	-	-	-	-	3	-	-	-	3	-
201	Hodgkin's disease	-	2	-	-	-	-	-	-	-	-	-	1	-	1	-	2
201.9	Unspecified	-	2	-	-	-	-	-	-	-	-	-	1	-	1	-	2
202	Other malignant neoplasm of lymphoid and histiocytic tissue	13	6	-	-	1	-	1	-	2	2	3	1	6	3	12	6
202.3	Malignant histiocytosis	1	-	-	-	1	-	1	-	-	-	-	-	-	-	-	-
202.8	Other lymphomas	12	6	-	-	-	-	-	-	2	2	3	1	6	3	12	6
203	Multiple myeloma and immunoproliferative neoplasms	1	-	-	-	-	-	-	-	-	-	-	-	-	-	1	-
203.1	Plasma cell leukaemia	1	-	-	-	-	-	-	-	-	-	-	-	-	-	1	-
204-208	Leukaemia	73	47	1	2	1	1	2	3	13	8	34	12	17	17	71	44
204	Lymphoid leukaemia	47	27	-	1	-	1	-	2	7	5	25	7	10	9	47	25
204.0	Acute	46	27	-	1	-	1	-	2	7	5	24	7	10	9	46	25
204.9	Unspecified	1	-	-	-	-	-	-	-	-	-	1	-	-	-	1	-
205	Myeloid leukaemia	20	17	1	1	1	-	2	1	4	3	7	4	6	6	18	16
205.0	Acute	18	15	1	1	1	-	2	1	4	3	6	3	5	5	16	14
205.1	Chronic	1	2	-	-	-	-	-	-	-	-	1	1	-	1	1	2
205.9	Unspecified	1	-	-	-	-	-	-	-	-	-	-	-	1	-	1	-

Table 6 - *continued*

ICD number	Cause of Death	All ages 28 days to 15 years Boys	Girls	Months 1-5 Boys	Girls	6-11 Boys	Girls	1-11 Boys	Girls	Years 1-4 Boys	Girls	5-9 Boys	Girls	10-14 Boys	Girls	1-15 Boys	Girls
208	Leukaemia of unspecified cell type	6	3	-	-	-	-	-	-	2	-	2	1	1	2	6	3
208.0	Acute	2	3	-	-	-	-	-	-	-	-	-	1	1	2	2	3
208.9	Unspecified	4	-	-	-	-	-	-	-	2	-	2	-	-	-	4	-
210-229	Benign neoplasms	6	7	1	1	1	1	2	2	1	1	-	2	3	1	4	5
212	Benign neoplasm of respiratory and intrathoracic organs	1	1	-	-	-	1	-	1	-	-	-	-	1	-	1	-
212.7	Heart	1	1	-	-	-	1	-	1	-	-	-	-	1	-	1	-
228	Haemangioma and lymphangioma, any site	2	1	1	1	-	-	1	1	1	-	-	-	-	-	1	-
228.0	Haemangioma, any site	-	1	-	1	-	-	-	1	-	-	-	-	-	-	-	-
228.1	Lymphangioma, any site	2	-	1	-	-	-	1	-	1	-	-	-	-	-	1	-
229	Benign neoplasm of other and unspecified sites	3	5	-	-	1	-	1	-	-	1	-	2	2	1	2	5
229.9	Site unspecified	3	5	-	-	1	-	1	-	-	1	-	2	2	1	2	5
235-239	Neoplasms of uncertain behaviour or unspecified nature	12	17	-	2	1	-	1	2	3	8	4	2	3	4	11	15
235	Neoplasm of uncertain behaviour of digestive and respiratory systems	-	1	-	1	-	-	-	1	-	-	-	-	-	-	-	-
235.3	Liver and biliary passages	-	1	-	1	-	-	-	1	-	-	-	-	-	-	-	-
237	Neoplasm of uncertain behaviour of endocrine glands and nervous system	3	-	-	-	-	-	-	-	-	-	-	-	3	-	3	-
237.0	Pituitary gland and craniopharyngeal duct	2	-											2	-	2	-
237.5	Brain and spinal cord	1	-	-	-	-	-	-	-	-	-	-	-	1	-	1	-
238	Neoplasm of uncertain behaviour of other and unspecified sites and tissues	1	1	-	-	-	-	-	-	-	-	1	1	-	-	1	1
238.7	Other lymphatic and haematopoietic tissues	1	1	-	-	-	-	-	-	-	-	1	1	-	-	1	1
239	Neoplasm of unspecified nature	8	15	-	1	1	-	1	1	3	8	3	1	-	4	7	14
239.0	Digestive system	3	1	-	-	1	-	1	-	1	-	-	-	-	-	2	1
239.6	Brain	5	11	-	1	-	-	-	1	2	6	3	1	-	3	5	10
239.7	Endocrine glands, and other parts of nervous system	-	1	-	-	-	-	-	-	-	-	-	-	-	1	-	1
239.8	Other specified sites	-	1	-	-	-	-	-	-	-	1	-	-	-	-	-	1
239.9	Site unspecified	-	1	-	-	-	-	-	-	-	1	-	-	-	-	-	1
240-279	**III Endocrine, nutritional and metabolic diseases and immunity disorders**	**55**	**46**	**14**	**3**	**9**	**8**	**23**	**11**	**12**	**13**	**5**	**7**	**12**	**13**	**32**	**35**
240-246	Disorders of thyroid gland	-	1	-	1	-	-	-	1	-	-	-	-	-	-	-	-
244	Acquired hypothyroidism	-	1	-	1	-	-	-	1	-	-	-	-	-	-	-	-
244.9	Unspecified hypothyroidism	-	1	-	1	-	-	-	1	-	-	-	-	-	-	-	-
250-259	Diseases of other endocrine glands	2	5	-	-	-	-	-	-	-	-	1	2	1	3	2	5
250	Diabetes mellitus	-	4	-	-	-	-	-	-	-	-	-	1	-	3	-	4
250.1	Diabetes with ketoacidosis	-	4	-	-	-	-	-	-	-	-	-	1	-	3	-	4
255	Disorders of adrenal glands	1	-	-	-	-	-	-	-	-	-	-	-	1	-	1	-
255.4	Corticoadrenal insufficiency	1	-	-	-	-	-	-	-	-	-	-	-	1	-	1	-
259	Other endocrine disorders	1	1	-	-	-	-	-	-	-	-	1	1	-	-	1	1
259.4	Dwarfism, not elsewhere classified	-	1	-	-	-	-	-	-	-	-	-	1	-	-	-	1
259.8	Other	1	-	-	-	-	-	-	-	-	-	1	-	-	-	1	-

Table 6 1995 Series DH3 no. 28

Table 6 - *continued*

ICD number	Cause of Death	Age at death															
		All ages															
		28 days to		Months						Years							
		15 years		1-5		6-11		1-11		1-4		5-9		10-14		1-15	
		Boys	Girls	Boys	Girls	Boys	Girls	Boys	Girls	Boys	Girls	Boys	Girls	Boys	Girls	Boys	Girls
260-269	Nutritional deficiencies	1	2	1	1	-	-	1	1	-	-	-	1	-	-	-	1
268	Vitamin D deficiency	1	-	1	-	-	-	1	-	-	-	-	-	-	-	-	-
268.0	Rickets, active	1	-	1	-	-	-	1	-	-	-	-	-	-	-	-	-
269	Other nutritional deficiencies	-	2	-	1	-	-	-	1	-	-	-	1	-	-	-	1
269.9	Unspecified	-	2	-	1	-	-	-	1	-	-	-	1	-	-	-	1
270-279	Other metabolic disorders and immunity disorders	52	38	13	1	9	8	22	9	12	13	4	4	11	10	30	29
270	Disorders of amino-acid transport and metabolism	2	1	-	-	1	-	1	-	-	1	-	-	-	-	1	1
270.2	Other disturbances of aromatic amino-acid metabolism	1	-	-	-	1	-	1	-	-	-	-	-	-	-	-	-
270.6	Disorders of urea cycle metabolism	1	1	-	-	-	-	-	-	-	1	-	-	-	-	1	1
271	Disorders of carbohydrate transport and metabolism	2	2	-	-	2	1	2	1	-	-	-	1	-	-	-	1
271.0	Glycogenosis	2	1	-	-	2	-	2	-	-	-	-	1	-	-	-	1
271.8	Other	-	1	-	-	-	1	-	1	-	-	-	-	-	-	-	-
272	Disorders of lipoid metabolism	2	4	-	-	1	2	1	2	1	1	-	1	-	-	1	2
272.7	Lipidoses	2	4	-	-	1	2	1	2	1	1	-	1	-	-	1	2
275	Disorders of mineral metabolism	3	1	2	-	1	1	3	1	-	-	-	-	-	-	-	-
275.0	Disorders of iron metabolism	2	-	2	-	-	-	2	-	-	-	-	-	-	-	-	-
275.3	Disorders of phosphorus metabolism	1	1	-	-	1	1	1	1	-	-	-	-	-	-	-	-
276	Disorders of fluid, electrolyte and acid-base balance	7	3	-	-	1	-	1	-	4	3	1	-	1	-	6	3
276.0	Hyperosmolality and/or hypernatraemia	1	-	-	-	1	-	1	-	-	-	-	-	-	-	-	-
276.1	Hyposmolality and/or hyponatraemia	-	1	-	-	-	-	-	-	-	1	-	-	-	-	-	1
276.2	Acidosis	5	2	-	-	-	-	-	-	3	2	1	-	1	-	5	2
276.5	Volume depletion	1	-	-	-	-	-	-	-	1	-	-	-	-	-	1	-
277	Other and unspecified disorders of metabolism	27	25	7	1	1	4	8	5	6	7	2	2	9	9	19	20
277.0	Cystic fibrosis	10	13	1	-	-	1	1	1	-	-	1	2	6	8	9	12
277.3	Amyloidosis	-	1	-	-	-	-	-	-	-	1	-	-	-	-	-	1
277.4	Disorders of bilirubin excretion	1	-	1	-	-	-	1	-	-	-	-	-	-	-	-	-
277.5	Mucopolysaccharidosis	5	2	-	-	-	-	-	-	2	2	-	-	3	-	5	2
277.6	Other deficiencies of circulating enzymes	-	1	-	-	-	1	-	1	-	-	-	-	-	-	-	-
277.8	Other	2	3	1	-	-	1	1	1	1	1	-	-	-	1	1	2
277.9	Unspecified	9	5	4	1	1	1	5	2	3	3	1	-	-	-	4	3
279	Disorders involving the immune mechanism	9	2	4	-	2	-	6	-	1	1	1	-	1	1	3	2
279.1	Deficiency of cell-mediated immunity	3	-	1	-	1	-	2	-	-	-	1	-	-	-	1	-
279.2	Combined immunity deficiency	2	1	1	-	1	-	2	-	-	-	-	-	-	1	-	1
279.3	Unspecified immunity deficiency	4	1	2	-	-	-	2	-	1	1	-	-	1	-	2	1
280-289	**IV Diseases of blood and blood-forming organs**	19	13	4	1	1	-	5	1	3	6	6	3	4	3	14	12
280-285	Anaemias	7	9	1	-	-	-	1	-	-	5	5	2	1	2	6	9
282	Hereditary haemolytic anaemias	3	4	-	-	-	-	-	-	-	1	2	2	1	1	3	4
282.4	Thalassaemias	2	2	-	-	-	-	-	-	-	-	1	1	1	1	2	2
282.6	Sickle-cell anaemia	1	2	-	-	-	-	-	-	-	1	1	1	-	-	1	2
283	Acquired haemolytic anaemias	-	3	-	-	-	-	-	-	-	-	-	2	-	1	-	3

Table 6 - *continued*

ICD number	Cause of Death	Age at death														
		All ages 28 days to 15 years		Months						Years						
				1-5		6-11		1-11		1-4		5-9		10-14		1-15	
		Boys	Girls	Boys	Girls	Boys	Girls	Boys	Girls	Boys	Girls	Boys	Girls	Boys	Girls	Boys	Girls
283.1	Non-autoimmune haemolytic anaemias	-	3	-	-	-	-	-	-	-	2	-	-	-	1	-	3
284	Aplastic anaemia	4	2	1	-	-	-	1	-	-	2	3	-	-	-	3	2
284.0	Constitutional aplastic anaemia	4	1	1	-	-	-	1	-	-	1	3	-	-	-	3	1
284.8	Other	-	1	-	-	-	-	-	-	-	1	-	-	-	-	-	1
286	Coagulation defects	7	2	3	1	-	-	3	1	3	1	1	-	-	-	4	1
286.3	Congenital deficiency of other clotting factors	1	-	1	-	-	-	1	-	-	-	-	-	-	-	-	-
286.6	Defibrination syndrome	6	2	2	1	-	-	2	1	3	1	1	-	-	-	4	1
287	Purpura and other haemorrhagic conditions	3	-	-	-	1	-	1	-	-	-	-	-	1	-	2	-
287.3	Primary thrombocytopenia	1	-	-	-	-	-	-	-	-	-	-	-	-	-	1	-
287.5	Thrombocytopenia, unspecified	2	-	-	-	1	-	1	-	-	-	-	-	1	-	1	-
289	Other diseases of blood and blood-forming organs	2	2	-	-	-	-	-	-	-	-	-	1	2	1	2	2
289.8	Other	1	1	-	-	-	-	-	-	-	-	-	-	1	1	1	1
289.9	Unspecified	1	1	-	-	-	-	-	-	-	-	-	1	1	-	1	1
290-319	**V Mental disorders**	11	6	-	-	-	-	-	-	-	-	1	-	2	5	11	6
304	Drug dependence	7	3	-	-	-	-	-	-	-	-	-	-	2	3	7	3
304.6	Other	7	3	-	-	-	-	-	-	-	-	-	-	2	3	7	3
305	Nondependent abuse of drugs	3	2	-	-	-	-	-	-	-	-	-	-	-	1	3	2
305.5	Morphine type	-	1	-	-	-	-	-	-	-	-	-	-	-	-	-	1
305.7	Amphetamine type	1	-	-	-	-	-	-	-	-	-	-	-	-	-	1	-
305.9	Other, mixed or unspecified	2	1	-	-	-	-	-	-	-	-	-	-	-	1	2	1
315	Specific delays in development	1	-	-	-	-	-	-	-	-	-	1	-	-	-	1	-
315.9	Unspecified	1	-	-	-	-	-	-	-	-	-	1	-	-	-	1	-
317-319	Mental retardation	-	1	-	-	-	-	-	-	-	-	-	-	-	1	-	1
319	Unspecified mental retardation	-	1	-	-	-	-	-	-	-	-	-	-	-	1	-	1
320-389	**VI Diseases of the nervous system and sense organs**	181	134	45	29	17	10	62	39	45	45	27	17	35	23	119	95
320-359	Diseases of nervous system	181	132	45	28	17	10	62	38	45	44	27	17	35	23	119	94
320-326	Inflammatory diseases of the central nervous system	17	20	6	6	-	1	6	7	3	8	5	-	2	4	11	13
320-322	Meningitis	14	16	4	6	-	1	4	7	3	5	4	-	2	3	10	9
320	Bacterial meningitis	7	8	3	4	-	1	3	5	2	2	-	-	2	-	4	3
320.1	Pneumococcal meningitis	3	3	1	1	-	-	1	1	1	2	-	-	1	-	2	2
320.2	Streptococcal meningitis	1	1	1	-	-	1	1	1	-	-	-	-	-	-	-	-
320.3	Staphylococcal meningitis	-	1	-	1	-	-	-	1	-	-	-	-	-	-	-	-
320.8	Meningitis due to other specified bacteria	-	1	-	1	-	-	-	1	-	-	-	-	-	-	-	-
320.9	Meningitis due to unspecified bacterium	3	2	1	1	-	-	1	1	1	-	-	-	1	-	2	1
322	Meningitis of unspecified cause	7	8	1	2	-	-	1	2	1	3	4	-	-	3	6	6
322.9	Meningitis, unspecified	7	8	1	2	-	-	1	2	1	3	4	-	-	3	6	6
323	Encephalitis, myelitis and encephalomyelitis	3	4	2	-	-	-	2	-	-	3	1	-	-	1	1	4
323.9	Unspecified cause	3	4	2	-	-	-	2	-	-	3	1	-	-	1	1	4
330-337	Hereditary and degenerative diseases of the central nervous system	59	42	20	11	9	3	29	14	15	14	5	9	9	4	30	28
330	Cerebral degenerations usually manifest in childhood	27	16	6	1	4	2	10	3	9	7	3	4	5	1	17	13
330.0	Leucodystrophy	11	6	1	-	1	1	2	1	2	3	2	2	5	-	9	5

Table 6 1995 Series DH3 no. 28

Table 6 - *continued*

ICD number	Cause of Death	All ages 28 days to 15 years		Months 1-5		6-11		1-11		Years 1-4		5-9		10-14		1-15	
		Boys	Girls	Boys	Girls	Boys	Girls	Boys	Girls	Boys	Girls	Boys	Girls	Boys	Girls	Boys	Girls
330.1	Cerebral lipidoses	8	8	-	-	1	1	1	1	6	3	1	2	-	1	7	7
330.8	Other cerebral degenerations in childhood	8	2	5	1	2	-	7	1	1	1	-	-	-	-	1	1
331	Other cerebral degenerations	9	10	3	1	1	-	4	1	2	3	1	3	2	3	5	9
331.3	Communicating hydrocephalus	1	-	1	-	-	-	1	-	-	-	-	-	-	-	-	-
331.4	Obstructive hydrocephalus	5	4	2	1	1	-	3	1	-	2	1	-	1	1	2	3
331.8	Other cerebral degeneration	1	4	-	-	-	-	-	-	1	-	-	3	-	1	1	4
331.9	Unspecified	2	2	-	-	-	-	-	-	1	1	-	-	1	1	2	2
333	Other extrapyramidal disease and abnormal movement disorders	-	1	-	-	-	-	-	-	-	1	-	-	-	-	-	1
333.0	Other degenerative diseases of the basal ganglia	-	1	-	-	-	-	-	-	-	1	-	-	-	-	-	1
334	Spinocerebellar disease	1	-	-	-	-	-	-	-	-	-	-	-	-	-	1	-
334.0	Friedreich's ataxia	1	-	-	-	-	-	-	-	-	-	-	-	-	-	1	-
335	Anterior horn cell disease	21	15	11	9	4	1	15	10	4	3	-	2	2	-	6	5
335.0	Werdnig-Hoffmann disease	5	5	3	3	2	-	5	3	-	2	-	-	-	-	-	2
335.1	Spinal muscular atrophy	15	10	8	6	2	1	10	7	3	1	-	2	2	-	5	3
335.2	Motor neurone disease	1	-	-	-	-	-	-	-	1	-	-	-	-	-	1	-
337	Disorders of the autonomic nervous system	1	-	-	-	-	-	-	-	-	-	1	-	-	-	1	-
337.9	Unspecified	1	-	-	-	-	-	-	-	-	-	1	-	-	-	1	-
340-349	Other disorders of the central nervous system	81	55	12	2	6	5	18	7	22	21	16	8	21	12	63	48
343	Infantile cerebral palsy	36	32	4	-	1	3	5	3	11	12	7	6	10	6	31	29
343.2	Quadriplegic	3	-	-	-	-	-	-	-	-	-	-	-	2	-	3	-
343.9	Unspecified	33	32	4	-	1	3	5	3	11	12	7	6	8	6	28	29
344	Other paralytic syndromes	4	1	-	-	-	1	-	1	1	-	2	-	1	-	4	-
344.0	Quadriplegia	4	-	-	-	-	-	-	-	1	-	2	-	1	-	4	-
344.6	Cauda equina syndrome	-	1	-	-	-	1	-	1	-	-	-	-	-	-	-	-
345	Epilepsy	21	16	1	-	3	-	4	-	6	8	3	1	7	6	17	16
345.1	Generalized convulsive epilepsy	4	2	-	-	1	-	1	-	2	-	1	-	-	2	3	2
345.3	Grand mal status	5	4	1	-	1	-	2	-	1	3	-	-	1	1	3	4
345.9	Unspecified	12	10	-	-	1	-	1	-	3	5	2	1	6	3	11	10
348	Other conditions of brain	14	4	6	2	2	1	8	3	2	-	2	-	2	-	6	1
348.1	Anoxic brain damage	4	2	3	2	-	-	3	2	1	-	-	-	-	-	1	-
348.3	Encephalopathy, unspecified	5	-	2	-	2	-	4	-	-	-	1	-	-	-	1	-
348.4	Compression of brain	1	-	-	-	-	-	-	-	1	-	-	-	-	-	1	-
348.5	Cerebral oedema	3	1	-	-	-	-	-	-	-	-	1	-	2	-	3	1
348.9	Unspecified	1	1	1	-	-	1	1	1	-	-	-	-	-	-	-	-
349	Other and unspecified disorders of the nervous system	6	2	1	-	-	-	1	-	2	1	2	1	1	-	5	2
349.8	Other	6	2	1	-	-	-	1	-	2	1	2	1	1	-	5	2
350-359	Diseases of the peripheral nervous system	24	15	7	9	2	1	9	10	5	1	1	-	3	3	15	5
355	Mononeuritis of lower limb	1	1	-	-	-	-	-	-	1	-	-	-	-	-	1	1
355.9	Mononeuritis of unspecified site	1	1	-	-	-	-	-	-	1	-	-	-	-	-	1	1
356	Hereditary and idiopathic peripheral neuropathy	2	1	-	-	-	-	-	-	-	1	1	-	-	-	2	1
356.3	Refsum's disease	1	-	-	-	-	-	-	-	-	-	1	-	-	-	1	-
356.9	Unspecified	1	1	-	-	-	-	-	-	-	1	-	-	-	-	1	1
358	Myoneural disorders	4	1	1	1	1	-	2	1	1	-	-	-	-	-	2	-
358.8	Other	4	1	1	1	1	-	2	1	1	-	-	-	-	-	2	-
359	Muscular dystrophies and other myopathies	17	12	6	8	1	1	7	9	3	-	-	-	3	3	10	3
359.0	Congenital hereditary muscular dystrophy	4	7	3	4	-	1	3	5	1	-	-	-	-	2	1	2
359.1	Hereditary progressive muscular dystrophy	7	1	-	1	-	-	-	1	-	-	-	-	3	-	7	-

Table 6 - *continued*

ICD number	Cause of Death	All ages 28 days to 15 years		Months 1-5		6-11		1-11		Years 1-4		5-9		10-14		1-15	
		Boys	Girls	Boys	Girls	Boys	Girls	Boys	Girls	Boys	Girls	Boys	Girls	Boys	Girls	Boys	Girls
359.2	Myotonic disorders	4	3	3	2	1	-	4	2	-	-	-	-	-	1	-	1
359.8	Other	1	-	-	-	-	-	-	-	1	-	-	-	-	-	1	-
359.9	Unspecified	1	1	-	1	-	-	-	1	1	-	-	-	-	-	1	-
380-389	Diseases of the ear and mastoid process	-	2	-	1	-	-	-	1	-	1	-	-	-	-	-	1
381-383	Otitis media and mastoiditis	-	2	-	1	-	-	-	1	-	1	-	-	-	-	-	1
382	Suppurative and unspecified otitis media	-	2	-	1	-	-	-	1	-	1	-	-	-	-	-	1
382.9	Unspecified otitis media	-	2	-	1	-	-	-	1	-	1	-	-	-	-	-	1
390-459	**VII Diseases of the circulatory system**	**90**	**72**	**25**	**18**	**7**	**6**	**32**	**24**	**17**	**18**	**14**	**14**	**25**	**13**	**58**	**48**
391	Rheumatic fever with heart involvement	-	1	-	-	-	-	-	-	-	-	-	1	-	-	-	1
391.2	Acute rheumatic myocarditis	-	1	-	-	-	-	-	-	-	-	-	1	-	-	-	1
393-398	Chronic rheumatic heart disease	2	1	2	-	-	-	2	-	-	-	-	1	-	-	-	1
394	Diseases of mitral valve	1	1	1	-	-	-	1	-	-	-	-	1	-	-	-	1
394.0	Mitral stenosis	1	-	1	-	-	-	1	-	-	-	-	-	-	-	-	-
394.9	Other and unspecified	-	1	-	-	-	-	-	-	-	-	-	1	-	-	-	1
397	Diseases of other endocardial structures	1	-	1	-	-	-	1	-	-	-	-	-	-	-	-	-
397.0	Diseases of tricuspid valve	1	-	1	-	-	-	1	-	-	-	-	-	-	-	-	-
410-414	Ischaemic heart disease	2	2	-	-	-	-	-	-	1	-	-	1	1	1	2	2
410	Acute myocardial infarction	1	-	-	-	-	-	-	-	-	-	-	-	1	-	1	-
414	Other forms of chronic ischaemic heart disease	1	2	-	-	-	-	-	-	1	-	-	1	-	1	1	2
414.0	Coronary atherosclerosis	-	1	-	-	-	-	-	-	-	-	-	-	-	1	-	1
414.8	Other	1	1	-	-	-	-	-	-	1	-	-	1	-	-	1	1
415-417	Diseases of pulmonary circulation	10	6	3	-	2	-	5	-	3	3	1	2	1	1	5	6
415	Acute pulmonary heart disease	1	1	-	-	-	-	-	-	1	1	-	-	-	-	1	1
415.1	Pulmonary embolism	1	1	-	-	-	-	-	-	1	1	-	-	-	-	1	1
416	Chronic pulmonary heart disease	8	4	3	-	2	-	5	-	2	2	-	2	1	-	3	4
416.0	Primary pulmonary hypertension	8	4	3	-	2	-	5	-	2	2	-	2	1	-	3	4
417	Other diseases of pulmonary circulation	1	1	-	-	-	-	-	-	-	-	1	-	-	1	1	1
417.9	Unspecified	1	1	-	-	-	-	-	-	-	-	1	-	-	1	1	1
420-429	Other forms of heart disease	38	43	5	14	1	4	6	18	10	11	9	6	13	6	32	25
421	Acute and subacute endocarditis	1	-	-	-	-	-	-	-	1	-	-	-	-	-	1	-
421.0	Acute and subacute bacterial endocarditis	1	-	-	-	-	-	-	-	1	-	-	-	-	-	1	-
422	Acute myocarditis	2	8	-	1	-	-	-	1	2	3	-	4	-	-	2	7
422.9	Other and unspecified acute myocarditis	2	8	-	1	-	-	-	1	2	3	-	4	-	-	2	7
424	Other diseases of endocardium	1	1	-	-	-	-	-	-	-	-	1	1	-	-	1	1
424.1	Aortic valve disorders	1	1	-	-	-	-	-	-	-	-	1	1	-	-	1	1
425	Cardiomyopathy	24	24	3	10	1	2	4	12	7	7	5	1	8	4	20	12

Table 6 1995 Series DH3 no. 28

Table 6 - *continued*

ICD number	Cause of Death	All ages 28 days to 15 years		Months 1-5		6-11		1-11		Years 1-4		5-9		10-14		1-15	
		Boys	Girls	Boys	Girls	Boys	Girls	Boys	Girls	Boys	Girls	Boys	Girls	Boys	Girls	Boys	Girls
425.1	Hypertrophic obstructive cardiomyopathy	3	-	1	-	-	-	1	-	-	-	-	-	2	-	2	-
425.3	Endocardial fibroelastosis	2	5	-	4	-	-	-	4	2	1	-	-	-	-	2	1
425.4	Other primary cardiomyopathies	19	19	2	6	1	2	3	8	5	6	5	1	6	4	16	11
426	Conduction disorders	1	-	-	-	-	-	-	-	-	-	-	-	1	-	1	-
426.7	Anomalous atrioventricular excitation	1	-	-	-	-	-	-	-	-	-	-	-	1	-	1	-
427	Cardiac dysrhythmias	4	3	1	1	-	-	1	1	-	-	1	-	2	1	3	2
427.5	Cardiac arrest	1	3	1	1	-	-	1	1	-	-	-	-	-	1	-	2
427.9	Unspecified	3	-	-	-	-	-	-	-	-	-	1	-	2	-	3	-
428	Heart failure	3	1	1	1	-	-	1	1	-	-	2	-	-	-	2	-
428.0	Congestive heart failure	1	-	1	-	-	-	1	-	-	-	-	-	-	-	-	-
428.9	Unspecified	2	1	-	1	-	-	-	1	-	-	2	-	-	-	2	-
429	Ill-defined descriptions and complications of heart disease	2	6	-	1	-	2	-	3	-	1	-	-	2	1	2	3
429.0	Myocarditis, unspecified	1	5	-	1	-	2	-	3	-	1	-	-	1	1	1	2
429.3	Cardiomegaly	-	1	-	-	-	-	-	-	-	-	-	-	-	-	-	1
429.9	Unspecified	1	-	-	-	-	-	-	-	-	-	-	-	1	-	1	-
430-438	Cerebrovascular disease	33	19	13	4	4	2	17	6	1	4	4	3	10	5	16	13
430	Subarachoid haemorrhage	4	2	-	-	1	-	1	-	-	1	1	1	2	-	3	2
431,432	Intracerebral and other intracranial haemorrhage	13	9	3	2	2	1	5	3	-	-	2	2	5	4	8	6
431	Intracerebral haemorrhage	11	8	2	2	2	1	4	3	-	-	1	2	5	3	7	5
432	Other and unspecified intracranial haemorrhage	2	3	1	-	-	-	1	-	-	1	1	-	-	2	1	3
432.1	Subdural haemorrhage	-	2	-	-	-	-	-	-	-	-	1	-	-	1	-	2
432.9	Unspecified intracranial haemorrhage	2	1	1	-	-	-	1	-	-	-	1	-	-	1	1	1
433	Occlusion and stenosis of precerebral arteries	1	-	-	-	-	-	-	-	-	-	-	-	1	-	1	-
433.1	Carotid artery	1	-	-	-	-	-	-	-	-	-	-	-	1	-	1	-
434	Occlusion of cerebral arteries	4	-	1	-	-	-	1	-	-	-	1	-	2	-	3	-
434.1	Cerebral embolism	1	-	-	-	-	-	-	-	-	-	1	-	-	-	1	-
434.9	Unspecified	3	-	1	-	-	-	1	-	-	-	-	-	2	-	2	-
436	Acute but ill-defined cerebrovascular disease	-	1	-	-	-	-	-	-	-	1	-	-	-	-	-	1
437	Other and ill-defined cerebrovascular disease	11	5	9	2	1	1	10	3	1	1	-	-	-	-	1	2
437.1	Other generalized ischaemic cerebrovascular disease	11	4	9	2	1	1	10	3	1	1	-	-	-	-	1	1
437.9	Unspecified	-	1	-	-	-	-	-	-	-	-	-	-	-	-	-	1
440-459	Other diseases of the circulatory system	5	-	2	-	-	-	2	-	2	-	-	-	-	-	3	-
440-448	Diseases of arteries, arterioles and capillaries	2	-	-	-	-	-	-	-	1	-	-	-	-	-	2	-
441	Aortic aneurysm	1	-	-	-	-	-	-	-	-	-	-	-	-	-	1	-
441.0	Dissecting aneurysm (any part)	1	-	-	-	-	-	-	-	-	-	-	-	-	-	1	-
447	Other disorders of arteries and arterioles	1	-	-	-	-	-	-	-	1	-	-	-	-	-	1	-
447.2	Rupture of artery	1	-	-	-	-	-	-	-	1	-	-	-	-	-	1	-
453	Other venous embolism and thrombosis	1	-	1	-	-	-	1	-	-	-	-	-	-	-	-	-
453.2	Of vena cava	1	-	1	-	-	-	1	-	-	-	-	-	-	-	-	-
456	Varicose veins of other sites	1	-	-	-	-	-	-	-	1	-	-	-	-	-	1	-
456.0	Oesophageal varices with bleeding	1	-	-	-	-	-	-	-	1	-	-	-	-	-	1	-

Table 6 - *continued*

ICD number	Cause of Death	Age at death All ages 28 days to 15 years		Months 1-5		6-11		1-11		Years 1-4		5-9		10-14		1-15	
		Boys	Girls	Boys	Girls	Boys	Girls	Boys	Girls	Boys	Girls	Boys	Girls	Boys	Girls	Boys	Girls
459	Other disorders of circulatory system	1	-	1	-	-	-	1	-	-	-	-	-	-	-	-	-
459.0	Haemorrhage, unspecified	1	-	1	-	-	-	1	-	-	-	-	-	-	-	-	-
460-519	**VIII Diseases of the respiratory system**	**135**	**118**	**52**	**38**	**22**	**14**	**74**	**52**	**28**	**30**	**15**	**14**	**14**	**22**	**61**	**66**
460-465, 470-478	Diseases of upper respiratory tract	4	5	1	4	1	-	2	4	1	1	1	-	-	-	2	1
464	Acute laryngitis and tracheitis	2	2	-	1	-	-	-	1	1	1	1	-	-	-	2	1
464.0	Acute laryngitis	1	2	-	1	-	-	-	1	-	1	1	-	-	-	1	1
464.3	Acute epiglottitis	1	-	-	-	-	-	-	-	1	-	-	-	-	-	1	-
465	Acute upper respiratory infections of multiple or unspecified site	1	2	-	2	1	-	1	2	-	-	-	-	-	-	-	-
465.9	Unspecified site	1	2	-	2	1	-	1	2	-	-	-	-	-	-	-	-
466	Acute bronchitis and bronchiolitis	20	7	6	3	6	2	12	5	7	2	1	-	-	-	8	2
466.0	Acute bronchitis	10	1	1	-	3	1	4	1	5	-	1	-	-	-	6	-
466.1	Acute bronchiolitis	10	6	5	3	3	1	8	4	2	2	-	-	-	-	2	2
478	Other diseases of upper respiratory tract	1	1	1	1	-	-	1	1	-	-	-	-	-	-	-	-
478.7	Other diseases of larynx, not elsewhere classified	1	1	1	1	-	-	1	1	-	-	-	-	-	-	-	-
480-486	Pneumonia	53	52	21	13	6	7	27	20	11	17	8	8	6	7	26	32
480	Viral pneumonia	7	2	3	-	1	1	4	1	2	1	1	-	-	-	3	1
480.1	Pneumonia due to respiratory syncytial virus	4	2	3	-	-	1	3	1	1	1	-	-	-	-	1	1
480.9	Viral pneumonia, unspecified	3	-	-	-	1	-	1	-	1	-	1	-	-	-	2	-
481	Pneumococcal pneumonia	2	-	-	-	-	-	-	-	-	-	-	-	2	-	2	-
482	Other bacterial pneumonia	2	3	-	2	-	-	-	2	1	1	-	-	1	-	2	1
482.2	Pneumonia due to Haemophilus influenzae (H.influenzae)	-	1	-	1	-	-	-	1	-	-	-	-	-	-	-	-
482.3	Pneumonia due to Streptococcus	1	-	-	-	-	-	-	-	1	-	-	-	-	-	1	-
482.4	Pneumonia due to Staphylococcus	1	1	-	1	-	-	-	1	-	-	-	-	1	-	1	-
482.9	Bacterial pneumonia, unspecified	-	1	-	-	-	-	-	-	-	1	-	-	-	-	-	1
483	Pneumonia due to other specified organism	-	1	-	-	-	1	-	1	-	-	-	-	-	-	-	-
485	Bronchopneumonia, organism unspecified	19	27	9	5	2	3	11	8	4	12	2	4	2	3	8	19
486	Pneumonia, organism unspecified	23	19	9	6	3	2	12	8	4	3	5	4	1	4	11	11
487	Influenza	-	4	-	1	-	1	-	2	-	2	-	-	-	-	-	2
487.0	With pneumonia	-	2	-	1	-	-	-	1	-	1	-	-	-	-	-	1
487.1	With other respiratory manifestations	-	2	-	-	-	1	-	1	-	1	-	-	-	-	-	1
490-496	Chronic obstructive pulmonary disease and allied conditions	12	16	2	1	1	-	3	1	2	2	2	3	4	10	9	15
490-493	Bronchitis, emphysema and asthma	12	15	2	1	1	-	3	1	2	2	2	3	4	9	9	14
490	Bronchitis, not specified as acute or chronic	3	3	1	-	1	-	2	-	1	1	-	1	-	1	1	3
491	Chronic bronchitis	2	1	1	1	-	-	1	1	-	-	-	-	1	-	1	-
491.1	Mucopurulent chronic bronchitis	1	1	-	1	-	-	-	1	-	-	-	-	1	-	1	-
491.8	Other chronic bronchitis	1	-	1	-	-	-	1	-	-	-	-	-	-	-	-	-

Table 6 1995 Series DH3 no. 28

Table 6 - *continued*

ICD number	Cause of Death	All ages 28 days to 15 years Boys	Girls	Months 1-5 Boys	Girls	6-11 Boys	Girls	1-11 Boys	Girls	Years 1-4 Boys	Girls	5-9 Boys	Girls	10-14 Boys	Girls	1-15 Boys	Girls
493	Asthma	7	11	-	-	-	-	-	-	1	1	2	2	3	8	7	11
493.0	Extrinsic asthma	5	11	-	-	-	-	-	-	-	1	1	2	3	8	5	11
493.9	Asthma, unspecified	2	-	-	-	-	-	-	-	1	-	1	-	-	-	2	-
494	Bronchiectasis	-	1	-	-	-	-	-	-	-	-	-	-	-	1	-	1
500-508	Pneumoconioses and other lung diseases due to external agents	3	3	-	1	1	-	1	1	1	-	-	2	1	-	2	2
507	Pneumonitis due to solids and liquids	3	3	-	1	1	-	1	1	1	-	-	2	1	-	2	2
507.0	Due to inhalation of food or vomit	3	3	-	1	1	-	1	1	1	-	-	2	1	-	2	2
510-519	Other diseases of respiratory system	43	31	22	15	7	4	29	19	6	6	3	1	3	5	14	12
510	Empyema	1	-	1	-	-	-	1	-	-	-	-	-	-	-	-	-
510.9	Without mention of fistula	1	-	1	-	-	-	1	-	-	-	-	-	-	-	-	-
512	Pneumothorax	2	-	1	-	-	-	1	-	-	-	-	-	-	-	1	-
516	Other alveolar and parietoalveolar pneumopathy	5	7	1	3	1	-	2	3	1	2	-	1	1	1	3	4
516.0	Pulmonary alveolar proteinosis	1	1	-	1	-	-	-	1	1	-	-	-	-	-	1	-
516.3	Idiopathic fibrosing alveolitis	-	1	-	-	-	-	-	-	-	-	-	1	-	-	-	1
516.8	Other	4	5	1	2	1	-	2	2	-	2	-	-	1	1	2	3
518	Other diseases of lung	15	13	13	8	1	3	14	11	1	1	-	-	-	1	1	2
518.1	Interstitial emphysema	-	1	-	-	-	1	-	1	-	-	-	-	-	-	-	-
518.5	Pulmonary insufficiency following trauma and surgery	1	2	1	-	-	-	1	-	-	1	-	-	-	1	-	2
518.8	Other diseases of lung, not elsewhere classified	14	10	12	8	1	2	13	10	1	-	-	-	-	-	1	-
519	Other diseases of respiratory system	20	11	6	4	5	1	11	5	4	3	3	-	2	3	9	6
519.1	Other diseases of trachea and bronchus, not elsewhere classified	3	1	1	-	2	1	3	1	-	-	-	-	-	-	-	-
519.8	Other diseases of respiratory system, not elsewhere classified	17	10	5	4	3	-	8	4	4	3	3	-	2	3	9	6
520-579	**IX Diseases of the digestive system**	**45**	**35**	**17**	**6**	**7**	**6**	**24**	**12**	**7**	**13**	**9**	**5**	**4**	**5**	**21**	**23**
530-537	Diseases of oesophagus, stomach and duodenum	9	7	3	2	2	1	5	3	2	3	1	-	1	1	4	4
530	Diseases of oesophagus	9	2	3	1	2	1	5	2	2	-	1	-	1	-	4	-
530.1	Oesophagitis	7	1	2	1	2	-	4	1	2	-	1	-	-	-	3	-
530.4	Perforation of oesophagus	1	-	-	-	-	-	-	-	-	-	-	-	1	-	1	-
530.8	Other disorders of oesophagus	1	1	1	-	-	1	1	1	-	-	-	-	-	-	-	-
531-533	Ulcer of stomach and duodenum	-	4	-	-	-	-	-	-	-	3	-	-	-	1	-	4
531	Gastric ulcer	-	3	-	-	-	-	-	-	-	2	-	-	-	1	-	3
531.0	Acute with haemorrhage	-	1	-	-	-	-	-	-	-	1	-	-	-	-	-	1
531.5	Chronic or unspecified with perforation	-	2	-	-	-	-	-	-	-	1	-	-	-	1	-	2
532	Duodenal ulcer	-	1	-	-	-	-	-	-	-	1	-	-	-	-	-	1
532.4	Chronic or unspecified with haemorrhage	-	1	-	-	-	-	-	-	-	1	-	-	-	-	-	1
537	Other disorders of stomach and duodenum	-	1	-	1	-	-	-	1	-	-	-	-	-	-	-	-

Table 6 - *continued*

ICD number	Cause of Death	Age at death														
		All ages		Months						Years							
		28 days to 15 years		1-5		6-11		1-11		1-4		5-9		10-14		1-15	
		Boys	Girls	Boys	Girls	Boys	Girls	Boys	Girls	Boys	Girls	Boys	Girls	Boys	Girls	Boys	Girls
537.9	Unspecified	-	1	-	1	-	-	-	1	-	-	-	-	-	-	-	-
540-543	Appendicitis	2	2	-	-	-	-	-	-	-	1	1	-	1	1	2	2
540	Acute appendicitis	2	2	-	-	-	-	-	-	-	1	1	-	1	1	2	2
540.0	With generalized peritonitis	1	2	-	-	-	-	-	-	-	1	1	-	-	1	1	2
540.1	With peritoneal abscess	1	-	-	-	-	-	-	-	-	-	-	-	1	-	1	-
550-553	Hernia of abdominal cavity	-	1	-	-	-	-	-	-	-	1	-	-	-	-	-	1
550	Inguinal hernia	-	1	-	-	-	-	-	-	-	1	-	-	-	-	-	1
550.1	Inguinal hernia, with obstruction, without mention of gangrene	-	1	-	-	-	-	-	-	-	1	-	-	-	-	-	1
555-558	Noninfective enteritis and colitis	8	9	4	1	-	2	4	3	2	3	1	2	1	1	4	6
558	Other noninfective gastroenteritis and colitis	8	9	4	1	-	2	4	3	2	3	1	2	1	1	4	6
560-569	Other diseases of intestine and peritoneum	14	5	5	1	2	2	7	3	2	-	4	1	-	1	7	2
560	Intestinal obstruction without mention of hernia	8	2	3	1	-	1	3	2	1	-	3	-	-	-	5	-
560.0	Intussusception	2	1	1	1	-	-	1	1	-	-	1	-	-	-	1	-
560.2	Volvulus	3	1	-	-	-	1	-	1	1	-	1	-	-	-	3	-
560.3	Impaction of intestine	1	-	-	-	-	-	-	-	-	-	1	-	-	-	1	-
560.8	Other intestinal obstruction	1	-	1	-	-	-	1	-	-	-	-	-	-	-	-	-
560.9	Unspecified intestinal obstruction	1	-	1	-	-	-	1	-	-	-	-	-	-	-	-	-
564	Functional digestive disorders, not elsewhere classified	1	1	1	-	-	1	1	1	-	-	-	-	-	-	-	-
564.9	Unspecified	1	1	1	-	-	1	1	1	-	-	-	-	-	-	-	-
567-569	Disorders of peritoneum and intestines nec	5	2	1	-	2	-	3	-	1	-	1	1	-	1	2	2
567	Peritonitis	-	1	-	-	-	-	-	-	-	-	-	-	-	1	-	1
567.9	Unspecified	-	1	-	-	-	-	-	-	-	-	-	-	-	1	-	1
568	Other disorders of peritoneum	2	-	-	-	-	-	-	-	1	-	1	-	-	-	2	-
568.0	Peritoneal adhesions	2	-	-	-	-	-	-	-	1	-	1	-	-	-	2	-
569	Other disorders of intestine	3	1	1	-	2	-	3	-	-	-	-	1	-	-	-	1
569.8	Other	2	1	1	-	1	-	2	-	-	-	-	1	-	-	-	1
569.9	Unspecified	1	-	-	-	1	-	1	-	-	-	-	-	-	-	-	-
570-579	Other diseases of digestive system	12	11	5	2	3	1	8	3	1	5	2	2	1	1	4	8
570	Acute and subacute necrosis of liver	2	2	1	1	-	-	1	1	1	-	-	-	-	1	1	1
571	Chronic liver disease and cirrhosis	2	1	1	-	1	-	2	-	-	-	-	1	-	-	-	1
571.5	Cirrhosis of liver without mention of alcohol	1	-	1	-	-	-	1	-	-	-	-	-	-	-	-	-
571.8	Other chronic nonalcoholic liver disease	1	1	-	-	1	-	1	-	-	-	-	1	-	-	-	1
572	Liver abscess and sequelae of chronic liver disease	4	3	1	1	2	1	3	2	-	1	1	-	-	-	1	1
572.8	Other sequelae of chronic liver disease	4	3	1	1	2	1	3	2	-	1	1	-	-	-	1	1
573	Other disorders of liver	2	2	1	-	-	-	1	-	-	2	1	-	-	-	1	2
573.8	Other	1	-	1	-	-	-	1	-	-	-	-	-	-	-	-	-
573.9	Unspecified	1	2	-	-	-	-	-	-	-	2	1	-	-	-	1	2

Table 6 1995 Series DH3 no. 28

Table 6 - *continued*

ICD number	Cause of Death	All ages 28 days to 15 years		Months 1-5		6-11		1-11		Years 1-4		5-9		10-14		1-15	
		Boys	Girls	Boys	Girls	Boys	Girls	Boys	Girls	Boys	Girls	Boys	Girls	Boys	Girls	Boys	Girls
575	Other disorders of gallbladder	1	-	1	-	-	-	1	-	-	-	-	-	-	-	-	-
575.8	Other	1	-	1	-	-	-	1	-	-	-	-	-	-	-	-	-
576	Other disorders of biliary tract	1	-	-	-	-	-	-	-	-	-	-	-	1	-	1	-
576.1	Cholangitis	1	-	-	-	-	-	-	-	-	-	-	-	1	-	1	-
578	Gastrointestinal haemorrhage	-	2	-	-	-	-	-	-	-	1	-	1	-	-	-	2
578.9	Haemorrage of gastrointestinal tract, unspecified	-	2	-	-	-	-	-	-	-	1	-	1	-	-	-	2
579	Intestinal malabsorption	-	1	-	-	-	-	-	-	-	1	-	-	-	-	-	1
579.9	Unspecified	-	1	-	-	-	-	-	-	-	1	-	-	-	-	-	1
580-629	**X Diseases of the genitourinary system**	9	2	3	1	1	1	4	2	3	-	1	-	-	-	5	-
580-599	Diseases of urinary tract	9	2	3	1	1	1	4	2	3	-	1	-	-	-	5	-
580-589	Nephritis, nephrotic syndrome and nephrosis	4	1	-	-	1	1	1	1	2	-	1	-	-	-	3	-
581	Nephrotic syndrome	1	1	-	-	-	1	-	1	1	-	-	-	-	-	1	-
581.9	Unspecified	1	1	-	-	-	1	-	1	1	-	-	-	-	-	1	-
584-586	Renal failure	3	-	-	-	1	-	1	-	1	-	1	-	-	-	2	-
585	Chronic renal failure	1	-	-	-	-	-	-	-	1	-	-	-	-	-	1	-
586	Renal failure, unspecified	2	-	-	-	1	-	1	-	-	-	1	-	-	-	1	-
590-599	Other diseases of urinary system	5	1	3	1	-	-	3	1	1	-	-	-	-	-	2	-
591	Hydronephrosis	1	1	-	1	-	-	-	1	-	-	-	-	-	-	1	-
593	Other disorders of kidney and ureter	2	-	2	-	-	-	2	-	-	-	-	-	-	-	-	-
593.4	Other ureteric obstruction	1	-	1	-	-	-	1	-	-	-	-	-	-	-	-	-
593.8	Other	1	-	1	-	-	-	1	-	-	-	-	-	-	-	-	-
596	Other disorders of bladder	1	-	-	-	-	-	-	-	1	-	-	-	-	-	1	-
596.9	Unspecified	1	-	-	-	-	-	-	-	1	-	-	-	-	-	1	-
599	Other disorders of urethra and urinary tract	1	-	1	-	-	-	1	-	-	-	-	-	-	-	-	-
599.9	Unspecified	1	-	1	-	-	-	1	-	-	-	-	-	-	-	-	-
630-676	**XI Complications of pregnancy, childbirth and the puerperium**	-	1	-	-	-	-	-	-	-	-	-	-	-	-	-	1
670	Major puerperal infection	-	1	-	-	-	-	-	-	-	-	-	-	-	-	-	1
680-709	**XII Diseases of the skin and subcutaneous tissue**	-	4	-	1	-	-	-	1	-	1	-	1	-	1	-	3
686	Other local infections of skin and subcutaneous tissue	-	1	-	-	-	-	-	-	-	1	-	-	-	-	-	1
686.1	Pyogenic granuloma	-	1	-	-	-	-	-	-	-	1	-	-	-	-	-	1
690-709	Other diseases of skin and subcutaneous tissue	-	3	-	1	-	-	-	1	-	-	-	1	-	1	-	2
693	Dermatitis due to substances taken internally	-	1	-	-	-	-	-	-	-	-	-	-	-	1	-	1
693.1	Due to food	-	1	-	-	-	-	-	-	-	-	-	-	-	1	-	1
695	Erythematous conditions	-	2	-	1	-	-	-	1	-	-	-	1	-	-	-	1
695.1	Erythema multiforme	-	1	-	-	-	-	-	-	-	-	-	1	-	-	-	1
695.9	Unspecified	-	1	-	1	-	-	-	1	-	-	-	-	-	-	-	1

Table 6 - *continued*

ICD number	Cause of Death	All ages 28 days to 15 years Boys	Girls	Months 1-5 Boys	Girls	6-11 Boys	Girls	1-11 Boys	Girls	Years 1-4 Boys	Girls	5-9 Boys	Girls	10-14 Boys	Girls	1-15 Boys	Girls
710-739	**XIII Diseases of the musculoskeletal system and connective tissue**	1	9	-	-	-	1	-	1	1	1	-	1	-	6	1	8
710	Diffuse diseases of connective tissue	-	2	-	-	-	-	-	-	-	-	-	-	-	2	-	2
710.0	Systemic lupus erythematosus	-	1	-	-	-	-	-	-	-	-	-	-	-	1	-	1
710.3	Dermatomyositis	-	1	-	-	-	-	-	-	-	-	-	-	-	1	-	1
716	Other and unspecified arthropathies	-	1	-	-	-	-	-	-	-	-	-	-	-	1	-	1
716.9	Unspecified	-	1	-	-	-	-	-	-	-	-	-	-	-	1	-	1
728	Disorders of muscle, ligament and fascia	-	1	-	-	-	-	-	-	-	1	-	-	-	-	-	1
728.8	Other disorders of muscle, ligament and fascia	-	1	-	-	-	-	-	-	-	1	-	-	-	-	-	1
733	Other disorders of bone and cartilage	1	1	-	-	-	1	-	1	1	-	-	-	-	-	1	-
733.0	Osteoporosis	1	1	-	-	-	1	-	1	1	-	-	-	-	-	1	-
737	Curvature of spine	-	4	-	-	-	-	-	-	-	-	-	1	-	3	-	4
737.3	Kyphoscoliosis and scoliosis	-	4	-	-	-	-	-	-	-	-	-	1	-	3	-	4
740-759	**XIV Congenital anomalies**	247	211	97	79	37	29	134	108	66	49	24	31	19	19	113	103
740-742	All deformities of central nervous system	30	35	9	11	4	3	13	14	6	11	9	6	2	4	17	21
741,742.3	Spina bifida and hydrocephalus	9	5	2	2	-	-	2	2	2	1	4	1	1	1	7	3
741	Spina bifida	1	4	-	1	1	-	1	1	-	-	-	1	-	2	-	3
741.0	With hydrocephalus	1	3	-	1	1	-	1	1	-	-	-	1	-	1	-	2
741.9	Without mention of hydrocephalus	-	1	-	-	-	-	-	-	-	-	-	-	-	1	-	1
742	Other congenital anomalies of nervous system	29	31	9	10	3	3	12	13	6	11	9	5	2	2	17	18
742.1	Microcephalus	6	8	1	2	1	2	2	4	2	2	2	1	-	1	4	4
742.2	Reduction deformities of brain	7	8	2	1	1	1	3	2	2	5	2	1	-	-	4	6
742.3	Congenital hydrocephalus	9	4	2	2	-	-	2	2	2	1	4	1	1	-	7	2
742.4	Other specified anomalies of brain	1	4	-	2	-	-	-	2	-	-	1	2	-	-	1	2
742.8	Other specified anomalies of nervous system	3	3	2	3	1	-	3	3	-	-	-	-	-	-	-	-
742.9	Unspecified anomalies of brain, spinal cord and nervous system	3	4	2	-	-	-	2	-	-	3	-	-	1	1	1	4
744	Congenital anomalies of ear, face and neck	1	-	-	-	-	-	-	-	-	-	-	-	1	-	1	-
744.5	Webbing of neck	1	-	-	-	-	-	-	-	-	-	-	-	1	-	1	-
745-747	Congenital anomalies of heart and circulatory system	132	105	52	42	19	15	71	57	38	19	7	15	13	12	61	48
745	Bulbus cordis anomalies and anomalies of cardiac septal closure	38	32	18	17	7	6	25	23	7	2	1	3	4	4	13	9
745.0	Common truncus	2	3	2	2	-	1	2	3	-	-	-	-	-	-	-	-
745.1	Transposition of great vessels	8	5	2	2	1	-	3	2	2	2	1	1	2	-	5	3
745.2	Tetralogy of Fallot	7	5	3	2	2	1	5	3	2	-	-	1	-	1	2	2
745.4	Ventricular septal defect	15	16	8	9	2	3	10	12	3	-	-	1	1	3	5	4
745.5	Ostium secundum type atrial septal defect	6	1	3	1	2	-	5	1	-	-	-	-	1	-	1	-
745.6	Endocardial cushion defects	-	2	-	1	-	1	-	2	-	-	-	-	-	-	-	-
746	Other congenital anomalies of heart	80	53	29	20	10	7	39	27	25	12	6	7	8	5	41	26
746.0	Anomalies of pulmonary valve	1	-	1	-	-	-	1	-	-	-	-	-	-	-	-	-

Table 6 1995 Series DH3 no. 28

Table 6 - *continued*

ICD number	Cause of Death	Age at death															
		All ages															
		28 days to		Months						Years							
		15 years		1-5		6-11		1-11		1-4		5-9		10-14		1-15	
		Boys	Girls	Boys	Girls	Boys	Girls	Boys	Girls	Boys	Girls	Boys	Girls	Boys	Girls	Boys	Girls
746.1	Tricuspid atresia and stenosis, congenital	1	2	-	-	-	-	-	-	1	2	-	-	-	-	1	2
746.3	Congenital stenosis of aortic valve	4	3	4	3	-	-	4	3	-	-	-	-	-	-	-	-
746.5	Congenital mitral stenosis	1	1	-	1	-	-	-	1	-	-	1	-	-	-	1	-
746.7	Hypoplastic left heart syndrome	6	2	4	2	1	-	5	2	1	-	-	-	-	-	1	-
746.8	Other specified anomalies of heart	10	7	5	2	-	2	5	4	3	1	-	1	2	1	5	3
746.9	Unspecified anomalies of heart	57	38	15	12	9	5	24	17	20	9	5	6	6	4	33	21
747	Other congenital anomalies of circulatory system	14	20	5	5	2	2	7	7	6	5	-	5	1	3	7	13
747.0	Patent ductus arteriosus	-	1	-	1	-	-	-	1	-	-	-	-	-	-	-	-
747.1	Coarctation of aorta	4	-	2	-	-	-	2	-	2	-	-	-	-	-	2	-
747.2	Other anomalies of aorta	-	1	-	-	-	-	-	-	-	1	-	-	-	-	-	1
747.3	Anomalies of pulmonary artery	6	9	2	3	2	-	4	3	1	3	-	3	1	-	2	6
747.4	Anomalies of great veins	2	3	1	1	-	1	1	2	1	1	-	-	-	-	1	1
747.6	Other anomalies of peripheral vascular system	1	-	-	-	-	-	-	-	1	-	-	-	-	-	1	-
747.8	Other specified anomalies of circulatory system	1	6	-	-	-	1	-	1	1	-	-	2	-	3	1	5
748	Congenital anomalies of respiratory system	7	6	5	2	-	3	5	5	1	1	1	-	-	-	2	1
748.3	Other anomalies of larynx, trachea and bronchus	1	1	1	-	-	1	1	1	-	-	-	-	-	-	-	-
748.5	Agenesis, hypoplasia and dysplasia of lung	4	2	2	1	-	1	2	2	1	-	1	-	-	-	2	-
748.6	Other anomalies of lung	1	3	1	1	-	1	1	2	-	1	-	-	-	-	-	1
748.9	Unspecified anomalies of respiratory system	1	-	1	-	-	-	1	-	-	-	-	-	-	-	-	-
749-751	Cleft palate and lip; other congenital anomalies of upper alimentary tract and digestive system	16	7	6	2	4	2	10	4	5	2	1	1	-	-	6	3
749	Cleft palate and cleft lip	3	-	1	-	-	-	1	-	2	-	-	-	-	-	2	-
749.0	Cleft palate	3	-	1	-	-	-	1	-	2	-	-	-	-	-	2	-
750	Other congenital anomalies of upper alimentary tract	2	-	1	-	1	-	2	-	-	-	-	-	-	-	-	-
750.5	Congenital hypertrophic pyloric stenosis	1	-	1	-	-	-	1	-	-	-	-	-	-	-	-	-
750.7	Other specified anomalies of stomach	1	-	-	-	1	-	1	-	-	-	-	-	-	-	-	-
751	Other congenital anomalies of digestive system	11	7	4	2	3	2	7	4	3	2	1	1	-	-	4	3
751.1	Atresia and stenosis of small intestine	-	1	-	1	-	-	-	1	-	-	-	-	-	-	-	-
751.3	Hirschsprung's disease and other congenital functional disorders of colon	2	-	-	-	2	-	2	-	-	-	-	-	-	-	-	-
751.4	Anomalies of intestinal fixation	1	-	-	-	1	-	1	-	-	-	-	-	-	-	-	-
751.5	Other anomalies of intestine	5	1	4	-	-	-	4	-	1	1	-	-	-	-	1	1
751.6	Anomalies of gallbladder, bile ducts and liver	3	5	-	1	-	2	-	3	2	1	1	1	-	-	3	2
753	Congenital anomalies of urinary system	4	2	2	1	-	-	2	1	-	1	1	-	1	-	2	1
753.0	Renal agenesis and dysgenesis	2	-	1	-	-	-	1	-	-	-	-	-	1	-	1	-
753.1	Cystic kidney disease	1	1	-	-	-	-	-	-	-	-	1	1	-	-	1	1
753.6	Atresia and stenosis of urethra and bladder neck	1	-	1	-	-	-	1	-	-	-	-	-	-	-	-	-
753.9	Unspecified anomalies of urinary system	-	1	-	1	-	-	-	1	-	-	-	-	-	-	-	-
755	Other congenital anomalies of limbs	-	2	-	-	-	-	-	-	-	-	-	2	-	-	-	2

Table 6 - *continued*

ICD number	Cause of Death	28 days to 15 years		Months 1-5		6-11		1-11		Years 1-4		5-9		10-14		1-15	
		Boys	Girls	Boys	Girls	Boys	Girls	Boys	Girls	Boys	Girls	Boys	Girls	Boys	Girls	Boys	Girls
755.8	Other specified anomalies of unspecified limb	-	2	-	-	-	-	-	-	-	-	-	2	-	-	-	2
756	Other congenital musculoskeletal anomalies	11	11	7	4	1	-	8	4	2	5	1	2	-	-	3	7
756.0	Anomalies of skull and face bones	1	4	1	1	-	-	1	1	-	2	-	1	-	-	-	3
756.1	Anomalies of spine	1	-	1	-	-	-	1	-	-	-	-	-	-	-	-	-
756.4	Chondrodystrophy	1	1	-	1	1	-	1	1	-	-	-	-	-	-	-	-
756.5	Osteodystrophies	2	2	1	1	-	-	1	1	1	1	-	-	-	-	1	1
756.6	Anomalies of diaphragm	2	2	2	1	-	-	2	1	-	1	-	-	-	-	-	1
756.7	Anomalies of abdominal wall	3	-	2	-	-	-	2	-	1	-	-	-	-	-	1	-
756.8	Other specified anomalies of muscle, tendon, fascia and connective tissue	1	2	-	-	-	-	-	-	-	1	1	1	-	-	1	2
757	Congenital anomalies of the integument	2	2	1	-	-	-	1	-	-	-	-	-	1	2	1	2
757.3	Other specified anomalies of skin	2	2	1	-	-	-	1	-	-	-	-	-	1	2	1	2
758	Chromosomal anomalies	22	23	8	10	5	5	13	15	4	5	3	1	1	1	9	8
758.0	Down's syndrome	9	7	3	3	1	-	4	3	2	1	1	1	1	1	5	4
758.1	Patau's syndrome	4	2	3	2	1	-	4	2	-	-	-	-	-	-	-	-
758.2	Edwards's syndrome	1	8	1	4	-	2	1	6	-	2	-	-	-	-	-	2
758.3	Autosomal deletion syndromes	2	-	-	-	1	-	1	-	1	-	-	-	-	-	1	-
758.5	Other conditions due to autosomal anomalies	1	-	1	-	-	-	1	-	-	-	-	-	-	-	-	-
758.9	Conditions due to anomaly of unspecified chromosome	5	6	-	1	2	3	2	4	1	2	2	-	-	-	3	2
759	Other and unspecified congenital anomalies	22	18	7	7	4	1	11	8	10	5	1	4	-	-	11	10
759.1	Anomalies of adrenal gland	2	-	1	-	-	-	1	-	1	-	-	-	-	-	1	-
759.6	Other hamartoses, not elsewhere classified	2	1	-	1	1	-	1	1	1	-	-	-	-	-	1	-
759.7	Multiple congenital anomalies, so described	4	3	1	1	-	1	1	2	3	1	-	-	-	-	3	1
759.8	Other specified anomalies	14	12	5	5	3	-	8	5	5	2	1	4	-	-	6	7
759.9	Congenital anomaly, unspecified	-	2	-	-	-	-	-	-	-	2	-	-	-	-	-	2
760-779	**XV Certain conditions originating in the perinatal period**	86	62	69	52	13	6	82	58	3	2	1	1	-	-	4	4
761-763	Obstetric complications affecting fetus or newborn	1	3	1	2	-	1	1	3	-	-	-	-	-	-	-	-
761	Fetus or newborn affected by maternal complications of pregnancy	1	2	1	1	-	1	1	2	-	-	-	-	-	-	-	-
761.2	Oligohydramnios	-	1	-	-	-	1	-	1	-	-	-	-	-	-	-	-
761.5	Multiple pregnancy	1	1	1	1	-	-	1	1	-	-	-	-	-	-	-	-
762	Fetus or newborn affected by complications of placenta, cord and membranes	-	1	-	1	-	-	-	1	-	-	-	-	-	-	-	-
762.1	Other forms of placental separation and haemorrhage	-	1	-	1	-	-	-	1	-	-	-	-	-	-	-	-
764	Slow fetal growth and fetal malnutrition	1	-	1	-	-	-	1	-	-	-	-	-	-	-	-	-
764.9	Fetal growth retardation, unspecified	1	-	1	-	-	-	1	-	-	-	-	-	-	-	-	-
765	Disorders relating to short gestation and unspecified low birthweight	6	4	5	4	1	-	6	4	-	-	-	-	-	-	-	-
765.0	Extreme immaturity	3	1	2	1	1	-	3	1	-	-	-	-	-	-	-	-
765.1	Other preterm infants	3	3	3	3	-	-	3	3	-	-	-	-	-	-	-	-
767	Birth trauma	2	1	1	-	1	-	2	-	-	-	-	-	1	-	-	1
767.0	Subdural and cerebral haemorrhage	2	1	1	-	1	-	2	-	-	-	-	-	1	-	-	1

Table 6 1995 Series DH3 no. 28

Table 6 - *continued*

ICD number	Cause of Death	Age at death															
		All ages															
		28 days to 15 years		Months						Years							
				1-5		6-11		1-11		1-4		5-9		10-14		1-15	
		Boys	Girls	Boys	Girls	Boys	Girls	Boys	Girls	Boys	Girls	Boys	Girls	Boys	Girls	Boys	Girls
768-770	Hypoxia, birth asphyxia and other respiratory conditions	65	48	52	41	10	5	62	46	3	2	-	-	-	-	3	2
768	Intrauterine hypoxia and birth asphyxia	1	7	-	6	-	-	-	6	1	1	-	-	-	-	1	1
768.5	Severe birth asphyxia	-	2	-	1	-	-	-	1	-	1	-	-	-	-	-	1
768.9	Unspecified birth asphyxia in liveborn infant	1	5	-	5	-	-	-	5	1	-	-	-	-	-	1	-
769	Respiratory distress syndrome	21	13	17	11	3	2	20	13	1	-	-	-	-	-	1	-
770	Other respiratory conditions of fetus and newborn	43	28	35	24	7	3	42	27	1	1	-	-	-	-	1	1
770.0	Congenital pneumonia	-	1	-	1	-	-	-	1	-	-	-	-	-	-	-	-
770.4	Primary atelectasis	2	1	1	1	1	-	2	1	-	-	-	-	-	-	-	-
770.7	Chronic respiratory disease arising in the perinatal period	41	26	34	22	6	3	40	25	1	1	-	-	-	-	1	1
771	Infections specific to the perinatal period	6	3	5	2	-	-	5	2	-	-	1	-	-	-	1	1
771.0	Congenital rubella	1	1	1	-	-	-	1	-	-	-	-	-	-	-	-	1
771.1	Congenital cytomegalovirus infection	-	1	-	1	-	-	-	1	-	-	-	-	-	-	-	-
771.2	Other congenital infections	2	-	1	-	-	-	1	-	-	-	1	-	-	-	1	-
771.7	Neonatal Candida infection	1	1	1	1	-	-	1	1	-	-	-	-	-	-	-	-
771.8	Other infection specific to the perinatal period	2	-	2	-	-	-	2	-	-	-	-	-	-	-	-	-
776	Haematological disorders of fetus and newborn	1	-	1	-	-	-	1	-	-	-	-	-	-	-	-	-
776.0	Haemorrhagic disease of newborn	1	-	1	-	-	-	1	-	-	-	-	-	-	-	-	-
777	Perinatal disorders of digestive system	4	3	3	3	1	-	4	3	-	-	-	-	-	-	-	-
777.5	Necrotizing enterocolitis in fetus or newborn	4	3	3	3	1	-	4	3	-	-	-	-	-	-	-	-
780-799	**XVI Signs, symptoms and ill-defined conditions**	**239**	**138**	**189**	**104**	**30**	**23**	**219**	**127**	**15**	**9**	**2**	**-**	**2**	**2**	**20**	**11**
780-789	Symptoms	1	2	1	1	-	-	1	1	-	-	-	-	-	1	-	1
785	Symptoms involving cardiovascular system	1	1	1	-	-	-	1	-	-	-	-	-	-	1	-	1
785.5	Shock without mention of trauma	1	1	1	-	-	-	1	-	-	-	-	-	-	1	-	1
786	Symptoms involving respiratory system and other chest symptoms	-	1	-	1	-	-	-	1	-	-	-	-	-	-	-	-
786.3	Haemoptysis	-	1	-	1	-	-	-	1	-	-	-	-	-	-	-	-
790	Nonspecific findings on examination of blood	2	-	-	-	-	-	-	-	2	-	-	-	-	-	2	-
790.6	Other abnormal blood chemistry	2	-	-	-	-	-	-	-	2	-	-	-	-	-	2	-
798	Sudden death, cause unknown	209	119	172	95	27	19	199	114	9	5	-	-	1	-	10	5
798.0	Sudden infant death syndrome	201	114	172	95	27	19	199	114	2	-	-	-	-	-	2	-
798.1	Instantaneous death	8	5	-	-	-	-	-	-	7	5	-	-	1	-	8	5
799	Other ill-defined and unknown causes of morbidity and mortality	27	17	16	8	3	4	19	12	4	4	2	-	1	1	8	5
799.0	Asphyxia	1	-	-	-	1	-	1	-	-	-	-	-	-	-	-	-
799.1	Respiratory failure	7	5	6	4	-	1	6	5	1	-	-	-	-	-	1	-
799.9	Other unknown and unspecified cause	19	12	10	4	2	3	12	7	3	4	2	-	1	1	7	5

Table 6 - *continued*

ICD number	Cause of Death	Age at death															
		All ages		Months						Years							
		28 days to		1-5		6-11		1-11		1-4		5-9		10-14		1-15	
		15 years															
		Boys	Girls	Boys	Girls	Boys	Girls	Boys	Girls	Boys	Girls	Boys	Girls	Boys	Girls	Boys	Girls
800-999	**XVII Injury and poisoning**	**394**	**196**	**15**	**15**	**18**	**10**	**33**	**25**	**94**	**67**	**79**	**42**	**145**	**39**	**361**	**171**
800-829	Fractures	55	16	1	1	1	-	2	1	7	4	12	5	26	4	53	15
800-804	Fracture of skull	47	13	1	1	1	-	2	1	5	3	11	5	21	3	45	12
800	Fracture of vault of skull	1	-	-	-	1	-	1	-	-	-	-	-	-	-	-	-
801	Fracture of base of skull	4	-	-	-	-	-	-	-	1	-	-	-	1	-	4	-
802	Fracture of face bones	1	1	-	-	-	-	-	-	-	-	-	1	1	-	1	1
803	Other and unqualified skull fractures	39	12	1	1	-	-	1	1	4	3	11	4	17	3	38	11
804	Multiple fractures involving skull or face with other bones	2	-	-	-	-	-	-	-	-	-	-	-	2	-	2	-
805-809	Fracture of neck and trunk	8	3	-	-	-	-	-	-	2	1	1	-	5	1	8	3
805	Fracture of vertebral column without mention of spinal cord lesion	3	2	-	-	-	-	-	-	2	1	1	-	-	1	3	2
806	Fracture of vertebral column with spinal cord lesion	4	1	-	-	-	-	-	-	-	-	-	-	4	-	4	1
808	Fracture of pelvis	1	-	-	-	-	-	-	-	-	-	-	-	1	-	1	-
830-839	Dislocation	2	1	-	-	-	-	-	-	1	-	1	1	-	-	2	1
839	Other, multiple and ill-defined dislocations	2	1	-	-	-	-	-	-	1	-	1	1	-	-	2	1
840-848	Sprains and strains of joints and adjacent muscles	1	-	-	-	-	-	-	-	-	-	-	-	1	-	1	-
847	Sprains and strains of other and unspecified parts of back	1	-	-	-	-	-	-	-	-	-	-	-	1	-	1	-
850-854	Intracranial injury, excluding those with skull fracture	91	41	4	5	2	-	6	5	17	15	16	12	40	7	85	36
851	Cerebral laceration and contusion	6	1	-	-	-	-	-	-	-	-	1	-	4	1	6	1
852	Subarachnoid, subdural and extradural haemorrhage, following injury	13	3	1	3	1	-	2	3	2	-	3	-	3	-	11	-
853	Other and unspecified intracranial haemorrhage following injury	1	2	-	2	-	-	-	2	-	-	1	-	-	-	1	-
854	Intracranial injury of other and unspecified nature	71	35	3	-	1	-	4	-	15	15	11	12	33	6	67	35
860-869	Internal injury of chest, abdomen and pelvis	61	28	-	1	-	1	-	2	13	6	13	7	25	6	61	26
861	Injury to heart and lung	6	1	-	-	-	-	-	-	1	-	1	1	2	-	6	1
862	Injury to other and unspecified intrathoracic organs	4	4	-	-	-	-	-	-	1	2	1	1	2	-	4	4
863	Injury to gastrointestinal tract	2	3	-	-	-	1	-	1	2	1	-	1	-	-	2	2
864	Injury to liver	3	1	-	-	-	-	-	-	2	-	-	1	1	-	3	1
868	Injury to other intraabdominal organs	3	-	-	-	-	-	-	-	2	-	1	-	-	-	3	-
869	Internal injury to unspecified or ill-defined organs	43	19	-	1	-	-	-	1	5	3	10	3	20	6	43	18

Table 6 1995 Series DH3 no. 28

Table 6 - *continued*

ICD number	Cause of Death	All ages 28 days to 15 years		Months 1-5		6-11		1-11		Years 1-4		5-9		10-14		1-15	
		Boys	Girls	Boys	Girls	Boys	Girls	Boys	Girls	Boys	Girls	Boys	Girls	Boys	Girls	Boys	Girls
870-897	Open wound	10	3	-	-	1	-	1	-	2	-	2	2	2	-	9	3
870-879	Open wound of head, neck and trunk	10	3	-	-	1	-	1	-	2	-	2	2	2	-	9	3
873	Other open wound of head	2	1	-	-	-	-	-	-	1	-	-	1	-	-	2	1
874	Open wound of neck	1	1	-	-	-	-	-	-	-	-	1	-	-	-	1	1
875	Open wound of chest (wall)	4	1	-	-	-	-	-	-	1	-	1	1	1	-	4	1
879	Open wound of other and unspecified sites, except limbs	3	-	-	-	1	-	1	-	-	-	-	-	1	-	2	-
900-904	Injury to blood vessels	1	-	-	-	-	-	-	-	-	-	-	-	1	-	1	-
901	Injury to blood vessels of thorax	1	-	-	-	-	-	-	-	-	-	-	-	1	-	1	-
901.0	Thoracic aorta	1	-	-	-	-	-	-	-	-	-	-	-	1	-	1	-
905-909	Late effects of injuries, poisonings, toxic effects and other external causes	3	2	-	-	-	-	-	-	-	2	1	-	2	-	3	2
907	Late effects of injuries to the nervous system	2	2	-	-	-	-	-	-	-	2	-	-	2	-	2	2
907.0	Late effect of intracranial injury without mention of skull fracture	2	2	-	-	-	-	-	-	-	2	-	-	2	-	2	2
909	Late effects of other and unspecified external causes	1	-	-	-	-	-	-	-	-	-	1	-	-	-	1	-
909.4	Late effect of certain other external causes	1	-	-	-	-	-	-	-	-	-	1	-	-	-	1	-
925-929	Crushing injury	-	1	-	-	-	-	-	-	-	1	-	-	-	-	-	1
925	Crushing injury of face, scalp and neck	-	1	-	-	-	-	-	-	-	1	-	-	-	-	-	1
930-939	Effects of foreign body entering through orifice	20	10	6	2	1	2	7	4	9	5	-	-	3	-	13	6
933	Foreign body in pharynx and larynx	20	8	6	1	1	1	7	2	9	5	-	-	3	-	13	6
934	Foreign body in trachea, bronchus and lung	-	2	-	1	-	1	-	2	-	-	-	-	-	-	-	-
940-949	Burns	20	10	-	-	-	1	-	1	14	4	4	4	2	1	20	9
947	Burn of internal organs	1	1	-	-	-	-	-	-	1	-	-	-	-	1	1	1
948	Burns classified according to extent of body surface involved	2	2	-	-	-	-	-	-	1	-	-	2	1	-	2	2
948.4	40-49%	1	-	-	-	-	-	-	-	1	-	-	-	-	-	1	-
948.7	70-79%	1	-	-	-	-	-	-	-	-	-	-	-	1	-	1	-
948.8	80-89%	-	1	-	-	-	-	-	-	-	-	-	1	-	-	-	1
948.9	90% or more	-	1	-	-	-	-	-	-	-	-	-	1	-	-	-	1
949	Burn, unspecified	17	7	-	-	-	1	-	1	12	4	4	2	1	-	17	6
950-957	Injury to nerves and spinal cord	1	1	-	-	-	-	-	-	-	-	-	-	1	1	1	1
952	Spinal cord lesion without evidence of spinal bone injury	1	-	-	-	-	-	-	-	-	-	-	-	1	-	1	-
957	Injury to other and unspecified nerves	-	1	-	-	-	-	-	-	-	-	-	-	-	1	-	1

Table 6 - *continued*

ICD number	Cause of Death	Age at death All ages 28 days to 15 years		Months 1-5		6-11		1-11		Years 1-4		5-9		10-14		1-15	
		Boys	Girls	Boys	Girls	Boys	Girls	Boys	Girls	Boys	Girls	Boys	Girls	Boys	Girls	Boys	Girls
958-959	Certain traumatic complications and unspecified injuries	11	7	2	-	-	-	2	-	2	1	3	2	4	1	9	7
958	Certain early complications of trauma	-	1	-	-	-	-	-	-	-	-	-	1	-	-	-	1
958.0	Air embolism	-	1	-	-	-	-	-	-	-	-	-	1	-	-	-	1
959	Injury, other and unspecified	11	6	2	-	-	-	2	-	2	1	3	1	4	1	9	6
959.0	Face and neck	-	1	-	-	-	-	-	-	-	-	-	-	-	-	-	1
959.8	Other specified sites, including multiple	5	2	-	-	-	-	-	-	2	-	1	1	2	-	5	2
959.9	Unspecified site	5	3	2	-	-	-	2	-	-	1	1	-	2	1	3	3
960-979	Poisoning by drugs, medicaments and biological substances	4	9	-	-	-	-	-	-	-	-	-	-	3	5	4	9
965	Poisoning by analgesics, antipyretics and antirheumatics	1	6	-	-	-	-	-	-	-	-	-	-	1	3	1	6
965.0	Opiates and related narcotics	-	2	-	-	-	-	-	-	-	-	-	-	-	1	-	2
965.4	Aromatic analgesics, not elsewhere classified	-	1	-	-	-	-	-	-	-	-	-	-	-	-	-	1
965.7	Other non-narcotic analgesics	1	1	-	-	-	-	-	-	-	-	-	-	1	1	1	1
965.8	Other	-	2	-	-	-	-	-	-	-	-	-	-	-	1	-	2
969	Poisoning by psychotropic agents	1	2	-	-	-	-	-	-	-	-	-	-	1	2	1	2
969.0	Antidepressants	1	2	-	-	-	-	-	-	-	-	-	-	1	2	1	2
977	Poisoning by other and unspecified drugs and medicaments	2	1	-	-	-	-	-	-	-	-	-	-	1	-	2	1
977.8	Other drugs and medicaments	2	1	-	-	-	-	-	-	-	-	-	-	1	-	2	1
980-989	Toxic effects of substances chiefly nonmedicinal as to source	31	33	-	1	1	-	1	1	12	18	13	8	5	5	30	32
981	Toxic effect of petroleum products	1	-	-	-	-	-	-	-	1	-	-	-	-	-	1	-
986	Toxic effect of carbon monoxide	13	16	-	-	-	-	-	-	4	9	6	5	3	2	13	16
987	Toxic effect of other gases, fumes or vapours	17	17	-	1	1	-	1	1	7	9	7	3	2	3	16	16
987.1	Other hydrocarbon gas	1	-	-	-	-	-	-	-	-	-	-	-	1	-	1	-
987.7	Hydrocyanic acid gas	-	1	-	-	-	-	-	-	-	1	-	-	-	-	-	1
987.8	Other	16	16	-	1	1	-	1	1	7	8	7	3	1	3	15	15
990-995	Other and unspecified effects of external causes	83	30	2	3	12	5	14	8	17	11	14	1	30	8	69	22
994	Effects of other external causes	83	30	2	3	12	5	14	8	17	11	14	1	30	8	69	22
994.1	Drowning and nonfatal submersion	28	12	1	-	5	3	6	3	10	6	6	-	6	2	22	9
994.2	Effects of hunger	-	1	-	-	-	1	-	1	-	-	-	-	-	-	-	-
994.7	Asphyxiation and strangulation	50	16	1	3	7	1	8	4	7	4	7	1	20	6	42	12
994.8	Electrocution and nonfatal effects of electric current	5	1	-	-	-	-	-	-	-	1	1	-	4	-	5	1
996-999	Complications of surgical and medical care not elslewhere classified	-	4	-	2	-	1	-	3	-	-	-	-	-	1	-	1
996	Complications peculiar to certain specified procedures	-	2	-	1	-	1	-	2	-	-	-	-	-	-	-	-
996.7	Other complications of internal prosthetic device, implant and graft	-	1	-	1	-	-	-	1	-	-	-	-	-	-	-	-

Table 6 1995 Series DH3 no. 28

Table 6 - *continued*

ICD number	Cause of Death	All ages 28 days to 15 years		Months 1-5		6-11		1-11		Years 1-4		5-9		10-14		1-15	
		Boys	Girls	Boys	Girls	Boys	Girls	Boys	Girls	Boys	Girls	Boys	Girls	Boys	Girls	Boys	Girls
996.8	Complications of transplanted organ	-	1	-	-	-	1	-	1	-	-	-	-	-	-	-	-
998	Other complications of procedures, not elsewhere classified	-	1	-	-	-	-	-	-	-	-	-	-	-	1	-	1
998.2	Accidental puncture or laceration during a procedure	-	1	-	-	-	-	-	-	-	-	-	-	-	1	-	1
999	Complications of medical care, not elsewhere classified	-	1	-	1	-	-	-	1	-	-	-	-	-	-	-	-
999.1	Air embolism	-	1	-	1	-	-	-	1	-	-	-	-	-	-	-	-
E800-E999	**XVII External causes of injury and poisoning**	**394**	**196**	**15**	**15**	**18**	**10**	**33**	**25**	**94**	**67**	**79**	**42**	**145**	**39**	**361**	**171**
E800-E848	Transport accidents	167	66	1	2	-	-	1	2	26	19	37	20	78	15	166	64
E800-E807	Railway accidents	2	-	-	-	-	-	-	-	-	-	1	-	1	-	2	-
E805	Hit by rolling stock	2	-	-	-	-	-	-	-	-	-	1	-	1	-	2	-
E805.2	Pedestrian	1	-	-	-	-	-	-	-	-	-	1	-	-	-	1	-
E805.9	Unspecified person	1	-	-	-	-	-	-	-	-	-	-	-	1	-	1	-
E810-E819	Motor vehicle traffic accidents	154	61	1	2	-	-	1	2	25	14	30	20	74	15	153	59
E812	Other motor vehicle traffic accident involving collision with another motor vehicle	17	15	1	-	-	-	1	-	5	6	4	4	3	2	16	15
E812.1	Passenger in motor vehicle other than motorcycle	15	15	1	-	-	-	1	-	5	6	4	4	2	2	14	15
E812.2	Motorcyclist	2	-	-	-	-	-	-	-	-	-	-	-	1	-	2	-
E813	Motor vehicle traffic accident involving collision with other vehicle	34	3	-	-	-	-	-	-	-	-	5	1	23	1	34	3
E813.6	Pedal cyclist	34	3	-	-	-	-	-	-	-	-	5	1	23	1	34	3
E814	Motor vehicle traffic accident involving collision with pedestrian	79	28	-	2	-	-	-	2	18	6	16	10	35	9	79	26
E814.7	Pedestrian	79	28	-	2	-	-	-	2	18	6	16	10	35	9	79	26
E815	Other motor vehicle traffic accident involving collision on the highway	4	1	-	-	-	-	-	-	-	-	-	-	2	-	4	1
E815.0	Driver of motor vehicle other than motorcycle	3	-	-	-	-	-	-	-	-	-	-	-	1	-	3	-
E815.1	Passenger in motor vehicle other than motorcycle	1	1	-	-	-	-	-	-	-	-	-	-	1	-	1	1
E816	Motor vehicle traffic accident due to loss of control, without collision on the highway	4	2	-	-	-	-	-	-	-	1	1	1	3	-	4	2
E816.1	Passenger in motor vehicle other than motorcycle	4	2	-	-	-	-	-	-	-	1	1	1	3	-	4	2
E818	Other noncollision motor vehicle traffic accident	1	1	-	-	-	-	-	-	-	-	1	-	-	1	1	1
E818.1	Passenger in motor vehicle other than motorcycle	1	1	-	-	-	-	-	-	-	-	1	-	-	1	1	1
E819	Motor vehicle traffic accident of unspecified nature	15	11	-	-	-	-	-	-	2	1	3	4	8	2	15	11
E819.1	Passenger in motor vehicle other than motorcycle	8	9	-	-	-	-	-	-	1	1	2	4	4	1	8	9
E819.9	Unspecified person	7	2	-	-	-	-	-	-	1	-	1	-	4	1	7	2

Table 6 - *continued*

ICD number	Cause of Death	Age at death														
		All ages 28 days to 15 years		Months						Years						
				1-5		6-11		1-11		1-4		5-9		10-14		1-15	
		Boys	Girls	Boys	Girls	Boys	Girls	Boys	Girls	Boys	Girls	Boys	Girls	Boys	Girls	Boys	Girls
E820-E825	Motor vehicle nontraffic accidents	4	4	-	-	-	-	-	-	-	4	3	-	-	-	4	4
E821	Nontraffic accident involving other off-road motor vehicle	3	-	-	-	-	-	-	-	-	-	2	-	-	-	3	-
E821.2	Motor cyclist	2	-	-	-	-	-	-	-	-	-	1	-	-	-	2	-
E821.7	Pedestrian	1	-	-	-	-	-	-	-	-	-	1	-	-	-	1	-
E822	Other motor vehicle nontraffic accident involving collision with moving object	1	4	-	-	-	-	-	-	-	4	1	-	-	-	1	4
E822.7	Pedestrian	1	4	-	-	-	-	-	-	-	4	1	-	-	-	1	4
E826-E829	Other road vehicle accidents	6	-	-	-	-	-	-	-	-	-	3	-	3	-	6	-
E826	Pedal cycle accident	6	-	-	-	-	-	-	-	-	-	3	-	3	-	6	-
E826.1	Pedal cyclist	6	-	-	-	-	-	-	-	-	-	3	-	3	-	6	-
E830-E838	Water transport accidents	1	-	-	-	-	-	-	-	1	-	-	-	-	-	1	-
E831	Accident to watercraft causing other injury	1	-	-	-	-	-	-	-	1	-	-	-	-	-	1	-
E831.3	Occupant of other watercraft - other than crew	1	-	-	-	-	-	-	-	1	-	-	-	-	-	1	-
E840-E845	Air and space transport accidents	-	1	-	-	-	-	-	-	-	1	-	-	-	-	-	1
E844	Other specified air transport accidents	-	1	-	-	-	-	-	-	-	1	-	-	-	-	-	1
E844.9	Other person	-	1	-	-	-	-	-	-	-	1	-	-	-	-	-	1
E850-E869	Accidental poisoning	4	2	-	-	-	-	-	-	1	-	-	-	3	1	4	2
E850-E858	Accidental poisoning by drugs, medicaments and biologicals	2	2	-	-	-	-	-	-	-	-	-	-	2	1	2	2
E850	Accidental poisoning by analgesics, antipyretics antirheumatics	-	1	-	-	-	-	-	-	-	-	-	-	-	1	-	1
E850.0	Opiates and related narcotics	-	1	-	-	-	-	-	-	-	-	-	-	-	1	-	1
E854	Accidental poisoning by other psychotropic agents	1	-	-	-	-	-	-	-	-	-	-	-	1	-	1	-
E854.0	Antidepressants	1	-	-	-	-	-	-	-	-	-	-	-	1	-	1	-
E858	Accidental poisoning by other drugs	1	1	-	-	-	-	-	-	-	-	-	-	1	-	1	1
E858.8	Other	1	1	-	-	-	-	-	-	-	-	-	-	1	-	1	1
E860-E869	Accidental poisoning by other solid and liquid substances, gases and vapours	2	-	-	-	-	-	-	-	1	-	-	-	1	-	2	-
E862	Accidental poisoning by petroleum products, other solvents and their vapours, not elsewhere classified	1	-	-	-	-	-	-	-	1	-	-	-	-	-	1	-
E862.0	Petroleum solvents	1	-	-	-	-	-	-	-	1	-	-	-	-	-	1	-

Table 6 1995 Series DH3 no. 28

Table 6 - *continued*

ICD number	Cause of Death	All ages 28 days to 15 years		Months 1-5		6-11		1-11		Years 1-4		5-9		10-14		1-15	
		Boys	Girls	Boys	Girls	Boys	Girls	Boys	Girls	Boys	Girls	Boys	Girls	Boys	Girls	Boys	Girls
E869	Accidental poisoning by other gases and vapours	1	-	-	-	-	-	-	-	-	-	-	-	1	-	1	-
E869.8	Other specified gases and vapours	1	-	-	-	-	-	-	-	-	-	-	-	1	-	1	-
E870-E879	Misadventures during medical care, abnormal reactions, late complications	-	4	-	2	-	1	-	3	-	-	-	-	-	1	-	1
E870-E876	Misadventures to patients during surgical nad medical care	-	3	-	2	-	-	-	2	-	-	-	-	-	1	-	1
E870	Accidental cut, puncture, perforation or haemorrhage during medical care	-	1	-	-	-	-	-	-	-	-	-	-	-	1	-	1
E870.8	Other	-	1	-	-	-	-	-	-	-	-	-	-	-	1	-	1
E876	Other and unspecified misadventures during medical care	-	2	-	2	-	-	-	2	-	-	-	-	-	-	-	-
E876.8	Other specified misadventures	-	2	-	2	-	-	-	2	-	-	-	-	-	-	-	-
E879	Other procedures, without mention of misadventure at the time of procedure, as the cause of abnormal reaction of patient, or of later complication	-	1	-	-	-	1	-	1	-	-	-	-	-	-	-	-
E879.8	Other	-	1	-	-	-	1	-	1	-	-	-	-	-	-	-	-
E880-E888	Accidental falls	14	5	1	-	1	-	2	-	2	3	2	-	6	1	12	5
E880	Fall on or from stairs or steps	2	-	-	-	-	-	-	-	2	-	-	-	-	-	2	-
E880.9	Other stairs or steps	2	-	-	-	-	-	-	-	2	-	-	-	-	-	2	-
E882	Fall from or out of building or other structure	3	3	-	-	-	-	-	-	-	1	2	-	1	1	3	3
E884	Other fall from one level to another	8	1	1	-	-	-	1	-	-	-	-	1	5	-	7	1
E884.1	Fall from cliff	1	-	-	-	-	-	-	-	-	-	-	-	1	-	1	-
E884.2	Fall from chair or bed	-	1	-	-	-	-	-	-	-	1	-	-	-	-	-	1
E884.9	Other fall from one level to another	7	-	1	-	-	-	1	-	-	-	-	-	4	-	6	-
E888	Other and unspecified fall	1	1	-	-	1	-	1	-	-	1	-	-	-	-	-	1
E890-E899	Accidents caused by fire and flames	33	31	-	1	1	1	1	2	16	19	12	5	4	5	32	29
E890	Conflagration in private dwelling	20	22	-	-	1	1	1	1	11	12	6	4	2	5	19	21
E890.2	Other smoke and fumes from conflagration	19	19	-	-	1	-	1	-	10	11	6	3	2	5	18	19
E890.3	Burning caused by conflagration	1	3	-	-	-	1	-	1	1	1	-	1	-	-	1	2
E892	Conflagration not in building or structure	1	-	-	-	-	-	-	-	1	-	-	-	-	-	1	-
E893	Accident caused by ignition of clothing	1	-	-	-	-	-	-	-	1	-	-	-	-	-	1	-
E893.0	From controlled fire in private dwelling	1	-	-	-	-	-	-	-	1	-	-	-	-	-	1	-
E894	Ignition of highly inflammable material	1	-	-	-	-	-	-	-	-	-	-	-	1	-	1	-
E895	Accident caused by controlled fire in private dwelling	1	-	-	-	-	-	-	-	-	-	1	-	-	-	1	-
E898	Accident caused by other specified fire and flames	5	6	-	1	-	-	-	1	3	5	2	-	-	-	5	5

Table 6 - *continued*

ICD number	Cause of Death	All ages 28 days to 15 years Boys	Girls	Months 1-5 Boys	Girls	6-11 Boys	Girls	1-11 Boys	Girls	Years 1-4 Boys	Girls	5-9 Boys	Girls	10-14 Boys	Girls	1-15 Boys	Girls
E898.0	Burning bedclothes	1	3	-	-	-	-	-	-	-	3	1	-	-	-	1	3
E898.1	Other	4	3	-	1	-	-	-	1	3	2	1	-	-	-	4	2
E899	Accident caused by unspecified fire	4	3	-	-	-	-	-	-	-	2	3	1	1	-	4	3
E900-E929	Other accidents, including late effects	114	41	7	7	14	4	21	11	33	19	15	6	39	4	93	30
E900-E909	Accidents due to natural and environmental factors	1	1	-	-	-	-	-	-	1	-	-	-	-	1	1	1
E901	Excessive cold	1	-	-	-	-	-	-	-	1	-	-	-	-	-	1	-
E901.9	Of unspecified origin	1	-	-	-	-	-	-	-	1	-	-	-	-	-	1	-
E906	Other injury caused by animals	-	1	-	-	-	-	-	-	-	-	-	-	-	1	-	1
E906.8	Other specified injury caused by animal	-	1	-	-	-	-	-	-	-	-	-	-	-	1	-	1
E910	Accidental drowning and submersion	24	10	-	-	5	3	5	3	8	5	5	-	6	2	19	7
E910.2	While engaged in other sport or recreational activity without diving equipment	6	1	-	-	-	-	-	-	-	-	1	-	5	1	6	1
E910.3	While swimming or diving for purposes other than recreation or sport	-	1	-	-	-	-	-	-	-	-	-	-	-	1	-	1
E910.4	In bathtub	6	3	-	-	4	3	4	3	1	-	1	-	-	-	2	-
E910.8	Other	5	2	-	-	1	-	1	-	2	2	1	-	1	-	4	2
E910.9	Unspecified	7	3	-	-	-	-	-	-	5	3	2	-	-	-	7	3
E911	Inhalation and ingestion of food causing obstruction of respiratory tract or suffocation	14	8	3	1	1	1	4	2	7	5	-	-	2	-	10	6
E912	Inhalation and ingestion of other object causing obstruction of respiratory tract or suffocation	6	1	3	1	-	-	3	1	2	-	-	-	1	-	3	-
E913	Accidental mechanical suffocation	34	7	1	3	7	-	8	3	6	3	4	-	13	1	26	4
E913.0	In bed or cradle	6	3	1	2	4	-	5	2	-	1	-	-	1	-	1	1
E913.1	By plastic bag	-	1	-	1	-	-	-	1	-	-	-	-	-	-	-	-
E913.3	By falling earth or other substance	2	-	-	-	-	-	-	-	-	-	1	-	1	-	2	-
E913.8	Other specified means	22	2	-	-	2	-	2	-	4	1	2	-	11	1	20	2
E913.9	Unspecified	4	1	-	-	1	-	1	-	2	1	1	-	-	-	3	1
E916-E928	Other accidents	32	13	-	2	1	-	1	2	9	5	5	6	15	-	31	11
E916	Struck accidentally by falling object	9	4	-	-	-	-	-	-	2	1	2	3	4	-	9	4
E917	Striking against or struck accidentally by objects or persons	3	2	-	-	-	-	-	-	-	1	1	1	2	-	3	2
E917.0	In sports	1	-	-	-	-	-	-	-	-	-	1	-	-	-	1	-
E917.9	Other	2	2	-	-	-	-	-	-	-	1	-	1	2	-	2	2
E919	Accidents caused by machinery	1	-	-	-	-	-	-	-	1	-	-	-	-	-	1	-
E919.0	Agricultural machines	1	-	-	-	-	-	-	-	1	-	-	-	-	-	1	-
E920	Accidents caused by cutting and piercing instruments or objects	2	-	-	-	-	-	-	-	1	-	-	-	1	-	2	-
E920.8	Other	2	-	-	-	-	-	-	-	1	-	-	-	1	-	2	-
E923	Accident caused by explosive material	-	1	-	-	-	-	-	-	-	-	-	1	-	-	-	1
E923.9	Unspecified	-	1	-	-	-	-	-	-	-	-	-	1	-	-	-	1

Table 6 1995 Series DH3 no. 28

Table 6 - *continued*

ICD number	Cause of Death	Age at death															
		All ages 28 days to 15 years		Months						Years							
				1-5		6-11		1-11		1-4		5-9		10-14		1-15	
		Boys	Girls	Boys	Girls	Boys	Girls	Boys	Girls	Boys	Girls	Boys	Girls	Boys	Girls	Boys	Girls
E924	Accident caused by hot substance or object, caustic or corrosive material and steam	4	1	-	-	-	-	-	-	4	1	-	-	-	-	4	1
E924.0	Hot liquids and vapours, including steam	4	1	-	-	-	-	-	-	4	1	-	-	-	-	4	1
E925	Accident caused by electric current	5	1	-	-	-	-	-	-	-	1	1	-	4	-	5	1
E925.0	Domestic wiring and appliances	-	1	-	-	-	-	-	-	-	1	-	-	-	-	-	1
E925.8	Other	5	-	-	-	-	-	-	-	-	-	1	-	4	-	5	-
E928	Other and unspecified environmental and accidental causes	8	4	-	2	1	-	1	2	1	1	1	1	4	-	7	2
E928.9	Unspecified accidents	8	4	-	2	1	-	1	2	1	1	1	1	4	-	7	2
E929	Late effects of accidental injury	3	1	-	-	-	-	-	-	-	1	1	-	2	-	3	1
E929.0	Late effects of motor vehicle accident	2	-	-	-	-	-	-	-	-	-	-	-	2	-	2	-
E929.8	Late effects of other accidents	1	1	-	-	-	-	-	-	-	1	1	-	-	-	1	1
E950-E959	Suicide and selfinflicted injury	3	6	-	-	-	-	-	-	-	-	-	-	1	4	3	6
E950	Suicide and selfinflicted poisoning by solid or liquid substances	1	2	-	-	-	-	-	-	-	-	-	-	1	1	1	2
E950.0	Analgesics, antipyretics and antirheumatics	1	1	-	-	-	-	-	-	-	-	-	-	1	-	1	1
E950.3	Tranquillizers and other psychotropic agents	-	1	-	-	-	-	-	-	-	-	-	-	-	1	-	1
E953	Suicide and selfinflicted injury by hanging, strangulation and suffocation	2	3	-	-	-	-	-	-	-	-	-	-	-	2	2	3
E953.0	Hanging	2	3	-	-	-	-	-	-	-	-	-	-	-	2	2	3
E957	Suicide and selfinflicted injuries by jumping from high places	-	1	-	-	-	-	-	-	-	-	-	-	-	1	-	1
E957.1	Other manmade structures	-	1	-	-	-	-	-	-	-	-	-	-	-	1	-	1
E960-E969	Homicide and injury purposely inflicted by other persons	25	18	2	1	1	2	3	3	7	4	9	8	6	1	22	15
E962	Assault by poisoning	3	4	-	-	-	-	-	-	-	-	3	3	-	-	3	4
E962.0	Drugs and medicaments	-	1	-	-	-	-	-	-	-	-	-	-	-	-	-	1
E962.2	Other gases and vapours	3	3	-	-	-	-	-	-	-	-	3	3	-	-	3	3
E963	Assault by hanging and strangulation	2	2	-	-	-	-	-	-	-	1	-	-	2	1	2	2
E966	Assault by cutting and piercing instrument	4	2	-	-	-	-	-	-	1	-	2	1	1	-	4	2
E967	Child battering and other maltreatment	4	1	1	-	-	-	1	-	3	1	-	-	-	-	3	1
E967.9	By unspecified person	4	1	1	-	-	-	1	-	3	1	-	-	-	-	3	1
E968	Assault by other and unspecified means	12	9	1	1	1	2	2	3	3	2	4	4	3	-	10	6
E968.0	Fire	5	4	-	-	-	-	-	-	3	1	2	3	-	-	5	4
E968.2	Striking by blunt or thrown object	-	1	-	-	-	1	-	1	-	-	-	-	-	-	-	1
E968.4	Criminal neglect	-	1	-	-	-	1	-	1	-	-	-	-	-	-	-	1
E968.8	Other specified means	2	-	1	-	-	-	1	-	-	-	-	-	1	-	1	-
E968.9	Unspecified means	5	3	-	1	1	-	1	1	-	1	2	1	2	-	4	2

Table 6 - *continued*

ICD number	Cause of Death	Age at death															
		All ages															
		28 days to		Months						Years							
		15 years		1-5		6-11		1-11		1-4		5-9		10-14		1-15	
		Boys	Girls	Boys	Girls	Boys	Girls	Boys	Girls	Boys	Girls	Boys	Girls	Boys	Girls	Boys	Girls
E970-E999	Other violence	34	23	4	2	1	2	5	4	9	3	4	3	8	7	29	19
E980-E989	Injury undetermined whether accidentally or purposely inflicted	34	23	4	2	1	2	5	4	9	3	4	3	8	7	29	19
E980	Poisoning by solid or liquid substances, undetermined, accidentally or purposely inflicted	-	4	-	-	-	-	-	-	-	-	-	-	-	3	-	4
E980.0	Analgesics, antipyretics and antirheumatics	-	3	-	-	-	-	-	-	-	-	-	-	-	2	-	3
E980.3	Tranquillizers and other psychotropic agents	-	1	-	-	-	-	-	-	-	-	-	-	-	1	-	1
E983	Hanging, strangulation or suffocation, undetermined whether accidentally or purposely inflicted	7	2	-	-	-	1	-	1	-	-	-	-	4	1	7	1
E983.0	Hanging	7	1	-	-	-	-	-	-	-	-	-	-	4	1	7	1
E983.8	Other specified means	-	1	-	-	-	1	-	1	-	-	-	-	-	-	-	-
E984	Submersion(drowning), undetermined whether accidentally or purposely inflicted	2	2	-	-	-	-	-	-	1	1	1	-	-	-	2	2
E985	Injury by firearms and explosives, undetermined whether accidentally or purposely inflicted	1	-	-	-	-	-	-	-	-	-	-	-	-	-	1	-
E985.1	Shot gun	1	-	-	-	-	-	-	-	-	-	-	-	-	-	1	-
E988	Injury by other and unspecified means, undetermined, whether accidentally or purposely inflicted	24	15	4	2	1	1	5	3	8	2	3	3	4	3	19	12
E988.1	Burns, fire	1	1	-	-	-	-	-	-	1	-	-	-	-	1	1	1
E988.8	Other specified means	20	13	4	1	1	1	5	2	6	2	3	3	3	2	15	11
E988.9	Unspecified means	3	1	-	1	-	-	-	1	1	-	-	-	1	-	3	-

Table 7 1995 Series DH3 no.28

Table 7   All infant deaths and linked infant deaths
England and Wales, 1980-95
Numbers and rates per 1,000 live births

England and Wales

Year	Numbers						Rates					
	Neonatal		Postneonatal		Infants		Neonatal		Postneonatal		Infants	
	All	Linked	All	Linked	All	Linked	All	Linked	All	Linked	All	Linked
1980	5,023	4,987	2,876	2,803	7,899	7,790	7.7	7.6	4.4	4.3	12.0	11.9
1981	4,213	4,176	2,741	2,709	6,954	6,885	6.6	6.6	4.3	4.3	11.0	10.9
1982	3,925	3,890	2,850	2,773	6,775	6,663	6.3	6.2	4.6	4.4	10.8	10.6
1983	3,682	3,653	2,699	2,631	6,381	6,284	5.9	5.8	4.3	4.2	10.1	10.0
1984	3,530	3,515	2,456	2,430	5,986	5,945	5.5	5.5	3.9	3.8	9.4	9.3
1985	3,531	3,489	2,610	2,538	6,141	6,027	5.4	5.3	4.0	3.9	9.4	9.2
1986	3,489	3,449	2,824	2,760	6,313	6,209	5.3	5.2	4.3	4.2	9.6	9.4
1987	3,448	3,413	2,824	2,742	6,272	6,155	5.1	5.0	4.1	4.0	9.2	9.0
1988	3,421	3,386	2,849	2,793	6,270	6,179	4.9	4.9	4.1	4.0	9.0	8.9
1989	3,272	3,223	2,536	2,478	5,808	5,701	4.8	4.7	3.7	3.6	8.4	8.3
1990	3,221	3,171	2,343	2,270	5,564	5,441	4.6	4.5	3.3	3.2	7.9	7.7
1991	3,052	3,006	2,106	2,049	5,158	5,055	4.4	4.3	3.0	2.9	7.4	7.2
1992	2,955	2,911	1,584	1,524	4,539	4,435	4.3	4.2	2.3	2.2	6.6	6.4
1993	2,796	2,771	1,446	1,405	4,242	4,176	4.2	4.1	2.2	2.1	6.3	6.2
1994	2,749	2,724	1,371	1,331	4,120	4,055	4.1	4.1	2.1	2.0	6.2	6.1
1995	2,698	2,669	1,284	1,244	3,982	3,913	4.2	4.1	2.0	1.9	6.1	6.0

Table 8: Live births, stillbirths and infant deaths   **England and Wales**
       ONS cause groups by birthweight
       Numbers, 1995

Cause group	Birthweight (grams)	Births		Deaths			
		Live births	Stillbirths	Early neonatal	Neonatal	Postneonatal	Infant
All causes	All	**648,001**	**3,597**	**2,084**	**2,669**	**1,244**	**3,913**
	<2500	47,324	2,426	1,425	1,789	488	2,277
	<1500	7,583	1,625	1,154	1,425	255	1,680
	<1000	2,879	1,119	941	1,124	168	1,292
	1000-1499	4,704	506	213	301	87	388
	1500-1999	9,679	399	134	167	91	258
	2000-2499	30,062	402	137	197	142	339
	2500-2999	109,436	429	150	217	238	455
	3000-3499	234,752	376	191	267	298	565
	3500-3999	185,122	198	128	179	147	326
	4000 & over	69,150	93	131	153	54	207
	not stated	2,217	75	59	64	19	83
Congenital anomalies	All		320	520	706	304	1,010
	<2500		270	294	373	99	472
	<1500		194	150	177	29	206
	<1000		130	78	89	12	101
	1000-1499		64	72	88	17	105
	1500-1999		38	74	94	22	116
	2000-2499		38	70	102	48	150
	2500-2999		25	79	115	77	192
	3000-3499		8	69	110	79	189
	3500-3999		4	43	68	34	102
	4000 & over		-	18	23	9	32
	not stated		13	17	17	6	23
Antepartum infections	All		12	17	22	6	28
	<2500		12	9	12	4	16
	<1500		10	6	7	-	7
	<1000		9	4	5	-	5
	1000-1499		1	2	2	-	2
	1500-1999		1	1	1	1	2
	2000-2499		1	2	4	3	7
	2500-2999		-	3	4	-	4
	3000-3499		-	2	2	1	3
	3500-3999		-	2	3	1	4
	4000 & over		-	1	1	-	1
	not stated		-	-	-	-	-
Immaturity related conditions	All		116	1,100	1,302	118	1,420
	<2500		111	935	1,121	110	1,231
	<1500		104	894	1,072	102	1,174
	<1000		87	791	924	82	1,006
	1000-1499		17	103	148	20	168
	1500-1999		5	25	30	6	36
	2000-2499		2	16	19	2	21
	2500-2999		1	15	17	2	19
	3000-3499		1	29	34	1	35
	3500-3999		-	27	29	-	29
	4000 & over		-	62	66	1	67
	not stated		3	32	35	4	39
Asphyxia anoxia or trauma (intrapartum)	All		173	283	348	9	357
	<2500		80	99	138	3	141
	<1500		60	49	78	2	80
	<1000		44	32	46	1	47
	1000-1499		16	17	32	1	33
	1500-1999		9	18	20	-	20
	2000-2499		11	32	40	1	41
	2500-2999		28	33	40	-	40
	3000-3499		27	61	66	3	69
	3500-3999		18	42	52	1	53
	4000 & over		19	40	44	2	46
	not stated		1	8	8	-	8

Table 8 1995 Series DH3 no.28

Table 8 - *continued*

Cause group	Birthweight (grams)	Births		Deaths			
		Live births	Stillbirths	Early neonatal	Neonatal	Postneonatal	Infant
External conditions	**All**		-	**3**	**7**	**59**	**66**
	<2500		-	-	-	7	7
	<1500		-	-	-	1	1
	<1000		-	-	-	1	1
	1000-1499		-	-	-	-	-
	1500-1999		-	-	-	3	3
	2000-2499		-	-	-	3	3
	2500-2999		-	-	1	18	19
	3000-3499		-	1	1	17	18
	3500-3999		-	2	3	13	16
	4000 & over		-	-	2	3	5
	not stated		-	-	-	1	1
Infections	**All**	**11**		**51**	**96**	**205**	**301**
	<2500	9		27	52	91	143
	<1500	8		13	29	53	82
	<1000	7		6	15	35	50
	1000-1499	1		7	14	18	32
	1500-1999	1		10	13	19	32
	2000-2499	-		4	10	19	29
	2500-2999	-		8	14	27	41
	3000-3499	1		11	16	48	64
	3500-3999	1		4	10	26	36
	4000 & over	-		-	2	9	11
	not stated	-		1	2	4	6
Other specific conditions	**All**	**118**		**25**	**30**	**34**	**64**
	<2500	78		13	15	10	25
	<1500	48		6	7	2	9
	<1000	25		4	5	1	6
	1000-1499	23		2	2	1	3
	1500-1999	14		2	2	6	8
	2000-2499	16		5	6	2	8
	2500-2999	13		5	6	6	12
	3000-3499	12		5	6	8	14
	3500-3999	6		1	2	6	8
	4000 & over	5		1	1	3	4
	not stated	4		-	-	1	1
Asphyxia, anoxia or trauma (antepartum death)	**All**	**1,068**		-	-	-	-
	<2500	732		-	-	-	-
	<1500	470		-	-	-	-
	<1000	316		-	-	-	-
	1000-1499	154		-	-	-	-
	1500-1999	138		-	-	-	-
	2000-2499	124		-	-	-	-
	2500-2999	142		-	-	-	-
	3000-3499	109		-	-	-	-
	3500-3999	52		-	-	-	-
	4000 & over	17		-	-	-	-
	not stated	16		-	-	-	-
Remaining antepartum deaths	**All**	**1,696**		-	-	-	-
	<2500	1,094		-	-	-	-
	<1500	705		-	-	-	-
	<1000	479		-	-	-	-
	1000-1499	226		-	-	-	-
	1500-1999	188		-	-	-	-
	2000-2499	201		-	-	-	-
	2500-2999	208		-	-	-	-
	3000-3499	203		-	-	-	-
	3500-3999	105		-	-	-	-
	4000 & over	49		-	-	-	-
	not stated	37		-	-	-	-

Table 8 - *continued*

Cause group	Birthweight (grams)	Births		Deaths			
		Live births	Stillbirths	Early neonatal	Neonatal	Postneonatal	Infant
Sudden infant deaths	**All**		-	**13**	**47**	**322**	**369**
	<2500		-	-	5	83	88
	<1500		-	-	-	20	20
	<1000		-	-	-	4	4
	1000-1499		-	-	-	16	16
	1500-1999		-	-	2	18	20
	2000-2499		-	-	3	45	48
	2500-2999		-	2	10	73	83
	3000-3499		-	7	20	103	123
	3500-3999		-	4	9	44	53
	4000 & over		-	-	2	17	19
	not stated		-	-	1	2	3
Other conditions	**All**	**83**	**72**	**111**	**187**	**298**	
	<2500	40	48	73	81	154	
	<1500	26	36	55	46	101	
	<1000	22	26	40	32	72	
	1000-1499	4	10	15	14	29	
	1500-1999	5	4	5	16	21	
	2000-2499	9	8	13	19	32	
	2500-2999	12	5	10	35	45	
	3000-3499	15	6	12	38	50	
	3500-3999	12	3	3	22	25	
	4000 & over	3	9	12	10	22	
	not stated	1	1	1	1	2	

Table 9 1995 Series DH3 no.28

Table 9: Live births, stillbirths and infant deaths
ONS cause groups by mother's age
Numbers, 1995

England and Wales

Cause group	Mother's age	Births		Deaths			
		Live births	Stillbirths	Early neonatal	Neonatal	Postneonatal	Infant
All causes	**All**	**648,001**	**3,597**	**2,084**	**2,669**	**1,244**	**3,913**
	<20	41,926	292	183	232	179	411
	20-24	130,729	728	486	613	333	946
	25-29	217,356	1,076	647	833	340	1,173
	30-34	181,140	932	496	641	241	882
	35-39	65,520	443	225	290	129	419
	40 & over	11,330	126	47	60	22	82
Congenital anomalies	**All**		**320**	**520**	**706**	**304**	**1,010**
	<20		22	41	54	18	72
	20-24		60	138	178	74	252
	25-29		99	153	215	99	314
	30-34		74	120	167	68	235
	35-39		47	55	75	36	111
	40 & over		18	13	17	9	26
Antepartum infections	**All**		**12**	**17**	**22**	**6**	**28**
	<20		-	4	5	1	6
	20-24		4	4	5	2	7
	25-29		2	4	6	2	8
	30-34		3	2	2	1	3
	35-39		3	3	3	-	3
	40 & over		-	-	1	-	1
Immaturity related conditions	**All**		**116**	**1,100**	**1,302**	**118**	**1,420**
	<20		9	109	131	14	145
	20-24		22	250	287	27	314
	25-29		42	336	394	25	419
	30-34		27	264	317	28	345
	35-39		15	113	141	23	164
	40 & over		1	28	32	1	33
Asphyxia anoxia or trauma (intrapartum)	**All**		**173**	**283**	**348**	**9**	**357**
	<20		14	16	21	-	21
	20-24		28	53	61	1	62
	25-29		61	99	127	6	133
	30-34		50	75	92	1	93
	35-39		17	36	41	1	42
	40 & over		3	4	6	-	6
External conditions	**All**		**-**	**3**	**7**	**59**	**66**
	<20		-	2	2	12	14
	20-24		-	-	3	16	19
	25-29		-	-	-	15	15
	30-34		-	1	1	10	11
	35-39		-	-	1	5	6
	40 & over		-	-	-	1	1
Infections	**All**		**11**	**51**	**96**	**205**	**301**
	<20		1	3	7	29	36
	20-24		3	12	28	56	84
	25-29		4	15	26	57	83
	30-34		2	15	27	39	66
	35-39		1	5	6	21	27
	40 & over		-	1	2	3	5
Other specific conditions	**All**		**118**	**25**	**30**	**34**	**64**
	<20		5	1	1	4	5
	20-24		25	4	4	10	14
	25-29		39	13	15	5	20
	30-34		27	3	5	12	17
	35-39		18	3	4	3	7
	40 & over		4	1	1	-	1

Table 9 - *continued*

Cause group	Mother's age	Births		Deaths			
		Live births	Stillbirths	Early neonatal	Neonatal	Postneonatal	Infant
Asphyxia, anoxia or trauma	**All**		1,068	-	-	-	-
(antepartum death)	<20		109	-	-	-	-
	20-24		213	-	-	-	-
	25-29		311	-	-	-	-
	30-34		266	-	-	-	-
	35-39		127	-	-	-	-
	40 & over		42	-	-	-	-
Remaining antepartum deaths	**All**		1,696	-	-	-	-
	<20		128	-	-	-	-
	20-24		360	-	-	-	-
	25-29		491	-	-	-	-
	30-34		459	-	-	-	-
	35-39		203	-	-	-	-
	40 & over		55	-	-	-	-
Sudden infant deaths	**All**		-	13	47	322	369
	<20		-	3	7	76	83
	20-24		-	1	13	103	116
	25-29		-	6	17	78	95
	30-34		-	-	5	42	47
	35-39		-	3	5	21	26
	40 & over		-	-	-	2	2
Other conditions	**All**	83	72	111	187	298	
	<20	4	4	4	25	29	
	20-24	13	24	34	44	78	
	25-29	27	21	33	53	86	
	30-34	24	16	25	40	65	
	35-39	12	7	14	19	33	
	40 & over	3	-	1	6	7	

Table 10 1995 Series DH3 no.28

Table 10: Live births, stillbirths and infant deaths
ONS cause groups by mother's country of birth
Numbers, 1995

England and Wales

Cause group	Country of birth	Births		Deaths			
		Live births	Stillbirths	Early neonatal	Neonatal	Postneonatal	Infant
All causes	**All**	**648,001**	**3,597**	**2,084**	**2,669**	**1,244**	**3,913**
	United Kingdom	566,331	2,970	1,769	2,282	1,038	3,320
	Irish Republic	5,166	35	14	21	9	30
	Rest of European Union	8,026	53	11	16	21	37
	Australia, Canada, New Zealand	3,052	21	7	12	8	20
	New Commonwealth**	47,337	413	217	258	140	398
	Bangladesh	6,783	62	18	22	16	38
	India	6,679	45	29	31	19	50
	Pakistan	12,332	133	73	85	54	139
	East Africa	5,122	38	12	16	12	28
	Caribbean	2,910	28	27	30	8	38
	Other*	18,089	105	66	80	28	108
Congenital anomalies	**All**		**320**	**520**	**706**	**304**	**1,010**
	United Kingdom		228	430	593	239	832
	Irish Republic		4	5	7	2	9
	Rest of European Union		12	3	4	4	8
	Australia, Canada, New Zealand		3	1	1	2	3
	New Commonwealth**		59	60	74	46	120
	Bangladesh		11	5	7	7	14
	India		2	8	8	7	15
	Pakistan		18	34	39	22	61
	East Africa		10	-	1	3	4
	Caribbean		3	3	4	1	5
	Other*		14	21	27	11	38
Antepartum infections	**All**		**12**	**17**	**22**	**6**	**28**
	United Kingdom		11	12	17	2	19
	Irish Republic		-	-	-	-	-
	Rest of European Union		-	-	-	1	1
	Australia, Canada, New Zealand		-	-	-	-	-
	New Commonwealth**		1	4	4	1	5
	Bangladesh		-	-	-	-	-
	India		-	-	-	1	1
	Pakistan		-	1	1	-	1
	East Africa		-	-	-	-	-
	Caribbean		-	-	-	-	-
	Other*		-	1	1	2	3
Immaturity related conditions	**All**		**116**	**1,100**	**1,302**	**118**	**1,420**
	United Kingdom		93	940	1,119	98	1,217
	Irish Republic		1	7	8	-	8
	Rest of European Union		2	6	8	1	9
	Australia, Canada, New Zealand		1	5	10	1	11
	New Commonwealth**		15	108	120	14	134
	Bangladesh		1	6	6	1	7
	India		2	13	13	1	14
	Pakistan		3	29	32	3	35
	East Africa		2	4	5	2	7
	Caribbean		2	22	23	4	27
	Other*		4	34	37	4	41
Asphyxia, anoxia or trauma (intrapartum)	**All**		**173**	**283**	**348**	**9**	**357**
	United Kingdom		150	252	308	6	314
	Irish Republic		2	-	1	-	1
	Rest of European Union		1	2	2	1	3
	Australia, Canada, New Zealand		2	1	1	-	1
	New Commonwealth**		16	22	29	2	31
	Bangladesh		-	5	6	-	6
	India		2	4	5	-	5
	Pakistan		3	3	3	-	3
	East Africa		-	3	4	-	4
	Caribbean		3	1	2	1	3
	Other*		2	6	7	-	7

* Including cases where no country of birth was stated
** A full list of countries included in the New Commonwealth is provided in the introduction

Table 10 - *continued*

Cause group	Country of birth	Births		Deaths			
		Live births	Stillbirths	Early neonatal	Neonatal	Postneonatal	Infant
External conditions	**All**		-	**3**	**7**	**59**	**66**
	United Kingdom		-	3	7	52	59
	Irish Republic		-	-	-	-	-
	Rest of European Union		-	-	-	2	2
	Australia, Canada, New Zealand		-	-	-	1	1
	New Commonwealth**		-	-	-	3	3
	Bangladesh		-	-	-	1	1
	India		-	-	-	1	1
	Pakistan		-	-	-	1	1
	East Africa		-	-	-	-	-
	Caribbean		-	-	-	-	-
	Other*		-	-	-	1	1
Infections	**All**		**11**	**51**	**96**	**205**	**301**
	United Kingdom		10	45	84	172	256
	Irish Republic		-	1	1	1	2
	Rest of European Union		-	-	-	5	5
	Australia, Canada, New Zealand		-	-	-	-	-
	New Commonwealth**		-	5	8	21	29
	Bangladesh		-	-	-	2	2
	India		-	1	1	3	4
	Pakistan		-	-	3	6	9
	East Africa		-	1	1	3	4
	Caribbean		-	1	1	-	1
	Other*		1	-	3	6	9
Other specific conditions	**All**		**118**	**25**	**30**	**34**	**64**
	United Kingdom		93	19	23	30	53
	Irish Republic		3	-	-	-	-
	Rest of European Union		2	-	1	2	3
	Australia, Canada, New Zealand		1	-	-	1	1
	New Commonwealth**		15	6	6	1	7
	Bangladesh		2	2	2	-	2
	India		-	1	1	-	1
	Pakistan		8	2	2	1	3
	East Africa		1	1	1	-	1
	Caribbean		-	-	-	-	-
	Other*		4	-	-	-	-
Asphyxia, anoxia or trauma (antepartum death)	**All**		**1,068**	**-**	**-**	**-**	**-**
	United Kingdom		911	-	-	-	-
	Irish Republic		9	-	-	-	-
	Rest of European Union		12	-	-	-	-
	Australia, Canada, New Zealand		3	-	-	-	-
	New Commonwealth**		106	-	-	-	-
	Bangladesh		12	-	-	-	-
	India		14	-	-	-	-
	Pakistan		35	-	-	-	-
	East Africa		12	-	-	-	-
	Caribbean		11	-	-	-	-
	Other*		27	-	-	-	-
Remaining antepartum deaths	**All**		**1,696**	**-**	**-**	**-**	**-**
	United Kingdom		1,405	-	-	-	-
	Irish Republic		16	-	-	-	-
	Rest of European Union		23	-	-	-	-
	Australia, Canada, New Zealand		11	-	-	-	-
	New Commonwealth**		191	-	-	-	-
	Bangladesh		30	-	-	-	-
	India		23	-	-	-	-
	Pakistan		66	-	-	-	-
	East Africa		13	-	-	-	-
	Caribbean		8	-	-	-	-
	Other*		50	-	-	-	-

* Including cases where no country of birth was stated
** A full list of countries included in the New Commonwealth is provided in the introduction

Table 10 1995 Series DH3 no.28

Table 10 - *continued*

Cause group	Country of birth	Births		Deaths			
		Live births	Stillbirths	Early neonatal	Neonatal	Postneonatal	Infant
Sudden infant deaths	**All**		-	**13**	**47**	**322**	**369**
	United Kingdom		-	10	41	294	335
	Irish Republic		-	-	2	5	7
	Rest of European Union		-	-	-	2	2
	Australia, Canada, New Zealand		-	-	-	1	1
	New Commonwealth**		-	2	3	20	23
	Bangladesh		-	-	-	1	1
	India		-	1	1	1	2
	Pakistan		-	-	-	9	9
	East Africa		-	-	1	1	2
	Caribbean		-	-	-	-	-
	Other*		-	1	1	-	1
Other conditions	**All**		83	**72**	**111**	**187**	**298**
	United Kingdom		69	58	90	145	235
	Irish Republic		-	1	2	1	3
	Rest of European Union		1	-	1	3	4
	Australia, Canada, New Zealand		-	-	-	2	2
	New Commonwealth**		10	10	14	32	46
	Bangladesh		6	-	1	4	5
	India		2	1	2	5	7
	Pakistan		-	4	5	12	17
	East Africa		-	3	3	3	6
	Caribbean		1	-	-	2	2
	Other*		3	3	4	4	8

* Including cases where no country of birth was stated
** A full list of countries included in the New Commonwealth is provided in the introduction

Table 11: Live births, stillbirths and infant deaths
ONS cause groups by parity, marital status and type of registration
Numbers, 1994

England and Wales

Cause group	Marital status	Parity/type of registration	Births		Deaths			
			Live births	Stillbirths	Early neonatal	Neonatal	Postneonatal	Infant
All causes	All		648,001	3,597	2,084	2,669	1,244	3,913
	Inside marriage							
		All	428,099	2,224	1,262	1,596	655	2,251
		0	166,798	584	573	701	224	925
		1	157,692	806	367	466	218	684
		2	67,233	423	184	248	121	369
		3 and over	36,376	411	138	181	92	273
	Outside marriage							
		All	219,902	1,373	822	1,073	589	1,662
		Joint regn/same address	127,800	729	462	607	280	887
		Joint regn/different address	44,175	297	214	270	127	397
		Sole registration	47,927	347	146	196	182	378
Congenital anomalies	All			320	520	706	304	1,010
	Inside marriage							
		All		217	331	449	202	651
		0		55	120	155	76	231
		1		86	122	163	70	233
		2		33	44	71	32	103
		3 and over		43	45	60	24	84
	Outside marriage							
		All		103	189	257	102	359
		Joint regn/same address		53	117	155	62	217
		Joint regn/different address		20	36	54	20	74
		Sole registration		30	36	48	20	68
Antepartum infections	All			12	17	22	6	28
	Inside marriage							
		All		5	8	9	2	11
		0		1	2	2	1	3
		1		3	2	2	1	3
		2		-	3	3	-	3
		3 and over		1	1	2	-	2
	Outside marriage							
		All		7	9	13	4	17
		Joint regn/same address		5	6	9	2	11
		Joint regn/different address		-	3	4	2	6
		Sole registration		2	-	-	-	-
Immaturity related conditions	All			116	1,100	1,302	118	1,420
	Inside marriage							
		All		66	633	743	69	812
		0		16	308	361	28	389
		1		25	171	196	21	217
		2		10	87	104	12	116
		3 and over		15	67	82	8	90
	Outside marriage							
		All		50	467	559	49	608
		Joint regn/same address		18	236	288	30	318
		Joint regn/different address		17	145	167	11	178
		Sole registration		15	86	104	8	112
Asphyxia, anoxia or trauma (intrapartum)	All			173	283	348	9	357
	Inside marriage							
		All		99	183	225	6	231
		0		30	98	115	2	117
		1		37	39	52	2	54
		2		18	32	39	2	41
		3 and over		14	14	19	-	19
	Outside marriage							
		All		74	100	123	3	126
		Joint regn/same address		35	65	79	-	79
		Joint regn/different address		21	21	24	2	26
		Sole registration		18	14	20	1	21

Table 11 1995 Series DH3 no.28

Table 11 - *continued*

Cause group	Marital status	Parity/type of registration	Births		Deaths			
			Live births	Stillbirths	Early neonatal	Neonatal	Postneonatal	Infant
External conditions	**All** **Inside marriage**			-	**3**	**7**	**59**	**66**
		All		-	**1**	**2**	**25**	**27**
		0		-	1	1	7	8
		1		-	-	1	12	13
		2		-	-	-	2	2
		3 and over		-	-	-	4	4
	Outside marriage							
		All		-	**2**	**5**	**34**	**39**
		Joint regn/same address		-	-	2	15	17
		Joint regn/different address		-	1	1	11	12
		Sole registration		-	1	2	8	10
Infections	**All** **Inside marriage**			**11**	**51**	**96**	**205**	**301**
		All		**5**	**29**	**48**	**107**	**155**
		0		1	11	21	40	61
		1		3	9	14	34	48
		2		1	5	8	21	29
		3 and over		-	4	5	12	17
	Outside marriage							
		All		**6**	**22**	**48**	**98**	**146**
		Joint regn/same address		4	15	32	41	73
		Joint regn/different address		-	3	9	21	30
		Sole registration		2	4	7	36	43
Other specific conditions	**All** **Inside marriage**			**118**	**25**	**30**	**34**	**64**
		All		**92**	**22**	**26**	**20**	**46**
		0		17	8	8	6	14
		1		40	9	11	4	15
		2		17	3	4	6	10
		3 and over		18	2	3	4	7
	Outside marriage							
		All		**26**	**3**	**4**	**14**	**18**
		Joint regn/same address		15	2	3	9	12
		Joint regn/different address		6	1	1	2	3
		Sole registration		5	-	-	3	3
Asphyxia, anoxia or trauma (antepartum death)	**All** **Inside marriage**			**1,068**	-	-	-	-
		All		**622**	-	-	-	-
		0		175	-	-	-	-
		1		197	-	-	-	-
		2		129	-	-	-	-
		3 and over		121	-	-	-	-
	Outside marriage							
		All		**446**	-	-	-	-
		Joint regn/same address		238	-	-	-	-
		Joint regn/different address		90	-	-	-	-
		Sole registration		118	-	-	-	-
Remaining antepartum deaths	**All** **Inside marriage**			**1,696**	-	-	-	-
		All		**1,065**	-	-	-	-
		0		272	-	-	-	-
		1		400	-	-	-	-
		2		204	-	-	-	-
		3 and over		189	-	-	-	-
	Outside marriage							
		All		**631**	-	-	-	-
		Joint regn/same address		345	-	-	-	-
		Joint regn/different address		133	-	-	-	-
		Sole registration		153	-	-	-	-

Table 11 - *continued*

Cause group	Marital status	Parity/type of registration	Births		Deaths			
			Live births	Stillbirths	Early neonatal	Neonatal	Postneonatal	Infant
Sudden infant deaths	**All**			-	**13**	**47**	**322**	**369**
	Inside marriage							
		All		-	9	22	109	131
		0		-	4	5	25	30
		1		-	3	8	38	46
		2		-	1	6	22	28
		3 and over		-	1	3	24	27
	Outside marriage							
		All		-	4	25	213	238
		Joint regn/same address		-	4	16	91	107
		Joint regn/different address		-	-	4	41	45
		Sole registration		-	-	5	81	86
Other conditions	**All**		83	72	111	187	298	
	Inside marriage							
		All	53	46	72	115	187	
		0	17	21	33	39	72	
		1	15	12	19	36	55	
		2	11	9	13	24	37	
		3 and over	10	4	7	16	23	
	Outside marriage							
		All	30	26	39	72	111	
		Joint regn/same address	16	17	23	30	53	
		Joint regn/different address	10	4	6	17	23	
		Sole registration	4	5	10	25	35	

Table 12 1995 Series DH3 no.28

Table 12: Live births*, stillbirths and infant deaths — England and Wales
ONS cause groups by father's social class (based on occupation at death registration)
Inside marriage and outside marriage/joint registration
Numbers, 1995

Cause group	Marital status / Social class	Live births*	Stillbirths	Early neonatal	Neonatal	Postneonatal	Infant
All causes	All**	59,962	3,250	1,938	2,473	1,062	3,535
	Inside marriage						
	All***	42,921	2,224	1,262	1,596	655	2,251
	I	4,051	171	97	124	47	171
	II	12,150	517	332	406	141	547
	IIIN	4,828	240	139	171	69	240
	IIIM	12,504	606	349	465	193	658
	IV	5,467	369	210	250	105	355
	V	1,799	154	65	91	47	138
	Other	2,122	167	63	79	43	122
	Outside marriage joint registration						
	All***	17,041	1,026	676	877	407	1,284
	I	493	27	16	21	14	35
	II	2,615	109	87	120	39	159
	IIIN	1,285	71	44	54	26	80
	IIIM	6,727	413	239	315	140	455
	IV	3,277	203	142	179	72	251
	V	1,626	118	84	106	46	152
	Other	1,018	85	57	71	56	127
Congenital anomalies	All**		290	484	658	284	942
	Inside marriage						
	All***		217	331	449	202	651
	I		22	24	37	19	56
	II		52	94	125	37	162
	IIIN		18	36	47	23	70
	IIIM		61	79	111	54	165
	IV		33	53	67	37	104
	V		13	17	28	13	41
	Other		18	25	31	18	49
	Outside marriage joint registration						
	All***		73	153	209	82	291
	I		3	6	6	8	14
	II		10	17	27	13	40
	IIIN		6	12	13	6	19
	IIIM		22	60	85	23	108
	IV		13	35	42	14	56
	V		9	17	23	8	31
	Other		10	6	12	10	22
Antepartum infections	All**		10	17	22	6	28
	Inside marriage						
	All***		5	8	9	2	11
	I		1	1	1	-	1
	II		1	1	1	-	1
	IIIN		-	3	3	1	4
	IIIM		1	2	2	1	3
	IV		-	1	1	-	1
	V		-	-	1	-	1
	Other		2	-	-	-	-
	Outside marriage joint registration						
	All***		5	9	13	4	17
	I		-	-	-	-	-
	II		2	1	1	2	3
	IIIN		-	-	-	-	-
	IIIM		1	4	5	-	5
	IV		-	2	4	-	4
	V		1	1	1	-	1
	Other		1	-	1	2	3

* Figures for live births are a 10 percent sample coded for father's occupation
** Inside marriage and outside marriage/joint registration including cases where father's occupation was not stated
*** Includes cases where father's occupation was not stated

80

Table 12 - *continued*

Cause group	Marital status Social class	Births		Deaths			
		Live births*	Stillbirths	Early neonatal	Neonatal	Postneonatal	Infant
Immaturity related conditions	**All**	**101**	**1,014**	**1,198**	**110**	**1,308**	
	Inside marriage						
	All*	66	633	743	69	812	
	I	5	45	51	8	59	
	II	13	159	183	18	201	
	IIIN	11	67	80	8	88	
	IIIM	18	191	237	17	254	
	IV	9	113	126	10	136	
	V	6	32	36	4	40	
	Other	4	24	28	4	32	
	Outside marriage joint registration						
	All*	35	381	455	41	496	
	I	1	10	15	1	16	
	II	-	47	61	4	65	
	IIIN	2	25	31	2	33	
	IIIM	19	134	156	17	173	
	IV	5	78	94	6	100	
	V	4	45	52	6	58	
	Other	4	41	44	4	48	
Asphyxia anoxia or trauma (intrapartum)	**All**	**155**	**269**	**328**	**8**	**336**	
	Inside marriage						
	All*	99	183	225	6	231	
	I	9	15	17	-	17	
	II	28	52	61	2	63	
	IIIN	9	22	25	-	25	
	IIIM	24	51	67	4	71	
	IV	15	24	30	-	30	
	V	8	7	11	-	11	
	Other	6	10	11	-	11	
	Outside marriage joint registration						
	All*	56	86	103	2	105	
	I	1	-	-	-	-	
	II	4	12	17	-	17	
	IIIN	5	5	7	-	7	
	IIIM	27	29	36	2	38	
	IV	6	19	20	-	20	
	V	9	12	13	-	13	
	Other	4	6	6	-	6	
External conditions	**All**	**-**	**2**	**5**	**51**	**56**	
	Inside marriage						
	All*	-	1	2	25	27	
	I	-	1	1	2	3	
	II	-	-	-	6	6	
	IIIN	-	-	-	2	2	
	IIIM	-	-	-	9	9	
	IV	-	-	-	-	-	
	V	-	-	-	1	1	
	Other	-	-	1	2	3	
	Outside marriage joint registration						
	All*	-	1	3	26	29	
	I	-	-	-	-	-	
	II	-	-	-	-	-	
	IIIN	-	-	-	-	-	
	IIIM	-	-	1	6	7	
	IV	-	-	-	3	3	
	V	-	-	-	2	2	
	Other	-	-	-	11	11	

* Figures for live births are a 10 percent sample coded for father's occupation
** Inside marriage and outside marriage/joint registration including cases where father's occupation was not stated
***Includes cases where father's occupation was not stated

Table 12 1995 Series DH3 no.28

Table 12 - *continued*

Cause group	Marital status Social class	Births		Deaths			
		Live births*	Stillbirths	Early neonatal	Neonatal	Postneonatal	Infant
Infections	All**		9	47	89	169	258
	Inside marriage						
	All***		5	29	48	107	155
	I		-	4	5	5	10
	II		2	8	12	28	40
	IIIN		-	3	5	10	15
	IIIM		1	6	12	34	46
	IV		-	4	6	15	21
	V		-	4	6	11	17
	Other		2	-	2	2	4
	Outside marriage joint registration						
	All***		4	18	41	62	103
	I		-	-	-	2	2
	II		-	2	5	6	11
	IIIN		-	2	3	3	6
	IIIM		2	4	14	21	35
	IV		-	3	7	9	16
	V		2	3	6	5	11
	Other		-	3	5	11	16
Other specific conditions	All**	113	25	30	31	61	
	Inside marriage						
	All***	92	22	26	20	46	
	I	10	1	1	3	4	
	II	20	6	6	3	9	
	IIIN	7	2	3	1	4	
	IIIM	23	7	10	6	16	
	IV	11	4	4	5	9	
	V	14	1	1	2	3	
	Other	7	1	1	-	1	
	Outside marriage joint registration						
	All***	21	3	4	11	15	
	I	3	-	-	-	-	
	II	-	-	-	1	1	
	IIIN	1	-	-	2	2	
	IIIM	10	1	1	4	5	
	IV	5	-	1	1	2	
	V	1	1	1	1	2	
	Other	1	1	1	1	2	
Asphyxia anoxia or trauma (antepartum)	All**	950	-	-	-	-	
	Inside marriage						
	All***	622	-	-	-	-	
	I	40	-	-	-	-	
	II	131	-	-	-	-	
	IIIN	76	-	-	-	-	
	IIIM	171	-	-	-	-	
	IV	98	-	-	-	-	
	V	42	-	-	-	-	
	Other	64	-	-	-	-	
	Outside marriage joint registration						
	All***	328	-	-	-	-	
	I	7	-	-	-	-	
	II	35	-	-	-	-	
	IIIN	26	-	-	-	-	
	IIIM	130	-	-	-	-	
	IV	72	-	-	-	-	
	V	36	-	-	-	-	
	Other	22	-	-	-	-	

*   Figures for live births are a 10 percent sample coded for father's occupation
**   Inside marriage and outside marriage/joint registration including cases where father's occupation was not stated
***Includes cases where father's occupation was not stated

Table 12 - *continued*

Cause group	Marital status Social class	Births		Deaths			
		Live births*	Stillbirths	Early neonatal	Neonatal	Postneonatal	Infant
Remaining antepartum deaths	**All****		1,543	-	-	-	-
	Inside marriage						
	All***		1,065	-	-	-	-
	I		77	-	-	-	-
	II		252	-	-	-	-
	IIIN		114	-	-	-	-
	IIIM		291	-	-	-	-
	IV		201	-	-	-	-
	V		69	-	-	-	-
	Other		61	-	-	-	-
	Outside marriage joint registration						
	All***		478	-	-	-	-
	I		12	-	-	-	-
	II		54	-	-	-	-
	IIIN		31	-	-	-	-
	IIIM		187	-	-	-	-
	IV		99	-	-	-	-
	V		55	-	-	-	-
	Other		40	-	-	-	-
Sudden infant deaths	**All****	-	13	42	241	283	
	Inside marriage						
	All***	-	9	22	109	131	
	I	-	2	2	4	6	
	II	-	2	3	16	19	
	IIIN	-	-	1	11	12	
	IIIM	-	2	9	40	49	
	IV	-	1	3	21	24	
	V	-	1	1	9	10	
	Other	-	1	1	6	7	
	Outside marriage joint registration						
	All***	-	4	20	132	152	
	I	-	-	-	1	1	
	II	-	2	3	10	13	
	IIIN	-	-	-	7	7	
	IIIM	-	2	9	51	60	
	IV	-	-	4	30	34	
	V	-	-	3	17	20	
	Other	-	-	1	13	14	
Other conditions	**All****	79	67	101	162	263	
	Inside marriage						
	All***	53	46	72	115	187	
	I	7	4	9	6	15	
	II	18	10	15	31	46	
	IIIN	5	6	7	13	20	
	IIIM	16	11	17	28	45	
	IV	2	10	13	17	30	
	V	2	3	7	7	14	
	Other	3	2	4	11	15	
	Outside marriage joint registration						
	All***	26	21	29	47	76	
	I	-	-	-	2	2	
	II	4	6	6	3	9	
	IIIN	-	-	-	6	6	
	IIIM	15	5	8	16	24	
	IV	3	5	7	9	16	
	V	1	5	7	7	14	
	Other	3	-	1	4	5	

* Figures for live births are a 10 percent sample coded for father's occupation
** Inside marriage and outside marriage/joint registration including cases where father's occupation was not stated
*** Includes cases where father's occupation was not stated

Table 13 1995 Series DH3 no.28

Table 13: **Stillbirths**
ONS cause groups by gestation and birthweight
Numbers, 1995

England and Wales

Cause group	Birthweight (grams)	Gestation (weeks)						
		All	24-27	28-31	32-35	36-39	40 & over	Not stated
All causes	**All**	**3,597**	**893**	**668**	**661**	**926**	**424**	**25**
	<2500	2,426	863	653	558	305	39	8
	<1500	1,625	853	533	182	49	5	3
	<1000	1,119	766	267	53	29	2	2
	1000-1499	506	87	266	129	20	3	1
	1500-1999	399	8	104	209	67	8	3
	2000-2499	402	2	16	167	189	26	2
	2500-2999	429	3	4	70	262	90	-
	3000-3499	376	1	1	17	216	140	1
	3500-3999	198	-	-	2	90	106	-
	4000 & over	93	1	-	2	44	46	-
	not stated	75	25	10	12	9	3	16
Congenital	**All**	**320**	**108**	**70**	**72**	**57**	**9**	**4**
anomalies	<2500	270	105	68	62	30	2	3
	<1500	194	101	53	31	9	-	-
	<1000	130	89	24	13	4	-	-
	1000-1499	64	12	29	18	5	-	-
	1500-1999	38	2	10	14	7	2	3
	2000-2499	38	2	5	17	14	-	-
	2500-2999	25	-	-	6	15	4	-
	3000-3499	8	-	-	1	5	2	-
	3500-3999	4	-	-	-	3	1	-
	4000 & over	-	-	-	-	-	-	-
	not stated	13	3	2	3	4	-	1
Antepartum	**All**	**12**	**8**	**2**	**2**	**-**	**-**	**-**
infections	<2500	12	8	2	2	-	-	-
	<1500	10	8	2	-	-	-	-
	<1000	9	7	2	-	-	-	-
	1000-1499	1	1	-	-	-	-	-
	1500-1999	1	-	-	1	-	-	-
	2000-2499	1	-	-	1	-	-	-
	2500-2999	-	-	-	-	-	-	-
	3000-3499	-	-	-	-	-	-	-
	3500-3999	-	-	-	-	-	-	-
	4000 & over	-	-	-	-	-	-	-
	not stated	-	-	-	-	-	-	-
Immaturity	**All**	**116**	**90**	**15**	**6**	**2**	**1**	**2**
related	<2500	111	88	15	5	1	1	1
conditions	<1500	104	88	11	2	1	1	1
	<1000	87	83	2	1	-	-	1
	1000-1499	17	5	9	1	1	1	-
	1500-1999	5	-	3	2	-	-	-
	2000-2499	2	-	1	1	-	-	-
	2500-2999	1	-	-	1	-	-	-
	3000-3499	1	-	-	-	1	-	-
	3500-3999	-	-	-	-	-	-	-
	4000 & over	-	-	-	-	-	-	-
	not stated	3	2	-	-	-	-	1
Asphyxia	**All**	**173**	**45**	**13**	**15**	**52**	**47**	**1**
anoxia	<2500	80	44	13	11	9	2	1
or trauma	<1500	60	44	11	4	1	-	-
(intrapartum)	<1000	44	41	2	-	1	-	-
	1000-1499	16	3	9	4	-	-	-
	1500-1999	9	-	2	6	1	-	-
	2000-2499	11	-	-	1	7	2	1
	2500-2999	28	-	-	4	18	6	-
	3000-3499	27	-	-	-	13	14	-
	3500-3999	18	-	-	-	7	11	-
	4000 & over	19	-	-	-	5	14	-
	not stated	1	1	-	-	-	-	-
External	**All**	**-**	**-**	**-**	**-**	**-**	**-**	**-**
conditions	<2500	-	-	-	-	-	-	-
	<1500	-	-	-	-	-	-	-
	<1000	-	-	-	-	-	-	-
	1000-1499	-	-	-	-	-	-	-
	1500-1999	-	-	-	-	-	-	-
	2000-2499	-	-	-	-	-	-	-
	2500-2999	-	-	-	-	-	-	-
	3000-3499	-	-	-	-	-	-	-
	3500-3999	-	-	-	-	-	-	-
	4000 & over	-	-	-	-	-	-	-
	not stated	-	-	-	-	-	-	-

Table 13 - *continued*

Cause group	Birthweight (grams)	Gestation (weeks)						
		All	24-27	28-31	32-35	36-39	40 & over	Not stated
Infections	**All**	**11**	**8**	**1**	**1**	**1**	-	-
	<2500	9	8	1	-	-	-	-
	<1500	8	8	-	-	-	-	-
	<1000	7	7	-	-	-	-	-
	1000-1499	1	1	-	-	-	-	-
	1500-1999	1	-	1	-	-	-	-
	2000-2499	-	-	-	-	-	-	-
	2500-2999	-	-	-	-	-	-	-
	3000-3499	1	-	-	1	-	-	-
	3500-3999	1	-	-	-	1	-	-
	4000 & over	-	-	-	-	-	-	-
	not stated	-	-	-	-	-	-	-
Other specific conditions	**All**	**118**	**33**	**29**	**27**	**26**	**2**	**1**
	<2500	78	32	27	13	4	2	-
	<1500	48	28	17	1	1	1	-
	<1000	25	18	6	-	-	1	-
	1000-1499	23	10	11	1	1	-	-
	1500-1999	14	4	8	2	-	-	-
	2000-2499	16	-	2	10	3	1	-
	2500-2999	13	-	1	8	4	-	-
	3000-3499	12	-	-	4	8	-	-
	3500-3999	6	-	-	-	6	-	-
	4000 & over	5	-	-	1	4	-	-
	not stated	4	1	1	1	-	-	1
Asphyxia anoxia or trauma (antepartum death)	**All**	**1,068**	**225**	**216**	**221**	**287**	**113**	**6**
	<2500	732	220	211	195	94	11	1
	<1500	470	220	177	61	11	-	1
	<1000	316	202	89	18	7	-	-
	1000-1499	154	18	88	43	4	-	1
	1500-1999	138	-	32	80	24	2	-
	2000-2499	124	-	2	54	59	9	-
	2500-2999	142	-	1	22	92	27	-
	3000-3499	109	1	-	2	69	36	1
	3500-3999	52	-	-	-	24	28	-
	4000 & over	17	-	-	-	7	10	-
	not stated	16	4	4	2	1	1	4
Remaining antepartum deaths	**All**	**1,696**	**358**	**312**	**312**	**479**	**224**	**11**
	<2500	1,094	340	306	265	162	19	2
	<1500	705	338	255	83	26	2	1
	<1000	479	301	139	21	17	-	1
	1000-1499	226	37	116	62	9	2	-
	1500-1999	188	2	46	101	35	4	-
	2000-2499	201	-	5	81	101	13	1
	2500-2999	208	3	2	29	125	49	-
	3000-3499	203	-	1	9	115	78	-
	3500-3999	105	-	-	2	46	57	-
	4000 & over	49	1	-	1	27	20	-
	not stated	37	14	3	6	4	1	9
Other conditions	**All**	**83**	**18**	**10**	**5**	**22**	**28**	-
	<2500	40	18	10	5	5	2	-
	<1500	26	18	7	-	-	1	-
	<1000	22	18	3	-	-	1	-
	1000-1499	4	-	4	-	-	-	-
	1500-1999	5	-	2	3	-	-	-
	2000-2499	9	-	1	2	5	1	-
	2500-2999	12	-	-	-	8	4	-
	3000-3499	15	-	-	-	5	10	-
	3500-3999	12	-	-	-	3	9	-
	4000 & over	3	-	-	-	1	2	-
	not stated	1	-	-	-	-	1	-

Table 14 1995 Series DH3 no.28

Table 14   Live births, stillbirths and infant deaths
Birthweight by mother's age
Numbers and rates*, 1995
    England and Wales

Birthweight (grams)	Mother's age	Numbers						Rates*				
		Births		Deaths								
		Live births	Still-births	Early neonatal	Neonatal	Postneo-natal	Infant	Still-birth	Peri-natal	Neo-natal	Postneo-natal	Infant
All	All	648,001	3,597	2,084	2,669	1,244	3,913	5.5	8.7	4.1	1.9	6.0
	<20	41,926	292	183	232	179	411	6.9	11.3	5.5	4.3	9.8
	20-24	130,729	728	486	613	333	946	5.5	9.2	4.7	2.5	7.2
	25-29	217,356	1,076	647	833	340	1,173	4.9	7.9	3.8	1.6	5.4
	30-34	181,140	932	496	641	241	882	5.1	7.8	3.5	1.3	4.9
	35-39	65,520	443	225	290	129	419	6.7	10.1	4.4	2.0	6.4
	40 & over	11,330	126	47	60	22	82	11.0	15.1	5.3	1.9	7.2
<2500	All	47,324	2,426	1,425	1,789	488	2,277	48.8	77.4	37.8	10.3	48.1
	<20	3,822	226	133	164	65	229	55.8	88.7	42.9	17.0	59.9
	20-24	10,625	512	345	425	111	536	46.0	77.0	40.0	10.4	50.4
	25-29	14,647	718	418	530	134	664	46.7	73.9	36.2	9.1	45.3
	30-34	12,083	603	343	432	109	541	47.5	74.6	35.8	9.0	44.8
	35-39	5,112	278	154	196	62	258	51.6	80.1	38.3	12.1	50.5
	40 & over	1,035	89	32	42	7	49	79.2	107.7	40.6	*6.8*	47.3
<1500	All	7,583	1,625	1,154	1,425	255	1,680	176.5	301.8	187.9	33.6	221.5
	<20	620	145	112	137	29	166	189.5	335.9	221.0	46.8	267.7
	20-24	1,657	347	284	335	51	386	173.2	314.9	202.2	30.8	233.0
	25-29	2,270	499	328	411	76	487	180.2	298.7	181.1	33.5	214.5
	30-34	1,923	383	283	357	53	410	166.1	288.8	185.6	27.6	213.2
	35-39	924	192	121	154	39	193	172.0	280.5	166.7	42.2	208.9
	40 & over	189	59	26	31	7	38	237.9	342.7	164.0	*37.0*	201.1
<1000	All	2,879	1,119	941	1,124	168	1,292	279.9	515.3	390.4	58.4	448.0
	<20	243	100	92	110	20	130	291.5	559.8	452.7	82.3	535.0
	20-24	642	238	230	272	34	306	270.5	531.8	423.7	53.0	476.6
	25-29	842	338	267	316	42	358	286.4	512.7	375.3	49.9	425.2
	30-34	740	258	232	278	39	317	258.5	491.0	375.7	52.7	428.4
	35-39	338	141	95	118	27	145	294.4	492.7	349.1	79.9	429.0
	40 & over	74	44	25	30	6	36	372.9	584.7	405.4	*81.1*	486.5
1000-1499	All	4,704	506	213	301	87	388	97.1	138.0	64.0	18.5	82.5
	<20	377	45	20	27	9	36	106.6	154.0	71.6	*23.9*	95.5
	20-24	1,015	109	54	63	17	80	97.0	145.0	62.1	*16.7*	78.8
	25-29	1,428	161	61	95	34	129	101.3	139.7	66.5	23.8	90.3
	30-34	1,183	125	51	79	14	93	95.6	134.6	66.8	*11.8*	78.6
	35-39	586	51	26	36	12	48	80.1	120.9	61.4	20.5	81.9
	40 & over	115	15	1	1	1	2	*115.4*	*123.1*	*8.7*	*8.7*	*17.4*
1500-1999	All	9,679	399	134	167	91	258	39.6	52.9	17.3	9.4	26.7
	<20	746	41	13	16	18	34	52.1	68.6	21.4	*24.1*	45.6
	20-24	2,090	74	29	39	22	61	34.2	47.6	18.7	10.5	29.2
	25-29	2,971	113	42	53	20	73	36.6	50.3	17.8	6.7	24.6
	30-34	2,542	109	30	35	22	57	41.1	52.4	13.8	8.7	22.4
	35-39	1,111	46	17	20	9	29	39.8	54.5	18.0	*8.1*	26.1
	40 & over	219	16	3	4	-	4	*68.1*	*80.9*	*18.3*	-	*18.3*
2000-2499	All	30,062	402	137	197	142	339	13.2	17.7	6.6	4.7	11.3
	<20	2,456	40	8	11	18	29	16.0	19.2	*4.5*	*7.3*	11.8
	20-24	6,878	91	32	51	38	89	13.1	17.6	7.4	5.5	12.9
	25-29	9,406	106	48	66	38	104	11.1	16.2	7.0	4.0	11.1
	30-34	7,618	111	30	40	34	74	14.4	18.2	5.3	4.5	9.7
	35-39	3,077	40	16	22	14	36	12.8	18.0	7.1	*4.5*	11.7
	40 & over	627	14	3	7	-	7	*21.8*	*26.5*	*11.2*	-	*11.2*
2500-2999	All	109,436	429	150	217	238	455	3.9	5.3	2.0	2.2	4.2
	<20	8,892	29	9	15	28	43	3.3	4.3	*1.7*	3.1	4.8
	20-24	25,557	98	38	56	86	142	3.8	5.3	2.2	3.4	5.6
	25-29	35,602	116	52	72	59	131	3.2	4.7	2.0	1.7	3.7
	30-34	27,174	120	33	48	39	87	4.4	5.6	1.8	1.4	3.2
	35-39	10,275	55	14	21	20	41	5.3	6.7	2.0	1.9	4.0
	40 & over	1,936	11	4	5	6	11	*5.6*	*7.7*	*2.6*	*3.1*	*5.7*

* Stillbirths and perinatal deaths per 1,000 live and stillbirths
   Neonatal, postneonatal and infant deaths per 1,000 live births

Table 14 - *continued*

Birthweight (grams)	Mother's age	Numbers						Rates*				
		Births		Deaths								
		Live births	Still-births	Early neonatal	Neonatal	Postneo-natal	Infant	Still-birth	Peri-natal	Neo-natal	Postneo-natal	Infant
3000-3499	All	234,752	376	191	267	298	565	1.6	2.4	1.1	1.3	2.4
	<20	16,201	20	15	18	55	73	1.2	2.2	1.1	3.4	4.5
	20-24	49,190	68	46	60	81	141	1.4	2.3	1.2	1.6	2.9
	25-29	79,404	125	66	94	78	172	1.6	2.4	1.2	1.0	2.2
	30-34	63,933	98	43	62	50	112	1.5	2.2	1.0	0.8	1.8
	35-39	22,217	50	18	28	29	57	2.2	3.1	1.3	1.3	2.6
	40 & over	3,807	15	3	5	5	10	3.9	4.7	1.3	1.3	2.6
3500-3999	All	185,122	198	128	179	147	326	1.1	1.8	1.0	0.8	1.8
	<20	10,035	9	10	19	20	39	0.9	1.9	1.9	2.0	3.9
	20-24	34,004	32	26	35	38	73	0.9	1.7	1.0	1.1	2.1
	25-29	63,426	63	47	64	48	112	1.0	1.7	1.0	0.8	1.8
	30-34	55,045	58	29	42	23	65	1.1	1.6	0.8	0.4	1.2
	35-39	19,431	29	11	14	15	29	1.5	2.1	0.7	0.8	1.5
	40 & over	3,181	7	5	5	3	8	2.2	3.8	1.6	0.9	2.5
4000 and over	All	69,150	93	131	153	54	207	1.3	3.2	2.2	0.8	3.0
	<20	2,816	5	10	10	5	15	1.8	5.3	3.6	1.8	5.3
	20-24	10,908	8	22	25	14	39	0.7	2.7	2.3	1.3	3.6
	25-29	23,551	33	46	54	17	71	1.4	3.3	2.3	0.7	3.0
	30-34	22,297	29	33	41	16	57	1.3	2.8	1.8	0.7	2.6
	35-39	8,247	14	18	21	1	22	1.7	3.9	2.5	0.1	2.7
	40 & over	1,331	4	2	2	1	3	3.0	4.5	1.5	0.8	2.3
Not stated	All	2,217	75	59	64	19	83	32.7	58.5	28.9	8.6	37.4
	<20	160	3	6	6	6	12	18.4	55.2	37.5	37.5	75.0
	20-24	445	10	9	12	3	15	22.0	41.8	27.0	6.7	33.7
	25-29	726	21	18	19	4	23	28.1	52.2	26.2	5.5	31.7
	30-34	608	24	15	16	4	20	38.0	61.7	26.3	6.6	32.9
	35-39	238	17	10	10	2	12	66.7	105.9	42.0	8.4	50.4
	40 & over	40	-	1	1	-	1	-	25.0	25.0	-	25.0

* Stillbirths and perinatal deaths per 1,000 live and stillbirths
  Neonatal, postneonatal and infant deaths per 1,000 live births

Table 15 1995 Series DH3 no.28

Table 15 Live births, stillbirths and infant deaths
Birthweight by mother's country of birth
Numbers and rates*, 1995

England and Wales

Birth-weight (grams)	Country of birth	Numbers						Rates*				
		Births		Deaths								
		Live births	Still-births	Early neonatal	Neonatal	Postneo-natal	Infant	Still-birth	Peri-natal	Neo-natal	Postneo-natal	Infant
All	**All**	**648,001**	**3,597**	**2,084**	**2,669**	**1,244**	**3,913**	**5.5**	**8.7**	**4.1**	**1.9**	**6.0**
	United Kingdom	566,331	2,970	1,769	2,282	1,038	3,320	5.2	8.3	4.0	1.8	5.9
	Irish Republic	5,166	35	14	21	9	30	6.7	9.4	4.1	1.7	5.8
	Rest of European Union	8,026	53	11	16	21	37	6.6	7.9	2.0	2.6	4.6
	Australia, Canada, New Zealand	3,052	21	7	12	8	20	6.8	9.1	3.9	2.6	6.6
	New Commonwealth***	47,337	413	217	258	140	398	8.6	13.2	5.5	3.0	8.4
	Bangladesh	6,783	62	18	22	16	38	9.1	11.7	3.2	2.4	5.6
	India	6,679	45	29	31	19	50	6.7	11.0	4.6	2.8	7.5
	Pakistan	12,332	133	73	85	54	139	10.7	16.5	6.9	4.4	11.3
	East Africa	5,122	38	12	16	12	28	7.4	9.7	3.1	2.3	5.5
	Caribbean	2,910	28	27	30	8	38	9.5	18.7	10.3	2.7	13.1
	Other**	18,089	105	66	80	28	108	5.8	9.4	4.4	1.5	6.0
<2500	**All**	**47,324**	**2,426**	**1,425**	**1,789**	**488**	**2,277**	**48.8**	**77.4**	**37.8**	**10.3**	**48.1**
	United Kingdom	40,412	2,020	1,222	1,540	406	1,946	47.6	76.4	38.1	10.0	48.2
	Irish Republic	363	24	10	13	3	16	62.0	87.9	35.8	8.3	44.1
	Rest of European Union	491	38	7	11	7	18	71.8	85.1	22.4	14.3	36.7
	Australia, Canada, New Zealand	152	11	5	9	4	13	67.5	98.2	59.2	26.3	85.5
	New Commonwealth***	4,828	267	133	159	56	215	52.4	78.5	32.9	11.6	44.5
	Bangladesh	746	32	8	10	4	14	41.1	51.4	13.4	5.4	18.8
	India	748	22	14	15	7	22	28.6	46.8	20.1	9.4	29.4
	Pakistan	1,279	93	49	54	16	70	67.8	103.5	42.2	12.5	54.7
	East Africa	623	33	7	9	6	15	50.3	61.0	14.4	9.6	24.1
	Caribbean	337	21	20	22	8	30	58.7	114.5	65.3	23.7	89.0
	Other**	1,078	66	48	57	12	69	57.7	99.7	52.9	11.1	64.0
<1500	**All**	**7,583**	**1,625**	**1,154**	**1,425**	**255**	**1,680**	**176.5**	**301.8**	**187.9**	**33.6**	**221.5**
	United Kingdom	6,484	1,361	994	1,231	204	1,435	173.5	300.2	189.9	31.5	221.3
	Irish Republic	63	12	8	10	1	11	160.0	266.7	158.7	15.9	174.6
	Rest of European Union	68	26	5	9	4	13	276.6	329.8	132.4	58.8	191.2
	Australia, Canada, New Zealand	29	9	5	9	2	11	236.8	368.4	310.3	69.0	379.3
	New Commonwealth***	747	179	105	123	35	158	193.3	306.7	164.7	46.9	211.5
	Bangladesh	64	17	5	7	2	9	209.9	271.6	109.4	31.3	140.6
	India	97	10	11	11	4	15	93.5	196.3	113.4	41.2	154.6
	Pakistan	174	68	37	40	6	46	281.0	433.9	229.9	34.5	264.4
	East Africa	83	22	6	7	4	11	209.5	266.7	84.3	48.2	132.5
	Caribbean	88	16	17	19	7	26	153.8	317.3	215.9	79.5	295.5
	Other**	192	38	37	43	9	52	165.2	326.1	224.0	46.9	270.8
<1000	**All**	**2,879**	**1,119**	**941**	**1,124**	**168**	**1,292**	**279.9**	**515.3**	**390.4**	**58.4**	**448.8**
	United Kingdom	2,412	939	806	967	130	1,097	280.2	520.7	400.9	53.9	454.8
	Irish Republic	24	9	7	8	-	8	272.7	484.8	333.3	-	333.3
	Rest of European Union	26	16	3	6	3	9	381.0	452.4	230.8	115.4	346.2
	Australia, Canada, New Zealand	11	6	4	6	2	8	352.9	588.2	545.5	181.8	727.3
	New Commonwealth***	321	125	91	102	26	128	280.3	484.3	317.8	81.0	398.8
	Bangladesh	19	10	4	5	1	6	344.8	482.8	263.2	52.6	315.8
	India	38	7	8	8	4	12	155.6	333.3	210.5	105.3	315.8
	Pakistan	81	50	32	34	4	38	381.7	626.0	419.8	49.4	469.1
	East Africa	34	14	4	5	4	9	291.7	375.0	147.1	117.6	264.7
	Caribbean	41	10	17	18	6	24	196.1	529.4	439.0	146.3	585.4
	Other**	85	24	30	35	7	42	220.2	495.4	411.8	82.4	494.1

*   Stillbirths and perinatal deaths per 1,000 live and stillbirths
    Neonatal, postneonatal and infant deaths per 1,000 live births
**   Including cases where no country of birth was stated
*** A full list of countries included in the New Commonwealth is provided in the introduction

Table 15 - *continued*

Birth-weight (grams)	Country of birth	Numbers						Rates*				
		Births		Deaths								
		Live births	Still-births	Early neonatal	Neonatal	Postneo-natal	Infant	Still-birth	Peri-natal	Neo-natal	Postneo-natal	Infant
1000-1499	**All**	**4,704**	**506**	**213**	**301**	**87**	**388**	**97.1**	**138.0**	**64.0**	**18.5**	**82.5**
	United Kingdom	4,072	422	188	264	74	338	93.9	135.7	64.8	18.2	83.0
	Irish Republic	39	3	1	2	1	3	71.4	95.2	51.3	25.6	76.9
	Rest of European Union	42	10	2	3	1	4	192.3	230.8	71.4	23.8	95.2
	Australia, Canada, New Zealand	18	3	1	3	-	3	142.9	190.5	166.7	-	166.7
	New Commonwealth***	426	54	14	21	9	30	112.5	141.7	49.3	21.1	70.4
	Bangladesh	45	7	1	2	1	3	134.6	153.8	44.4	22.2	66.7
	India	59	3	3	3	-	3	48.4	96.8	50.8	-	50.8
	Pakistan	93	18	5	6	2	8	162.2	207.2	64.5	21.5	86.0
	East Africa	49	8	2	2	-	2	140.4	175.4	40.8	-	40.8
	Caribbean	47	6	-	1	1	2	113.2	113.2	21.3	21.3	42.6
	Other**	107	14	7	8	2	10	115.7	173.6	74.8	18.7	93.5
1500-1999	**All**	**9,679**	**399**	**134**	**167**	**91**	**258**	**39.6**	**52.9**	**17.3**	**9.4**	**26.7**
	United Kingdom	8,430	327	117	141	81	222	37.3	50.7	16.7	9.6	26.3
	Irish Republic	80	6	1	2	1	3	69.8	81.4	25.0	12.5	37.5
	Rest of European Union	86	8	1	1	2	3	85.1	95.7	11.6	23.3	34.9
	Australia, Canada, New Zealand	30	2	-	-	1	1	62.5	62.5	-	33.3	33.3
	New Commonwealth***	881	43	13	18	5	23	46.5	60.6	20.4	5.7	26.1
	Bangladesh	121	9	1	1	-	1	69.2	76.9	8.3	-	8.3
	India	136	7	2	2	-	2	49.0	62.9	14.7	-	14.7
	Pakistan	238	11	5	6	4	10	44.2	64.3	25.2	16.8	42.0
	East Africa	116	5	-	1	-	1	41.3	41.3	8.6	-	8.6
	Caribbean	66	2	2	2	-	2	29.4	58.8	30.3	-	30.3
	Other**	172	13	2	5	1	6	70.3	81.1	29.1	5.8	34.9
2000-2499	**All**	**30,062**	**402**	**137**	**197**	**142**	**339**	**13.2**	**17.7**	**6.6**	**4.7**	**11.3**
	United Kingdom	25,498	332	111	168	121	289	12.9	17.2	6.6	4.7	11.3
	Irish Republic	220	6	1	1	1	2	26.5	31.0	4.5	4.5	9.1
	Rest of European Union	337	4	1	1	1	2	11.7	14.7	3.0	3.0	5.9
	Australia, Canada, New Zealand	93	-	-	-	1	1	-	-	-	10.8	10.8
	New Commonwealth***	3,200	45	15	18	16	34	13.9	18.5	5.6	5.0	10.6
	Bangladesh	561	6	2	2	2	4	10.6	14.1	3.6	3.6	7.1
	India	515	5	1	2	3	5	9.6	11.5	3.9	5.8	9.7
	Pakistan	867	14	7	8	6	14	15.9	23.8	9.2	6.9	16.1
	East Africa	424	6	1	1	2	3	14.0	16.3	2.4	4.7	7.1
	Caribbean	183	3	1	1	1	2	16.1	21.5	5.5	5.5	10.9
	Other**	714	15	9	9	2	11	20.6	32.9	12.6	2.8	15.4
2500-2999	**All**	**109,436**	**429**	**150**	**217**	**238**	**455**	**3.9**	**5.3**	**2.0**	**2.2**	**4.2**
	United Kingdom	92,255	349	127	179	193	372	3.8	5.1	1.9	2.1	4.0
	Irish Republic	736	7	1	3	2	5	9.4	10.8	4.1	2.7	6.8
	Rest of European Union	1,284	6	2	3	6	9	4.7	6.2	2.3	4.7	7.0
	Australia, Canada, New Zealand	403	2	1	1	2	3	4.9	7.4	2.5	5.0	7.4
	New Commonwealth***	11,821	54	17	27	28	55	4.5	6.0	2.3	2.4	4.7
	Bangladesh	2,146	9	3	4	9	13	4.2	5.6	1.9	4.2	6.1
	India	1,971	14	4	5	3	8	7.1	9.1	2.5	1.5	4.1
	Pakistan	3,231	16	4	11	13	24	4.9	6.2	3.4	4.0	7.4
	East Africa	1,432	-	4	4	3	7	-	2.8	2.8	2.1	4.9
	Caribbean	566	6	-	-	-	-	10.5	10.5	-	-	-
	Other**	2,937	11	2	4	7	11	3.7	4.4	1.4	2.4	3.7

* Stillbirths and perinatal deaths per 1,000 live and stillbirths
  Neonatal, postneonatal and infant deaths per 1,000 live births
** Including cases where no country of birth was stated
*** A full list of countries included in the New Commonwealth is provided in the introduction

Table 15 1995 Series DH3 no.28

Table 15 - *continued*

Birth-weight (grams)	Country of birth	Numbers						Rates*				
		Births		Deaths				Still-birth	Peri-natal	Neo-natal	Postneo-natal	Infant
		Live births	Still-births	Early neonatal	Neonatal	Postneo-natal	Infant					
3000-3499	All	234,752	376	191	267	298	565	1.6	2.4	1.1	1.3	2.4
	United Kingdom	203,992	304	157	225	247	472	1.5	2.3	1.1	1.2	2.3
	Irish Republic	1,804	1	-	1	1	2	0.6	0.6	0.6	0.6	1.1
	Rest of European Union	2,972	4	2	2	4	6	1.3	2.0	0.7	1.3	2.0
	Australia, Canada, New Zealand	1,079	4	-	1	1	2	3.7	3.7	0.9	0.9	1.9
	New Commonwealth***	18,020	52	25	29	40	69	2.9	4.3	1.6	2.2	3.8
	Bangladesh	2,642	14	3	4	1	5	5.3	6.4	1.5	0.4	1.9
	India	2,633	7	6	6	7	13	2.7	4.9	2.3	2.7	4.9
	Pakistan	4,732	14	9	9	18	27	2.9	4.8	1.9	3.8	5.7
	East Africa	1,876	3	1	3	2	5	1.6	2.1	1.6	1.1	2.7
	Caribbean	1,080	1	1	1	-	1	0.9	1.9	0.9	-	0.9
	Other**	6,885	11	7	9	5	14	1.6	2.6	1.3	0.7	2.0
3500-3999	All	185,122	198	128	179	147	326	1.1	1.8	1.0	0.8	1.8
	United Kingdom	165,231	165	109	158	126	284	1.0	1.7	1.0	0.8	1.7
	Irish Republic	1,557	1	2	3	2	5	0.6	1.9	1.9	1.3	3.2
	Rest of European Union	2,404	-	-	-	2	2	-	-	-	0.8	0.8
	Australia, Canada, New Zealand	978	2	-	-	1	1	2.0	2.0	-	1.0	1.0
	New Commonwealth***	9,660	25	13	13	12	25	2.6	3.9	1.3	1.2	2.6
	Bangladesh	1,005	4	2	2	1	3	4.0	5.9	2.0	1.0	3.0
	India	1,076	1	3	3	2	5	0.9	3.7	2.8	1.9	4.6
	Pakistan	2,420	6	2	2	6	8	2.5	3.3	0.8	2.5	3.3
	East Africa	908	2	-	-	-	-	2.2	2.2	-	-	-
	Caribbean	679	-	4	4	-	4	-	5.9	5.9	-	5.9
	Other**	5,292	5	4	5	4	9	0.9	1.7	0.9	0.8	1.7
4000 & over	All	69,150	93	131	153	54	207	1.3	3.2	2.2	0.8	3.0
	United Kingdom	62,620	76	110	131	50	181	1.2	3.0	2.1	0.8	2.9
	Irish Republic	685	1	-	-	1	1	1.5	1.5	-	1.5	1.5
	Rest of European Union	842	1	-	-	1	1	1.2	1.2	-	1.2	1.2
	Australia, Canada, New Zealand	425	1	-	-	-	-	2.3	2.3	-	-	-
	New Commonwealth***	2,788	9	19	20	2	22	3.2	10.0	7.2	0.7	7.9
	Bangladesh	217	2	2	2	-	2	9.1	18.3	9.2	-	9.2
	India	233	1	1	1	-	1	4.3	8.5	4.3	-	4.3
	Pakistan	632	4	4	4	-	4	6.3	12.6	6.3	-	6.3
	East Africa	263	-	-	-	1	1	-	-	-	3.8	3.8
	Caribbean	228	-	2	3	-	3	-	8.8	13.2	-	13.2
	Other**	1,790	5	2	2	-	2	2.8	3.9	1.1	-	1.1
Not stated	All	2,217	75	59	64	19	83	32.7	58.5	28.9	8.6	37.4
	United Kingdom	1,821	56	44	49	16	65	29.8	53.3	26.9	8.8	35.7
	Irish Republic	21	1	1	1	-	1	45.5	90.9	47.6	-	47.6
	Rest of European Union	33	4	-	-	1	1	108.1	108.1	-	30.3	30.3
	Australia, Canada, New Zealand	15	1	1	1	-	1	62.5	125.0	66.7	-	66.7
	New Commonwealth***	220	6	10	10	2	12	26.5	70.8	45.5	9.1	54.5
	Bangladesh	27	1	-	-	1	1	35.7	35.7	-	37.0	37.0
	India	18	-	1	1	-	1	-	55.6	55.6	-	55.6
	Pakistan	38	-	5	5	1	6	-	131.6	131.6	26.3	157.9
	East Africa	20	-	-	-	-	-	-	-	-	-	-
	Caribbean	20	-	-	-	-	-	-	-	-	-	-
	Other**	107	7	3	3	-	3	61.4	87.7	28.0	-	28.0

* Stillbirths and perinatal deaths per 1,000 live and stillbirths
    Neonatal, postneonatal and infant deaths per 1,000 live births
** Including cases where no country of birth was stated
*** A full list of countries included in the New Commonwealth is provided in the introduction

Table 16 Live births, stillbirths and infant deaths
 Birthweight by parity, marital status and type of registration
 Numbers and rates*, 1995

England and Wales

Birth-weight (grams)	Marital status Parity/type of registration	Numbers						Rates*				
		Births		Deaths								
		Live births	Still-births	Early neonatal	Neo-natal	Postneo-natal	Infant	Still-birth	Peri-natal	Neo-natal	Postneo-natal	Infant
All	**All**	**648,001**	**3,597**	**2,084**	**2,669**	**1,244**	**3,913**	**5.5**	**8.7**	**4.1**	**1.9**	**6.0**
	Inside marriage											
	All	**428,099**	**2,224**	**1,262**	**1,596**	**655**	**2,251**	**5.2**	**8.1**	**3.7**	**1.5**	**5.3**
	0	166,798	584	573	701	224	925	3.5	6.9	4.2	1.3	5.5
	1	157,692	806	367	466	218	684	5.1	7.4	3.0	1.4	4.3
	2	67,233	423	184	248	121	369	6.3	9.0	3.7	1.8	5.5
	3 and over	36,376	411	138	181	92	273	11.2	14.9	5.0	2.5	7.5
	Outside marriage											
	All	**219,902**	**1,373**	**822**	**1,073**	**589**	**1,662**	**6.2**	**9.9**	**4.9**	**2.7**	**7.6**
	Joint regn/same address	127,800	729	462	607	280	887	5.7	9.3	4.7	2.2	6.9
	Joint regn/different address	44,175	297	214	270	127	397	6.7	11.5	6.1	2.9	9.0
	Sole registration	47,927	347	146	196	182	378	7.2	10.2	4.1	3.8	7.9
<2500	**All**	**47,324**	**2,426**	**1,425**	**1,789**	**488**	**2,277**	**48.8**	**77.4**	**37.8**	**10.3**	**48.1**
	Inside marriage											
	All	**28,457**	**1,461**	**841**	**1,045**	**263**	**1,308**	**48.8**	**76.9**	**36.7**	**9.2**	**46.0**
	0	13,968	412	391	486	101	587	28.7	55.8	34.8	7.2	42.0
	1	8,206	528	229	278	87	365	60.5	86.7	33.9	10.6	44.5
	2	3,769	263	123	155	47	202	65.2	95.7	41.1	12.5	53.6
	3 and over	2,514	258	98	126	28	154	93.1	128.4	50.1	11.1	61.3
	Outside marriage											
	All	**18,867**	**965**	**584**	**744**	**225**	**969**	**48.7**	**78.1**	**39.4**	**11.9**	**51.4**
	Joint regn/same address	10,119	502	319	409	113	522	47.3	77.3	40.4	11.2	51.6
	Joint regn/different address	4,119	213	156	196	50	246	49.2	85.2	47.6	12.1	59.7
	Sole registration	4,629	250	109	139	62	201	51.2	73.6	30.0	13.4	43.4
<1500	**All**	**7,583**	**1,625**	**1,154**	**1,425**	**255**	**1,680**	**176.5**	**301.8**	**187.9**	**33.6**	**221.5**
	Inside marriage											
	All	**4,478**	**969**	**671**	**828**	**148**	**976**	**177.9**	**301.1**	**184.9**	**33.1**	**218.0**
	0	2,372	275	324	396	66	462	103.9	226.3	166.9	27.8	194.8
	1	1,149	349	172	212	39	251	233.0	347.8	184.5	33.9	218.5
	2	546	173	101	122	27	149	240.6	381.1	223.4	49.5	272.9
	3 and over	411	172	74	98	16	114	295.0	422.0	238.4	*38.9*	277.4
	Outside marriage											
	All	**3,105**	**656**	**483**	**597**	**107**	**704**	**174.4**	**302.8**	**192.3**	**34.5**	**226.7**
	Joint regn/same address	1,617	344	264	329	56	385	175.4	310.0	203.5	34.6	238.1
	Joint regn/different address	768	146	134	161	27	188	159.7	306.3	209.6	35.2	244.8
	Sole registration	720	166	85	107	24	131	187.4	283.3	148.6	33.3	181.9
<1000	**All**	**2,879**	**1,119**	**941**	**1,124**	**168**	**1,292**	**279.9**	**515.3**	**390.4**	**58.4**	**448.8**
	Inside marriage											
	All	**1,681**	**665**	**547**	**645**	**104**	**749**	**283.5**	**516.6**	**383.7**	**61.9**	**445.6**
	0	877	195	271	315	49	364	181.9	434.7	359.2	55.9	415.1
	1	421	234	139	164	26	190	357.3	569.5	389.5	61.8	451.3
	2	219	110	79	95	19	114	334.3	574.5	433.8	*86.8*	520.5
	3 and over	164	126	58	71	10	81	434.5	634.5	432.9	*61.0*	493.9
	Outside marriage											
	All	**1,198**	**454**	**394**	**479**	**64**	**543**	**274.8**	**513.3**	**399.8**	**53.4**	**453.3**
	Joint regn/same address	617	247	206	254	31	285	285.9	524.3	411.7	50.2	461.9
	Joint regn/different address	332	100	120	141	21	162	231.5	509.3	424.7	63.3	488.0
	Sole registration	249	107	68	84	12	96	300.6	491.6	337.3	*48.2*	385.5

* Stillbirths and perinatal deaths per 1,000 live and stillbirths,
 neonatal, postneonatal and infant deaths per 1,000 live births

Table 16 1995 Series DH3 no.28

Birth-weight (grams)	Marital status Parity/type of registration	Numbers						Rates*				
		Births		Deaths				Still-birth	Peri-natal	Neo-natal	Postneo-natal	Infant
		Live births	Still-births	Early neonatal	Neo-natal	Postneo-natal	Infant					
1000-1499	All	4,704	506	213	301	87	388	97.1	138.0	64.0	18.5	82.5
	Inside marriage											
	All	2,797	304	124	183	44	227	98.0	138.0	65.4	15.7	81.2
	0	1,495	80	53	81	17	98	50.8	84.4	54.2	*11.4*	65.6
	1	728	115	33	48	13	61	136.4	175.6	65.9	*17.9*	83.8
	2	327	63	22	27	8	35	161.5	217.9	82.6	*24.5*	107.0
	3 and over	247	46	16	27	6	33	157.0	211.6	109.3	*24.3*	133.6
	Outside marriage											
	All	1,907	202	89	118	43	161	95.8	138.0	61.9	22.5	84.4
	Joint regn/same address	1,000	97	58	75	25	100	88.4	141.3	75.0	25.0	100.0
	Joint regn/different address	436	46	14	20	6	26	95.4	124.5	45.9	*13.8*	59.6
	Sole registration	471	59	17	23	12	35	111.3	143.4	48.8	*25.5*	74.3
1500-1999	All	9,679	399	134	167	91	258	39.6	52.9	17.3	9.4	26.7
	Inside marriage											
	All	5,814	246	81	102	49	151	40.6	54.0	17.5	8.4	26.0
	0	2,934	80	31	37	10	47	26.5	36.8	12.6	*3.4*	16.0
	1	1,641	84	29	34	24	58	48.7	65.5	20.7	14.6	35.3
	2	724	45	8	15	9	24	58.5	68.9	*20.7*	*12.4*	33.1
	3 and over	515	37	13	16	6	22	67.0	90.6	*31.1*	*11.7*	42.7
	Outside marriage											
	All	3,865	153	53	65	42	107	38.1	51.3	16.8	10.9	27.7
	Joint regn/same address	2,048	76	32	40	17	57	35.8	50.8	19.5	*8.3*	27.8
	Joint regn/different address	826	31	12	16	11	27	36.2	50.2	*19.4*	*13.3*	32.7
	Sole registration	991	46	9	9	14	23	44.4	53.0	*9.1*	*14.1*	23.2
2000-2499	All	30,062	402	137	197	142	339	13.2	17.7	6.6	4.7	11.3
	Inside marriage											
	All	18,165	246	89	115	66	181	13.4	18.2	6.3	3.6	10.0
	0	8,662	57	36	53	25	78	6.5	10.7	6.1	2.9	9.0
	1	5,416	95	28	32	24	56	17.2	22.3	5.9	4.4	10.3
	2	2,499	45	14	18	11	29	17.7	23.2	7.2	*4.4*	11.6
	3 and over	1,588	49	11	12	6	18	29.9	36.7	*7.6*	*3.8*	*11.3*
	Outside marriage											
	All	11,897	156	48	82	76	158	12.9	16.9	6.9	6.4	13.3
	Joint regn/same address	6,454	82	23	40	40	80	12.5	16.1	6.2	6.2	12.4
	Joint regn/different address	2,525	36	10	19	12	31	14.1	18.0	*7.5*	*4.8*	12.3
	Sole registration	2,918	38	15	23	24	47	12.9	17.9	7.9	8.2	16.1
2500-2999	All	109,436	429	150	217	238	455	3.9	5.3	2.0	2.2	4.2
	Inside marriage											
	All	67,957	268	95	132	123	255	3.9	5.3	1.9	1.8	3.8
	0	30,544	63	35	41	52	93	2.1	3.2	1.3	1.7	3.0
	1	22,055	92	33	48	32	80	4.2	5.6	2.2	1.5	3.6
	2	9,461	47	12	21	19	40	4.9	6.2	2.2	*2.0*	4.2
	3 and over	5,897	66	15	22	20	42	11.1	13.6	3.7	3.4	7.1
	Outside marriage											
	All	41,479	161	55	85	115	200	3.9	5.2	2.0	2.8	4.8
	Joint regn/same address	22,632	98	31	45	49	94	4.3	5.7	2.0	2.2	4.2
	Joint regn/different address	8,755	26	16	25	25	50	3.0	4.8	2.9	2.9	5.7
	Sole registration	10,092	37	8	15	41	56	3.7	4.4	*1.5*	4.1	5.5

* Stillbirths and perinatal deaths per 1,000 live and stillbirths,
  neonatal, postneonatal and infant deaths per 1,000 live births

Table 16 - *continued*

Birth-weight (grams)	Marital status Parity/type of registration	Numbers						Rates*				
		Births		Deaths								
		Live births	Still-births	Early neonatal	Neo-natal	Postneo-natal	Infant	Still-birth	Peri-natal	Neo-natal	Postneo-natal	Infant
3000-3499	All	234,752	376	191	267	298	565	1.6	2.4	1.1	1.3	2.4
	Inside marriage											
	All	153,075	259	123	172	155	327	1.7	2.5	1.1	1.0	2.1
	0	62,532	48	53	68	39	107	0.8	1.6	1.1	0.6	1.7
	1	55,205	107	39	54	63	117	1.9	2.6	1.0	1.1	2.1
	2	22,974	63	21	35	30	65	2.7	3.6	1.5	1.3	2.8
	3 and over	12,364	41	10	15	23	38	3.3	4.1	*1.2*	1.9	3.1
	Outside marriage											
	All	81,677	117	68	95	143	238	1.4	2.3	1.2	1.8	2.9
	Joint regn/same address	47,181	58	42	59	65	124	1.2	2.1	1.3	1.4	2.6
	Joint regn/different address	16,393	26	14	17	33	50	1.6	2.4	*1.0*	2.0	3.1
	Sole registration	18,103	33	12	19	45	64	1.8	2.5	*1.0*	2.5	3.5
3500-3999	All	185,122	198	128	179	147	326	1.1	1.8	1.0	0.8	1.8
	Inside marriage											
	All	127,413	124	79	108	70	178	1.0	1.6	0.8	0.5	1.4
	0	44,691	27	41	46	21	67	0.6	1.5	1.0	0.5	1.5
	1	50,973	40	20	34	20	54	0.8	1.2	0.7	0.4	1.1
	2	21,145	31	12	21	13	34	1.5	2.0	1.0	*0.6*	1.6
	3 and over	10,604	26	6	7	16	23	2.4	3.0	*0.7*	*1.5*	2.2
	Outside marriage											
	All	57,709	74	49	71	77	148	1.3	2.1	1.2	1.3	2.6
	Joint regn/same address	35,203	45	32	45	35	80	1.3	2.2	1.3	1.0	2.3
	Joint regn/different address	11,192	17	10	14	18	32	*1.5*	2.4	*1.3*	*1.6*	2.9
	Sole registration	11,314	12	7	12	24	36	*1.1*	*1.7*	*1.1*	2.1	3.2
4000 and over	All	69,150	93	131	153	54	207	1.3	3.2	2.2	0.8	3.0
	Inside marriage											
	All	49,806	69	84	96	33	129	1.4	3.1	1.9	0.7	2.6
	0	14,318	18	33	38	8	46	1.3	3.6	2.7	*0.6*	3.2
	1	20,884	27	31	36	11	47	1.3	2.8	1.7	*0.5*	2.3
	2	9,708	15	12	12	11	23	*1.5*	2.8	*1.2*	*1.1*	*2.4*
	3 and over	4,896	9	8	10	3	13	*1.8*	*3.5*	*2.0*	*0.6*	*2.7*
	Outside marriage											
	All	19,344	24	47	57	21	78	1.2	3.7	2.9	1.1	4.0
	Joint regn/same address	12,248	12	29	38	13	51	*1.0*	3.3	3.1	*1.1*	4.2
	Joint regn/different address	3,508	8	11	11	-	11	*2.3*	*5.4*	*3.1*	-	*3.1*
	Sole registration	3,588	4	7	8	8	16	*1.1*	*3.1*	*2.2*	*2.2*	*4.5*
Not stated	All	2,217	75	59	64	19	83	32.7	58.5	28.9	8.6	37.4
	Inside marriage											
	All	1,391	43	40	43	11	54	30.0	57.9	30.9	7.9	38.8
	0	745	16	20	22	3	25	*21.0*	47.3	29.5	*4.0*	33.6
	1	369	12	15	16	5	21	*31.5*	70.9	*43.4*	*13.6*	56.9
	2	176	4	4	4	1	5	*22.2*	*44.4*	*22.7*	*5.7*	*28.4*
	3 and over	101	11	1	1	2	3	*98.2*	*107.1*	*9.9*	*19.8*	*29.7*
	Outside marriage											
	All	826	32	19	21	8	29	37.3	59.4	25.4	9.7	35.1
	Joint regn/same address	417	14	9	11	5	16	*32.5*	53.4	*26.4*	*12.0*	*38.4*
	Joint regn/different address	208	7	7	7	1	8	*32.6*	*65.1*	*33.7*	*4.8*	*38.5*
	Sole registration	201	11	3	3	2	5	*51.9*	*66.0*	*14.9*	*10.0*	*24.9*

* Stillbirths and perinatal deaths per 1,000 live and stillbirths,
  neonatal, postneonatal and infant deaths per 1,000 live births

Table 17 1995 Series DH3 no.28

Table 17 Live births**, stillbirths and infant deaths
Birthweight by father's social class (based on occupation at death registration)
Inside marriage and outside marriage/joint registration
Numbers and rates*, 1995

England and Wales

Birthweight (grams)	Marital Status Social class	Numbers						Rates*				
		Births		Deaths								
		Live births**	Still-births	Early neonatal	Neonatal	Postneo-natal	Infant	Still-birth	Peri-natal	Neo-natal	Postneo-natal	Infant
All	All***	59,962	3,250	1,938	2,473	1,062	3,535	5.4	8.6	4.1	1.8	5.9
	Inside marriage											
	All†	42,921	2,224	1,262	1,596	655	2,251	5.2	8.1	3.7	1.5	5.2
	I	4,051	171	97	124	47	171	4.2	6.6	3.1	1.2	4.2
	II	12,150	517	332	406	141	547	4.2	7.0	3.3	1.2	4.5
	IIIN	4,828	240	139	171	69	240	4.9	7.8	3.5	1.4	5.0
	IIIM	12,504	606	349	465	193	658	4.8	7.6	3.7	1.5	5.3
	IV	5,467	369	210	250	105	355	6.7	10.5	4.6	1.9	6.5
	V	1,799	154	65	91	47	138	8.5	12.1	5.1	2.6	7.7
	Other	2,122	167	63	79	43	122	7.8	10.8	3.7	2.0	5.7
	Outside marriage joint registration											
	All†	17,041	1,026	676	877	407	1,284	6.0	9.9	5.1	2.4	7.5
	I	493	27	16	21	14	35	5.4	8.7	4.3	2.8	7.1
	II	2,615	109	87	120	39	159	4.2	7.5	4.6	1.5	6.1
	IIIN	1,285	71	44	54	26	80	5.5	8.9	4.2	2.0	6.2
	IIIM	6,727	413	239	315	140	455	6.1	9.6	4.7	2.1	6.8
	IV	3,277	203	142	179	72	251	6.2	10.5	5.5	2.2	7.7
	V	1,626	118	84	106	46	152	7.2	12.3	6.5	2.8	9.3
	Other	1,018	85	57	71	56	127	8.3	13.8	7.0	5.5	12.5
<2500	All***	4,312	2,176	1,316	1,650	426	2,076	48.0	77.1	38.3	9.9	48.1
	Inside marriage											
	All†	2,888	1,461	841	1,045	263	1,308	48.2	75.9	36.2	9.1	45.3
	I	215	106	59	75	18	93	47.0	73.1	34.9	8.4	43.3
	II	719	334	214	257	65	322	44.4	72.8	35.7	9.0	44.8
	IIIN	322	166	85	105	29	134	49.0	74.1	32.6	9.0	41.6
	IIIM	900	409	245	319	66	385	43.5	69.5	35.4	7.3	42.8
	IV	427	233	152	175	47	222	51.7	85.5	41.0	11.0	52.0
	V	147	103	40	55	16	71	65.5	90.9	37.4	10.9	48.3
	Other	158	110	41	53	17	70	65.1	89.3	33.5	10.8	44.3
	Outside marriage joint registration											
	All†	1,424	715	475	605	163	768	47.8	79.6	42.5	11.4	53.9
	I	31	20	10	13	7	20	60.6	90.9	41.9	22.6	64.5
	II	188	72	55	75	14	89	36.9	65.1	39.9	7.4	47.3
	IIIN	108	55	27	35	17	52	48.5	72.2	32.4	15.7	48.1
	IIIM	541	271	157	206	54	260	47.7	75.3	38.1	10.0	48.1
	IV	305	150	119	147	30	177	46.9	84.1	48.2	9.8	58.0
	V	150	87	57	69	21	90	54.8	90.7	46.0	14.0	60.0
	Other	101	60	48	55	18	73	56.1	100.9	54.5	17.8	72.3
<1500	All***	710	1,459	1,069	1,318	231	1,549	170.5	295.4	185.6	32.5	218.2
	Inside marriage											
	All†	466	969	671	828	148	976	172.1	291.3	177.7	31.8	209.4
	I	34	67	48	59	8	67	164.6	282.6	173.5	23.5	197.1
	II	115	226	170	203	44	247	164.2	287.8	176.5	38.3	214.8
	IIIN	60	111	68	85	17	102	156.1	251.8	141.7	28.3	170.0
	IIIM	153	272	201	261	35	296	150.9	262.5	170.6	22.9	193.5
	IV	60	157	116	134	24	158	207.4	360.6	223.3	40.0	263.3
	V	25	69	34	45	9	54	216.3	322.9	180.0	36.0	216.0
	Other	19	67	31	38	8	46	260.7	381.3	200.0	42.1	242.1
	Outside marriage joint registration											
	All†	244	490	398	490	83	573	167.2	303.1	200.8	34.0	234.8
	I	7	16	9	12	5	17	186.0	290.7	171.4	71.4	242.9
	II	30	52	49	66	7	73	147.7	286.9	220.0	23.3	243.3
	IIIN	23	37	23	29	11	40	138.6	224.7	126.1	47.8	173.9
	IIIM	89	188	130	157	29	186	174.4	295.0	176.4	32.6	209.0
	IV	49	103	96	118	12	130	173.7	335.6	240.8	24.5	265.3
	V	27	52	52	62	13	75	161.5	323.0	229.6	48.1	277.8
	Other	19	42	38	44	5	49	181.0	344.8	231.6	26.3	257.9

*   Stillbirths and perinatal mortality rates are estimates per 1,000 live and stillbirths
       Neonatal, postneonatal and infant mortality rates are estimates per 1,000 livebirths
**   Figures for live births are a 10 percent sample coded for father's occupation
***   Inside marriage and outside marriage/joint registration including cases where father's occupation was not stated
†   Includes cases where father's occupation was not stated

Table 17 - *continued*

Birthweight (grams)	Marital Status Social class	Numbers						Rates*				
		Births		Deaths								
		Live births**	Still-births	Early neonatal	Neonatal	Postneo-natal	Infant	Still-birth	Peri-natal	Neo-natal	Postneo-natal	Infant
<1000	All***	258	1,012	873	1,040	156	1,196	281.7	524.8	403.1	60.5	463.6
	Inside marriage											
	All†	166	665	547	645	104	749	286.0	521.3	388.6	62.7	451.2
	I	9	46	39	45	8	53	338.2	625.0	500.0	88.9	588.9
	II	41	148	132	154	32	186	265.2	501.8	375.6	78.0	453.7
	IIIN	19	86	56	67	10	77	311.6	514.5	352.6	52.6	405.3
	IIIM	57	186	164	203	25	228	246.0	463.0	356.1	43.9	400.0
	IV	23	104	99	107	15	122	311.4	607.8	465.2	65.2	530.4
	V	8	48	29	37	6	43	375.0	601.6	462.5	75.0	537.5
	Other	9	47	25	29	7	36	343.1	525.5	322.2	77.8	400.0
	Outside marriage joint registration											
	All†	92	347	326	395	52	447	273.9	531.2	429.3	56.5	485.9
	I	4	10	8	10	3	13	200.0	360.0	250.0	75.0	325.0
	II	13	36	40	53	6	59	216.9	457.8	407.7	46.2	453.8
	IIIN	11	27	21	27	9	36	197.1	350.4	245.5	81.8	327.3
	IIIM	28	131	105	124	17	141	318.7	574.2	442.9	60.7	503.6
	IV	19	69	70	88	8	96	266.4	536.7	463.2	42.1	505.3
	V	10	40	47	53	7	60	285.7	621.4	530.0	70.0	600.0
	Other	7	34	34	38	2	40	326.9	653.8	542.9	28.6	571.4
1000-1499	All***	452	447	196	278	75	353	90.0	129.5	61.5	16.6	78.1
	Inside marriage											
	All†	300	304	124	183	44	227	92.0	129.5	61.0	14.7	75.7
	I	25	21	9	14	-	14	77.5	110.7	56.0	-	56.0
	II	74	78	38	49	12	61	95.4	141.8	66.2	16.2	82.4
	IIIN	41	25	12	18	7	25	57.5	85.1	43.9	17.1	61.0
	IIIM	96	86	37	58	10	68	82.2	117.6	60.4	10.4	70.8
	IV	37	53	17	27	9	36	125.3	165.5	73.0	24.3	97.3
	V	17	21	5	8	3	11	109.9	136.1	47.1	17.6	64.7
	Other	10	20	6	9	1	10	166.7	216.7	90.0	10.0	100.0
	Outside marriage joint registration											
	All†	152	143	72	95	31	126	86.0	129.3	62.5	20.4	82.9
	I	3	6	1	2	2	4	166.7	194.4	66.7	66.7	133.3
	II	17	16	9	13	1	14	86.0	134.4	76.5	5.9	82.4
	IIIN	12	10	2	2	2	4	76.9	92.3	16.7	16.7	33.3
	IIIM	61	57	25	33	12	45	85.5	122.9	54.1	19.7	73.8
	IV	30	34	26	30	4	34	101.8	179.6	100.0	13.3	113.3
	V	17	12	5	9	6	15	65.9	93.4	52.9	35.3	88.2
	Other	12	8	4	6	3	9	62.5	93.8	50.0	25.0	75.0
1500-1999	All***	883	353	125	158	77	235	38.4	52.1	17.9	8.7	26.6
	Inside marriage											
	All†	591	246	81	102	49	151	40.0	53.1	17.3	8.3	25.5
	I	43	15	3	4	6	10	33.7	40.4	9.3	14.0	23.3
	II	139	60	20	25	9	34	41.4	55.2	18.0	6.5	24.5
	IIIN	57	29	9	10	5	15	48.4	63.4	17.5	8.8	26.3
	IIIM	204	60	21	30	15	45	28.6	38.6	14.7	7.4	22.1
	IV	78	39	21	23	7	30	47.6	73.3	29.5	9.0	38.5
	V	36	23	3	4	2	6	60.1	67.9	11.1	5.6	16.7
	Other	34	20	4	6	4	10	55.6	66.7	17.6	11.8	29.4
	Outside marriage joint registration											
	All†	292	107	44	56	28	84	35.3	49.9	19.2	9.6	28.8
	I	8	3	1	1	-	1	36.1	48.2	12.5	-	12.5
	II	36	13	2	4	3	7	34.9	40.2	11.1	8.3	19.4
	IIIN	24	9	4	5	3	8	36.1	52.2	20.8	12.5	33.3
	IIIM	100	35	15	22	7	29	33.8	48.3	22.0	7.0	29.0
	IV	69	26	13	14	8	22	36.3	54.5	20.3	11.6	31.9
	V	32	14	4	5	1	6	41.9	53.9	15.6	3.1	18.8
	Other	23	7	4	4	5	9	29.5	46.4	17.4	21.7	39.1

* Stillbirths and perinatal mortality rates are estimates per 1,000 live and stillbirths
  Neonatal, postneonatal and infant mortality rates are estimates per 1,000 livebirths
** Figures for live births are a 10 percent sample coded for father's occupation
*** Inside marriage and outside marriage/joint registration including cases where father's occupation was not stated
† Includes cases where father's occupation was not stated

Table 17 1995 Series DH3 no.28

Table 17 - *continued*

Birthweight (grams)	Marital Status Social class	Numbers						Rates*				
		Births		Deaths								
		Live births**	Still-births	Early neonatal	Neonatal	Postneo-natal	Infant	Still-birth	Peri-natal	Neo-natal	Postneo-natal	Infant
2000-2499	All***	2,719	364	122	174	118	292	13.2	17.6	6.4	4.3	10.7
	Inside marriage											
	All†	1,831	246	89	115	66	181	13.3	18.1	6.3	3.6	9.9
	I	138	24	8	12	4	16	17.1	22.8	8.7	2.9	11.6
	II	465	48	24	29	12	41	10.2	15.3	6.2	2.6	8.8
	IIIN	205	26	8	10	7	17	12.5	16.4	4.9	3.4	8.3
	IIIM	543	77	23	28	16	44	14.0	18.2	5.2	2.9	8.1
	IV	289	37	15	18	16	34	12.6	17.8	6.2	5.5	11.8
	V	86	11	3	6	5	11	12.6	16.1	7.0	5.8	12.8
	Other	105	23	6	9	5	14	21.4	27.0	8.6	4.8	13.3
	Outside marriage joint registration											
	All†	888	118	33	59	52	111	13.1	16.8	6.6	5.9	12.5
	I	16	1	-	-	2	2	6.2	6.2	-	12.5	12.5
	II	122	7	4	5	4	9	5.7	9.0	4.1	3.3	7.4
	IIIN	61	9	-	1	3	4	14.5	14.5	1.6	4.9	6.6
	IIIM	352	48	12	27	18	45	13.5	16.8	7.7	5.1	12.8
	IV	187	21	10	15	10	25	11.1	16.4	8.0	5.3	13.4
	V	91	21	1	2	7	9	22.6	23.6	2.2	7.7	9.9
	Other	59	11	6	7	8	15	18.3	28.3	11.9	13.6	25.4
2500-2999	All***	9,922	392	142	202	197	399	3.9	5.4	2.0	2.0	4.0
	Inside marriage											
	All†	6,813	268	95	132	123	255	3.9	5.3	1.9	1.8	3.7
	I	582	26	9	11	8	19	4.4	6.0	1.9	1.4	3.3
	II	1,683	57	22	25	19	44	3.4	4.7	1.5	1.1	2.6
	IIIN	781	28	16	18	12	30	3.6	5.6	2.3	1.5	3.8
	IIIM	2,029	71	19	35	31	66	3.5	4.4	1.7	1.5	3.3
	IV	1,010	41	20	24	23	47	4.0	6.0	2.4	2.3	4.7
	V	351	26	5	12	16	28	7.4	8.8	3.4	4.6	8.0
	Other	377	19	3	6	12	18	5.0	5.8	1.6	3.2	4.8
	Outside marriage joint registration											
	All†	3,109	124	47	70	74	144	4.0	5.5	2.3	2.4	4.6
	I	76	3	3	5	2	7	3.9	7.9	6.6	2.6	9.2
	II	429	15	7	9	8	17	3.5	5.1	2.1	1.9	4.0
	IIIN	203	9	5	6	4	10	4.4	6.9	3.0	2.0	4.9
	IIIM	1,234	51	19	29	24	53	4.1	5.6	2.4	1.9	4.3
	IV	628	23	5	8	14	22	3.6	4.4	1.3	2.2	3.5
	V	326	14	6	8	7	15	4.3	6.1	2.5	2.1	4.6
	Other	213	9	2	5	11	16	4.2	5.1	2.3	5.2	7.5
3000-3499	All***	21,484	343	179	248	253	501	1.6	2.4	1.2	1.2	2.3
	Inside marriage											
	All†	15,180	259	123	172	155	327	1.7	2.5	1.1	1.0	2.2
	I	1,461	21	12	16	13	29	1.4	2.3	1.1	0.9	2.0
	II	4,321	67	32	49	31	80	1.5	2.3	1.1	0.7	1.9
	IIIN	1,706	26	16	23	19	42	1.5	2.5	1.3	1.1	2.5
	IIIM	4,437	68	32	42	52	94	1.5	2.3	0.9	1.2	2.1
	IV	1,875	47	13	21	22	43	2.5	3.2	1.1	1.2	2.3
	V	623	13	7	9	5	14	2.1	3.2	1.4	0.8	2.2
	Other	757	17	10	10	11	21	2.2	3.6	1.3	1.5	2.8
	Outside marriage joint registration											
	All†	6,304	84	56	76	98	174	1.3	2.2	1.2	1.6	2.8
	I	169	2	1	1	4	5	1.2	1.8	0.6	2.4	3.0
	II	963	13	8	14	7	21	1.3	2.2	1.5	0.7	2.2
	IIIN	487	4	3	4	2	6	0.8	1.4	0.8	0.4	1.2
	IIIM	2,497	42	26	31	37	68	1.7	2.7	1.2	1.5	2.7
	IV	1,207	11	6	9	17	26	0.9	1.4	0.7	1.4	2.2
	V	594	8	8	12	14	26	1.3	2.7	2.0	2.4	4.4
	Other	387	4	1	2	14	16	1.0	1.3	0.5	3.6	4.1

* Stillbirths and perinatal mortality rates are estimates per 1,000 live and stillbirths
  Neonatal, postneonatal and infant mortality rates are estimates per 1,000 livebirths
** Figures for live births are a 10 percent sample coded for father's occupation
*** Inside marriage and outside marriage/joint registration including cases where father's occupation was not stated
† Includes cases where father's occupation was not stated

Table 17 - *continued*

Birthweight (grams)	Marital Status Social class	Numbers						Rates*				
		Births		Deaths								
		Live births**	Still-births	Early neonatal	Neonatal	Postneo-natal	Infant	Still-birth	Peri-natal	Neo-natal	Postneo-natal	Infant
3500-3999	All***	17,562	186	121	167	123	290	1.1	1.7	1.0	0.7	1.7
	Inside marriage											
	All†	12,983	124	79	108	70	178	1.0	1.6	0.8	0.5	1.4
	I	1,252	7	7	11	5	16	0.6	1.1	0.9	0.4	1.3
	II	3,909	28	22	29	13	42	0.7	1.3	0.7	0.3	1.1
	IIIN	1,447	13	8	9	6	15	0.9	1.4	0.6	0.4	1.0
	IIIM	3,698	31	21	31	27	58	0.8	1.4	0.8	0.7	1.6
	IV	1,579	25	14	17	10	27	1.6	2.5	1.1	0.6	1.7
	V	499	8	6	8	6	14	1.6	2.8	1.6	1.2	2.8
	Other	599	12	1	2	3	5	2.0	2.2	0.3	0.5	0.8
	Outside marriage joint registration											
	All†	4,579	62	42	59	53	112	1.4	2.3	1.3	1.2	2.4
	I	159	1	2	2	1	3	0.6	1.9	1.3	0.6	1.9
	II	754	5	7	10	6	16	0.7	1.6	1.3	0.8	2.1
	IIIN	348	-	2	2	2	4	-	0.6	0.6	0.6	1.1
	IIIM	1,827	30	13	19	17	36	1.6	2.3	1.0	0.9	2.0
	IV	841	10	6	9	9	18	1.2	1.9	1.1	1.1	2.1
	V	416	8	9	11	4	15	1.9	4.1	2.6	1.0	3.6
	Other	234	8	1	4	11	15	3.4	3.8	1.7	4.7	6.4
4000 & over	All***	6,484	89	124	145	46	191	1.4	3.3	2.2	0.7	2.9
	Inside marriage											
	All†	4,924	69	84	96	33	129	1.4	3.1	1.9	0.7	2.6
	I	524	5	7	8	2	10	1.0	2.3	1.5	0.4	1.9
	II	1,481	19	27	31	7	38	1.3	3.1	2.1	0.5	2.6
	IIIN	562	4	9	10	2	12	0.7	2.3	1.8	0.4	2.1
	IIIM	1,397	19	21	26	15	41	1.4	2.9	1.9	1.1	2.9
	IV	562	16	9	10	3	13	2.8	4.4	1.8	0.5	2.3
	V	175	1	4	4	3	7	0.6	2.9	2.3	1.7	4.0
	Other	223	5	7	7	-	7	2.2	5.4	3.1	-	3.1
	Outside marriage joint registration											
	All†	1,560	20	40	49	13	62	1.3	3.8	3.1	0.8	4.0
	I	55	1	-	-	-	-	1.8	1.8	-	-	-
	II	269	2	6	8	4	12	0.7	3.0	3.0	1.5	4.5
	IIIN	136	2	5	5	1	6	1.5	5.1	3.7	0.7	4.4
	IIIM	611	9	18	23	4	27	1.5	4.4	3.8	0.7	4.4
	IV	281	4	6	6	2	8	1.4	3.6	2.1	0.7	2.8
	V	132	-	2	3	-	3	-	1.5	2.3	-	2.3
	Other	76	2	3	3	2	5	2.6	6.6	3.9	2.6	6.6
Not stated	All***	198	64	56	61	17	78	31.3	58.7	30.8	8.6	39.4
	Inside marriage											
	All†	133	43	40	43	11	54	31.3	60.5	32.3	8.3	40.6
	I	17	6	3	3	1	4	34.1	51.1	17.6	5.9	23.5
	II	37	12	15	15	6	21	31.4	70.7	40.5	16.2	56.8
	IIIN	10	3	5	6	1	7	29.1	77.7	60.0	10.0	70.0
	IIIM	43	8	11	12	2	14	18.3	43.4	27.9	4.7	32.6
	IV	14	7	2	3	-	3	47.6	61.2	21.4	-	21.4
	V	4	3	3	3	1	4	69.8	139.5	75.0	25.0	100.0
	Other	8	4	1	1	-	1	47.6	59.5	12.5	-	12.5
	Outside marriage joint registration											
	All†	65	21	16	18	6	24	31.3	55.1	27.7	9.2	36.9
	I	3	-	-	-	-	-	-	-	-	-	-
	II	12	2	4	4	-	4	16.4	49.2	33.3	-	33.3
	IIIN	3	1	2	2	-	2	32.3	96.8	66.7	-	66.7
	IIIM	17	10	6	7	4	11	55.6	88.9	41.2	23.5	64.7
	IV	15	5	-	-	-	-	32.3	32.3	-	-	-
	V	8	1	2	3	-	3	12.3	37.0	37.5	-	37.5
	Other	7	2	2	2	-	2	27.8	55.6	28.6	-	28.6

* Stillbirths and perinatal mortality rates are estimates per 1,000 live and stillbirths
Neonatal, postneonatal and infant mortality rates are estimates per 1,000 livebirths
** Figures for live births are a 10 percent sample coded for father's occupation
*** Inside marriage and outside marriage/joint registration including cases where father's occupation was not stated
† Includes cases where father's occupation was not stated

Table 18 1995 Series DH3 no.28

Table 18 Live births, stillbirths and infant deaths
   Mother's age by country of birth
   Numbers and rates*, 1995

England and Wales

Mother's age	Country of birth	Numbers						Rates*				
		Births		Deaths								
		Live births	Still-births	Early neonatal	Neonatal	Postneo-natal	Infant	Still-birth	Peri-natal	Neo-natal	Postneo-natal	Infant
All	**All**	**648,001**	**3,597**	**2,084**	**2,669**	**1,244**	**3,913**	**5.5**	**8.7**	**4.1**	**1.9**	**6.0**
	United Kingdom	566,331	2,970	1,769	2,282	1,038	3,320	5.2	8.3	4.0	1.8	5.9
	Irish Republic	5,166	35	14	21	9	30	6.7	9.4	4.1	1.7	5.8
	Rest of European Union	8,026	53	11	16	21	37	6.6	7.9	2.0	2.6	4.6
	Australia, Canada, New Zealand	3,052	21	7	12	8	20	6.8	9.1	3.9	2.6	6.6
	New Commonwealth***	47,337	413	217	258	140	398	8.6	13.2	5.5	3.0	8.4
	Bangladesh	6,783	62	18	22	16	38	9.1	11.7	3.2	2.4	5.6
	India	6,679	45	29	31	19	50	6.7	11.0	4.6	2.8	7.5
	Pakistan	12,332	133	73	85	54	139	10.7	16.5	6.9	4.4	11.3
	East Africa	5,122	38	12	16	12	28	7.4	9.7	3.1	2.3	5.5
	Caribbean	2,910	28	27	30	8	38	9.5	18.7	10.3	2.7	13.1
	Other**	18,089	105	66	80	28	108	5.8	9.4	4.4	1.5	6.0
< 20	**All**	**41,926**	**292**	**183**	**232**	**179**	**411**	**6.9**	**11.3**	**5.5**	**4.3**	**9.8**
	United Kingdom	38,995	275	172	219	167	386	7.0	11.4	5.6	4.3	9.9
	Irish Republic	197	1	2	3	2	5	5.1	15.2	15.2	10.2	25.4
	Rest of European Union	406	6	1	1	-	1	14.6	17.0	2.5	-	2.5
	Australia, Canada, New Zealand	58	1	-	-	1	1	16.9	16.9	-	17.2	17.2
	New Commonwealth***	1,695	8	1	2	9	11	4.7	5.3	1.2	5.3	6.5
	Bangladesh	642	5	-	-	4	4	7.7	7.7	-	6.2	6.2
	India	99	-	-	-	-	-	-	-	-	-	-
	Pakistan	586	2	1	2	4	6	3.4	5.1	3.4	6.8	10.2
	East Africa	54	-	-	-	-	-	-	-	-	-	-
	Caribbean	93	-	-	-	-	-	-	-	-	-	-
	Other**	575	1	7	7	-	7	1.7	13.9	12.2	-	12.2
20-24	**All**	**130,729**	**728**	**486**	**613**	**333**	**946**	**5.5**	**9.2**	**4.7**	**2.5**	**7.2**
	United Kingdom	114,495	593	415	526	287	813	5.2	8.8	4.6	2.5	7.1
	Irish Republic	691	5	5	7	1	8	7.2	14.4	10.1	1.4	11.6
	Rest of European Union	1,345	10	3	3	6	9	7.4	9.6	2.2	4.5	6.7
	Australia, Canada, New Zealand	414	2	4	6	1	7	4.8	14.4	14.5	2.4	16.9
	New Commonwealth***	10,817	96	51	60	33	93	8.8	13.5	5.5	3.1	8.6
	Bangladesh	3,115	24	9	11	4	15	7.6	10.5	3.5	1.3	4.8
	India	1,470	10	4	4	5	9	6.8	9.5	2.7	3.4	6.1
	Pakistan	3,971	43	27	30	17	47	10.7	17.4	7.6	4.3	11.8
	East Africa	537	5	3	3	2	5	9.2	14.8	5.6	3.7	9.3
	Caribbean	254	2	4	4	-	4	7.8	23.4	15.7	-	15.7
	Other**	2,967	22	8	11	5	16	7.4	10.0	3.7	1.7	5.4
25-29	**All**	**217,356**	**1,076**	**647**	**833**	**340**	**1,173**	**4.9**	**7.9**	**3.8**	**1.6**	**5.4**
	United Kingdom	192,339	893	566	734	287	1,021	4.6	7.6	3.8	1.5	5.3
	Irish Republic	1,458	12	2	2	-	2	8.2	9.5	1.4	-	1.4
	Rest of European Union	2,610	11	5	6	8	14	4.2	6.1	2.3	3.1	5.4
	Australia, Canada, New Zealand	919	7	1	2	1	3	7.6	8.6	2.2	1.1	3.3
	New Commonwealth***	14,232	125	57	70	35	105	8.7	12.7	4.9	2.5	7.4
	Bangladesh	1,667	22	5	6	5	11	13.0	16.0	3.6	3.0	6.6
	India	2,333	18	7	8	4	12	7.7	10.6	3.4	1.7	5.1
	Pakistan	3,977	36	21	24	13	37	9.0	14.2	6.0	3.3	9.3
	East Africa	1,577	11	3	6	2	8	6.9	8.8	3.8	1.3	5.1
	Caribbean	483	7	4	4	1	5	14.3	22.4	8.3	2.1	10.4
	Other**	5,798	28	16	19	9	28	4.8	7.6	3.3	1.6	4.8

*   Stillbirths and perinatal mortality rates per 1,000 live and stillbirths
      Neonatal, postneonatal and infant mortality rates per 1,000 livebirths
**   Including cases where no country of birth was stated
*** A full list of countries included in the New Commonwealth is provided in the introduction

Table 18 - *continued*

Mother's age	Country of birth	Numbers						Rates*				
		Births		Deaths								
		Live births	Still-births	Early neonatal	Neonatal	Postneo-natal	Infant	Still-birth	Peri-natal	Neo-natal	Postneo-natal	Infant
30-34	**All**	**181,140**	**932**	**496**	**641**	**241**	**882**	**5.1**	**7.8**	**3.5**	**1.3**	**4.9**
	United Kingdom	157,656	776	415	537	187	724	4.9	7.5	3.4	1.2	4.6
	Irish Republic	1,742	7	3	4	3	7	*4.0*	*5.7*	*2.3*	*1.7*	*4.0*
	Rest of European Union	2,549	19	2	2	4	6	*7.4*	*8.2*	*0.8*	*1.6*	*2.4*
	Australia, Canada, New Zealand	1,009	7	1	3	4	7	*6.9*	*7.9*	*3.0*	*4.0*	*6.9*
	New Commonwealth***	12,613	90	56	71	39	110	7.1	11.5	5.6	3.1	8.7
	Bangladesh	758	5	3	4	1	5	*6.6*	*10.5*	*5.3*	*1.3*	*6.6*
	India	1,893	6	10	11	8	19	*3.2*	*8.4*	*5.8*	*4.2*	*10.0*
	Pakistan	2,247	27	13	17	12	29	*11.9*	*17.6*	*7.6*	*5.3*	*12.9*
	East Africa	1,958	13	3	4	6	10	*6.6*	*8.1*	*2.0*	*3.1*	*5.1*
	Caribbean	847	4	7	10	2	12	*4.7*	*12.9*	*11.8*	*2.4*	*14.2*
	Other**	5,571	33	19	24	4	28	*5.9*	*9.3*	*4.3*	*0.7*	*5.0*
35-39	**All**	**65,520**	**443**	**225**	**290**	**129**	**419**	**6.7**	**10.1**	**4.4**	**2.0**	**6.4**
	United Kingdom	54,067	346	169	225	96	321	6.4	9.5	4.2	1.8	5.9
	Irish Republic	871	6	1	2	3	5	*6.8*	*8.0*	*2.3*	*3.4*	*5.7*
	Rest of European Union	924	5	-	4	1	5	*5.4*	*5.4*	*4.3*	*1.1*	*5.4*
	Australia, Canada, New Zealand	555	3	1	1	1	2	*5.4*	*7.2*	*1.8*	*1.8*	*3.6*
	New Commonwealth***	6,543	69	45	46	20	66	10.4	17.2	7.0	3.1	10.1
	Bangladesh	389	4	1	1	1	2	*10.2*	*12.7*	*2.6*	*2.6*	*5.1*
	India	741	10	6	6	2	8	*13.3*	*21.3*	*8.1*	*2.7*	*10.8*
	Pakistan	1,268	20	9	9	7	16	*15.5*	*22.5*	*7.1*	*5.5*	*12.6*
	East Africa	864	8	3	3	1	4	*9.2*	*12.6*	*3.5*	*1.2*	*4.6*
	Caribbean	998	10	11	11	5	16	*9.9*	*20.8*	*11.0*	*5.0*	*16.0*
	Other**	2,560	14	9	12	8	20	*5.4*	*8.9*	*4.7*	*3.1*	*7.8*
40 and over	**All**	**11,330**	**126**	**47**	**60**	**22**	**82**	**11.0**	**15.1**	**5.3**	**1.9**	**7.2**
	United Kingdom	8,779	87	32	41	14	55	9.8	13.4	4.7	1.6	6.3
	Irish Republic	207	4	1	3	-	3	*19.0*	*23.7*	*14.5*	-	*14.5*
	Rest of European Union	192	2	-	-	2	2	*10.3*	*10.3*	-	*10.4*	*10.4*
	Australia, Canada, New Zealand	97	1	-	-	-	-	*10.2*	*10.2*	-	-	-
	New Commonwealth***	1,437	25	7	9	4	13	17.1	21.9	6.3	2.8	9.0
	Bangladesh	212	2	-	-	1	1	*9.3*	*9.3*	-	*4.7*	*4.7*
	India	143	1	2	2	-	2	*6.9*	*20.8*	*14.0*	-	*14.0*
	Pakistan	283	5	2	3	1	4	*17.4*	*24.3*	*10.6*	*3.5*	*14.1*
	East Africa	132	1	-	-	1	1	*7.5*	*7.5*	-	*7.6*	*7.6*
	Caribbean	235	5	1	1	-	1	*20.8*	*25.0*	*4.3*	-	*4.3*
	Other**	618	7	7	7	2	9	*11.2*	*22.4*	*11.3*	*3.2*	*14.6*

*   Stillbirths and perinatal mortality rates per 1,000 live and stillbirths
      Neonatal, postneonatal and infant mortality rates per 1,000 livebirths
**   Including cases where no country of birth was stated
*** A full list of countries included in the New Commonwealth is provided in the introduction

Table 19 1995 Series DH3 no.28

Table 19   Live births, stillbirths and infant deaths   England and Wales
Mother's age by parity (inside marriage), marital status and type of registration
Numbers and rates, 1995

Mother's age	Marital status Parity/type of registration	Numbers						Rates*				
		Births		Deaths				Still-birth	Peri-natal	Neo-natal	Postneo-natal	Infant
		Live births	Still-births	Early neonatal	Neonatal	Postneo-natal	Infant					
All	**All**	**648,001**	**3,597**	**2,084**	**2,669**	**1,244**	**3,913**	**5.5**	**8.7**	**4.1**	**1.9**	**6.0**
	Inside marriage											
	All	**428,099**	**2,224**	**1,262**	**1,596**	**655**	**2,251**	**5.2**	**8.1**	**3.7**	**1.5**	**5.3**
	0	166,798	584	573	701	224	925	3.5	6.9	4.2	1.3	5.5
	1	157,692	806	367	466	218	684	5.1	7.4	3.0	1.4	4.3
	2	67,233	423	184	248	121	369	6.3	9.0	3.7	1.8	5.5
	3 & over	36,376	411	138	181	92	273	11.2	14.9	5.0	2.5	7.5
	Outside marriage											
	All	**219,902**	**1,373**	**822**	**1,073**	**589**	**1,662**	**6.2**	**9.9**	**4.9**	**2.7**	**7.6**
	Joint regn/same address	127,800	729	462	607	280	887	5.7	9.3	4.7	2.2	6.9
	Joint regn/difft address	44,175	297	214	270	127	397	6.7	11.5	6.1	2.9	9.0
	Sole registration	47,927	347	146	196	182	378	7.2	10.2	4.1	3.8	7.9
< 20	**All**	**41,926**	**292**	**183**	**232**	**179**	**411**	**6.9**	**11.3**	**5.5**	**4.3**	**9.8**
	Inside marriage											
	All	**5,622**	**36**	**21**	**27**	**21**	**48**	**6.4**	**10.1**	**4.8**	**3.7**	**8.5**
	0	4,295	14	19	23	14	37	*3.2*	7.7	5.4	*3.3*	8.6
	1	1,196	16	1	3	6	9	*13.2*	*14.0*	*2.5*	*5.0*	*7.5*
	2	120	5	1	1	1	2	*40.0*	*48.0*	*8.3*	*8.3*	*16.7*
	3 & over	11	1	-	-	-	-	*83.3*	*83.3*	-	-	-
	Outside marriage											
	All	**36,304**	**256**	**162**	**205**	**158**	**363**	**7.0**	**11.4**	**5.6**	**4.4**	**10.0**
	Joint regn/same address	14,427	105	70	86	63	149	7.2	12.0	6.0	4.4	10.3
	Joint regn/difft address	9,995	68	50	67	37	104	6.8	11.7	6.7	3.7	10.4
	Sole registration	11,882	83	42	52	58	110	6.9	10.4	4.4	4.9	9.3
20-24	**All**	**130,729**	**728**	**486**	**613**	**333**	**946**	**5.5**	**9.2**	**4.7**	**2.5**	**7.2**
	Inside marriage											
	All	**61,034**	**349**	**219**	**268**	**144**	**412**	**5.7**	**9.3**	**4.4**	**2.4**	**6.8**
	0	32,113	143	121	151	63	214	4.4	8.2	4.7	2.0	6.7
	1	20,666	127	66	76	46	122	6.1	9.3	3.7	2.2	5.9
	2	6,580	48	25	32	24	56	7.2	11.0	4.9	3.6	8.5
	3 & over	1,675	31	7	9	11	20	18.2	22.3	*5.4*	*6.6*	11.9
	Outside marriage											
	All	**69,695**	**379**	**267**	**345**	**189**	**534**	**5.4**	**9.2**	**5.0**	**2.7**	**7.7**
	Joint regn/same address	39,273	189	153	194	89	283	4.8	8.7	4.9	2.3	7.2
	Joint regn/difft address	14,791	99	81	99	37	136	6.6	12.1	6.7	2.5	9.2
	Sole registration	15,631	91	33	52	63	115	5.8	7.9	3.3	4.0	7.4
25-29	**All**	**217,356**	**1,076**	**647**	**833**	**340**	**1,173**	**4.9**	**7.9**	**3.8**	**1.6**	**5.4**
	Inside marriage											
	All	**157,811**	**731**	**455**	**577**	**218**	**795**	**4.6**	**7.5**	**3.7**	**1.4**	**5.0**
	0	70,556	204	220	265	74	339	2.9	6.0	3.8	1.0	4.8
	1	57,196	281	129	164	78	242	4.9	7.1	2.9	1.4	4.2
	2	20,731	133	56	87	48	135	6.4	9.1	4.2	2.3	6.5
	3 & over	9,328	113	50	61	18	79	12.0	17.3	6.5	*1.9*	8.5
	Outside marriage											
	All	**59,545**	**345**	**192**	**256**	**122**	**378**	**5.8**	**9.0**	**4.3**	**2.0**	**6.3**
	Joint regn/same address	38,361	215	121	162	60	222	5.6	8.7	4.2	1.6	5.8
	Joint regn/difft address	10,310	57	43	57	28	85	5.5	9.6	5.5	2.7	8.2
	Sole registration	10,874	73	28	37	34	71	6.7	9.2	3.4	3.1	6.5

* Stillbirths and perinatal mortality rates per 1,000 live and stillbirths
  Neonatal, postneonatal and infant mortality rates per 1,000 live births
  Inside marriage total is not a sum of the categories because one or more of the birth records did not specify the
  number of previous births

Table 19 - *continued*

Mother's age	Marital status Parity/type of registration	Numbers						Rates*				
		Births		Deaths								
		Live births	Still-births	Early neonatal	Neonatal	Postneo-natal	Infant	Still-birth	Peri-natal	Neo-natal	Postneo-natal	Infant
30-34	**All**	**181,140**	**932**	**496**	**641**	**241**	**882**	**5.1**	**7.8**	**3.5**	**1.3**	**4.9**
	Inside marriage											
	All	**144,153**	**706**	**369**	**473**	**165**	**638**	**4.9**	**7.4**	**3.3**	**1.1**	**4.4**
	0	46,157	167	147	178	41	219	3.6	6.8	3.9	0.9	4.7
	1	58,269	252	121	161	62	223	4.3	6.4	2.8	1.1	3.8
	2	26,240	146	61	76	27	103	5.5	7.8	2.9	1.0	3.9
	3 & over	13,487	141	40	58	35	93	10.3	13.3	4.3	2.6	6.9
	Outside marriage											
	All	**36,987**	**226**	**127**	**168**	**76**	**244**	**6.1**	**9.5**	**4.5**	**2.1**	**6.6**
	Joint regn/same address	24,384	123	73	105	43	148	5.0	8.0	4.3	1.8	6.1
	Joint regn/difft address	6,125	35	23	28	19	47	5.7	9.4	4.6	*3.1*	7.7
	Sole registration	6,478	68	31	35	14	49	10.4	15.1	5.4	*2.2*	7.6
35-39	**All**	**65,520**	**443**	**225**	**290**	**129**	**419**	**6.7**	**10.1**	**4.4**	**2.0**	**6.4**
	Inside marriage											
	All	**51,119**	**314**	**166**	**212**	**92**	**304**	**6.1**	**9.3**	**4.1**	**1.8**	**5.9**
	0	11,928	46	59	74	30	104	3.8	8.8	6.2	2.5	8.7
	1	17,988	105	39	50	19	69	5.8	8.0	2.8	*1.1*	3.8
	2	11,771	68	37	48	17	65	5.7	8.9	4.1	*1.4*	5.5
	3 & over	9,432	95	31	40	26	66	10.0	13.2	4.2	2.8	7.0
	Outside marriage											
	All	**14,401**	**129**	**59**	**78**	**37**	**115**	**8.9**	**12.9**	**5.4**	**2.6**	**8.0**
	Joint regn/same address	9,427	74	38	49	24	73	7.8	11.8	5.2	2.5	7.7
	Joint regn/difft address	2,448	31	13	14	5	19	12.5	17.7	*5.7*	*2.0*	*7.8*
	Sole registration	2,526	24	8	15	8	23	9.4	12.5	5.9	*3.2*	9.1
40 & over	**All**	**11,330**	**126**	**47**	**60**	**22**	**82**	**11.0**	**15.1**	**5.3**	**1.9**	**7.2**
	Inside marriage											
	All	**8,360**	**88**	**32**	**39**	**15**	**54**	**10.4**	**14.2**	**4.7**	*1.8*	**6.5**
	0	1,749	10	7	10	2	12	*5.7*	*9.7*	*5.7*	*1.1*	*6.9*
	1	2,377	25	11	12	7	19	10.4	15.0	*5.0*	*2.9*	*8.0*
	2	1,791	23	4	4	4	8	12.7	14.9	*2.2*	*2.2*	*4.5*
	3 & over	2,443	30	10	13	2	15	12.1	16.2	*5.3*	*0.8*	*6.1*
	Outside marriage											
	All	**2,970**	**38**	**15**	**21**	**7**	**28**	**12.6**	**17.6**	**7.1**	*2.4*	**9.4**
	Joint regn/same address	1,928	23	7	11	1	12	11.8	15.4	*5.7*	*0.5*	*6.2*
	Joint regn/difft address	506	7	4	5	1	6	*13.6*	*21.4*	*9.9*	*2.0*	*11.9*
	Sole registration	536	8	4	5	5	10	*14.7*	*22.1*	*9.3*	*9.3*	*18.7*

* Stillbirths and perinatal mortality rates per 1,000 live and stillbirths
  Neonatal, postneonatal and infant mortality rates per 1,000 live births
  Inside marriage total is not a sum of the categories because one or more of the birth records did not specify the number of previous births

Table 20 1995 Series DH3 no.28

Table 20   Live births, stillbirths and infant deaths**
Mother's age by father's social class (based on occupation at death registration)
Inside marriage and outside marriage/joint registration
Numbers and rates*, 1995

England and Wales

Mother's age	Marital status Social class	Numbers						Rates*				
		Births		Deaths								
		Live births**	Still-births	Early neonatal	Neonatal	Postneo-natal	Infant	Still-birth	Peri-natal	Neo-natal	Postneo-natal	Infant
All	All***	59,962	3,250	1,938	2,473	1,062	3,535	5.4	8.6	4.1	1.8	5.9
	Inside marriage											
	All†	42,921	2,224	1,262	1,596	655	2,251	5.2	8.1	3.7	1.5	5.2
	I	4,051	171	97	124	47	171	4.2	6.6	3.1	1.2	4.2
	II	12,150	517	332	406	141	547	4.2	7.0	3.3	1.2	4.5
	IIIN	4,828	240	139	171	69	240	4.9	7.8	3.5	1.4	5.0
	IIIM	12,504	606	349	465	193	658	4.8	7.6	3.7	1.5	5.3
	IV	5,467	369	210	250	105	355	6.7	10.5	4.6	1.9	6.5
	V	1,799	154	65	91	47	138	8.5	12.1	5.1	2.6	7.7
	Other	2,122	167	63	79	43	122	7.8	10.8	3.7	2.0	5.7
	Outside Marriage Joint registration											
	All†	17,041	1,026	676	877	407	1,284	6.0	9.9	5.1	2.4	7.5
	I	493	27	16	21	14	35	5.4	8.7	4.3	2.8	7.1
	II	2,615	109	87	120	39	159	4.2	7.5	4.6	1.5	6.1
	IIIN	1,285	71	44	54	26	80	5.5	8.9	4.2	2.0	6.2
	IIIM	6,727	413	239	315	140	455	6.1	9.6	4.7	2.1	6.8
	IV	3,277	203	142	179	72	251	6.2	10.5	5.5	2.2	7.7
	V	1,626	118	84	106	46	152	7.2	12.3	6.5	2.8	9.3
	Other	1,018	85	57	71	56	127	8.3	13.8	7.0	5.5	12.5
< 20	All***	3,074	209	141	180	121	301	6.8	11.3	5.9	3.9	9.8
	Inside marriage											
	All†	570	36	21	27	21	48	6.3	9.9	4.7	3.7	8.4
	I	12	-	-	-	-	-	-	-	-	-	-
	II	86	5	1	1	2	3	5.8	6.9	1.2	2.3	3.5
	IIIN	51	2	1	1	1	2	3.9	5.9	2.0	2.0	3.9
	IIIM	183	9	9	11	8	19	4.9	9.8	6.0	4.4	10.4
	IV	101	9	3	4	5	9	8.8	11.8	4.0	5.0	8.9
	V	36	5	2	3	4	7	13.7	19.2	8.3	11.1	19.4
	Other	101	6	5	7	1	8	5.9	10.8	6.9	1.0	7.9
	Outside Marriage Joint registration											
	All†	2,504	173	120	153	100	253	6.9	11.6	6.1	4.0	10.1
	I	17	2	1	2	-	2	11.6	17.4	11.8	-	11.8
	II	156	7	8	10	5	15	4.5	9.6	6.4	3.2	9.6
	IIIN	170	8	11	13	10	23	4.7	11.1	7.6	5.9	13.5
	IIIM	909	69	36	48	35	83	7.5	11.5	5.3	3.9	9.1
	IV	593	37	27	32	15	47	6.2	10.7	5.4	2.5	7.9
	V	343	23	13	18	15	33	6.7	10.4	5.2	4.4	9.6
	Other	316	27	18	24	12	36	8.5	14.1	7.6	3.8	11.4
20-24	All***	11,486	637	453	561	270	831	5.5	9.4	4.9	2.4	7.2
	Inside marriage											
	All†	6,133	349	219	268	144	412	5.7	9.2	4.4	2.3	6.7
	I	198	4	4	5	4	9	2.0	4.0	2.5	2.0	4.5
	II	1,029	47	37	44	15	59	4.5	8.1	4.3	1.5	5.7
	IIIN	609	38	22	23	19	42	6.2	9.8	3.8	3.1	6.9
	IIIM	2,127	101	62	79	44	123	4.7	7.6	3.7	2.1	5.8
	IV	1,211	87	55	62	31	93	7.1	11.6	5.1	2.6	7.7
	V	423	29	17	25	12	37	6.8	10.8	5.9	2.8	8.7
	Other	536	43	21	27	17	44	8.0	11.8	5.0	3.2	8.2
	Outside Marriage Joint registration											
	All†	5,353	288	234	293	126	419	5.4	9.7	5.5	2.4	7.8
	I	89	5	1	1	2	3	5.6	6.7	1.1	2.2	3.4
	II	567	27	24	28	6	34	4.7	9.0	4.9	1.1	6.0
	IIIN	405	18	14	16	6	22	4.4	7.9	4.0	1.5	5.4
	IIIM	2,271	115	79	106	44	150	5.0	8.5	4.7	1.9	6.6
	IV	1,142	68	63	76	26	102	5.9	11.4	6.7	2.3	8.9
	V	576	35	31	39	18	57	6.0	11.4	6.8	3.1	9.9
	Other	303	20	21	24	21	45	6.6	13.4	7.9	6.9	14.9

*   Stillbirths and perinatal mortality rates are estimates per 1,000 live and stillbirths
    Neonatal, postneonatal and infant mortality rates are estimates per 1,000 live births
**   Figures for live births are a 10 percent sample coded for father's occupation
***   Inside Marriage and outside marriage/Joint registration including cases where father's occupation was not stated
†   Includes cases where father's occupation was not stated

Table 20 - *continued*

Mother's age	Marital status Social class	Numbers						Rates*				
		Births		Deaths				Still-birth	Peri-natal	Neo-natal	Postneo-natal	Infant
		Live births**	Still-births	Early neonatal	Neonatal	Postneo-natal	Infant					
25-29	All***	20,589	1,003	619	796	306	1,102	4.8	7.8	3.9	1.5	5.4
	Inside marriage											
	All†	15,796	731	455	577	218	795	4.6	7.5	3.7	1.4	5.0
	I	1,196	60	34	42	11	53	5.0	7.8	3.5	0.9	4.4
	II	4,036	149	94	117	52	169	3.7	6.0	2.9	1.3	4.2
	IIIN	1,840	73	56	73	26	99	4.0	7.0	4.0	1.4	5.4
	IIIM	5,070	213	140	180	70	250	4.2	6.9	3.6	1.4	4.9
	IV	2,137	118	85	105	27	132	5.5	9.4	4.9	1.3	6.2
	V	725	61	25	35	18	53	8.3	11.8	4.8	2.5	7.3
	Other	792	57	20	23	10	33	7.1	9.7	2.9	1.3	4.2
	Outside Marriage Joint registration											
	All†	4,793	272	164	219	88	307	5.6	9.0	4.6	1.8	6.4
	I	143	6	7	8	3	11	4.2	9.1	5.6	2.1	7.7
	II	803	35	29	39	8	47	4.3	7.9	4.9	1.0	5.9
	IIIN	340	31	9	14	3	17	9.0	11.7	4.1	0.9	5.0
	IIIM	1,943	109	57	76	35	111	5.6	8.5	3.9	1.8	5.7
	IV	916	48	31	41	16	57	5.2	8.6	4.5	1.7	6.2
	V	414	26	23	29	8	37	6.2	11.8	7.0	1.9	8.9
	Other	234	17	8	11	15	26	7.2	10.6	4.7	6.4	11.1
30-34	All***	17,555	864	465	606	227	833	4.9	7.5	3.5	1.3	4.7
	Inside marriage											
	All†	14,536	706	369	473	165	638	4.8	7.4	3.3	1.1	4.4
	I	1,773	77	35	45	19	64	4.3	6.3	2.5	1.1	3.6
	II	4,836	191	128	152	40	192	3.9	6.6	3.1	0.8	4.0
	IIIN	1,717	77	39	50	15	65	4.5	6.7	2.9	0.9	3.8
	IIIM	3,802	186	96	137	45	182	4.9	7.4	3.6	1.2	4.8
	IV	1,481	95	45	54	28	82	6.4	9.4	3.6	1.9	5.5
	V	434	41	11	15	6	21	9.4	11.9	3.5	1.4	4.8
	Other	493	39	13	18	9	27	7.8	10.5	3.7	1.8	5.5
	Outside Marriage Joint registration											
	All†	3,019	158	96	133	62	195	5.2	8.4	4.4	2.1	6.5
	I	139	5	1	3	5	8	3.6	4.3	2.2	3.6	5.8
	II	704	21	16	26	14	40	3.0	5.2	3.7	2.0	5.7
	IIIN	237	9	6	7	6	13	3.8	6.3	3.0	2.5	5.5
	IIIM	1,145	64	40	52	15	67	5.6	9.0	4.5	1.3	5.9
	IV	468	28	15	23	13	36	5.9	9.1	4.9	2.8	7.7
	V	213	17	11	13	3	16	7.9	13.0	6.1	1.4	7.5
	Other	113	14	7	8	4	12	12.2	18.4	7.1	3.5	10.6
35-39	All***	6,194	419	217	275	121	396	6.7	10.2	4.4	2.0	6.4
	Inside marriage											
	All†	5,046	314	166	212	92	304	6.2	9.5	4.2	1.8	6.0
	I	748	22	19	27	12	39	2.9	5.5	3.6	1.6	5.2
	II	1,840	104	60	77	25	102	5.6	8.9	4.2	1.4	5.5
	IIIN	514	42	18	21	7	28	8.1	11.6	4.1	1.4	5.4
	IIIM	1,153	71	36	50	25	75	6.1	9.2	4.3	2.2	6.5
	IV	466	49	19	22	12	34	10.4	14.4	4.7	2.6	7.3
	V	147	12	8	9	6	15	8.1	13.5	6.1	4.1	10.2
	Other	178	14	3	3	4	7	7.8	9.5	1.7	2.2	3.9
	Outside Marriage Joint registration											
	All†	1,148	105	51	63	29	92	9.1	13.5	5.5	2.5	8.0
	I	82	7	3	4	3	7	8.5	12.1	4.9	3.7	8.5
	II	323	16	8	13	6	19	4.9	7.4	4.0	1.9	5.9
	IIIN	113	5	4	4	1	5	4.4	7.9	3.5	0.9	4.4
	IIIM	385	40	23	27	11	38	10.3	16.2	7.0	2.9	9.9
	IV	137	21	4	5	2	7	15.1	18.0	3.6	1.5	5.1
	V	65	14	6	6	2	8	21.1	30.1	9.2	3.1	12.3
	Other	43	2	3	4	3	7	4.6	11.6	9.3	7.0	16.3

*   Stillbirths and perinatal mortality rates are estimates per 1,000 live and stillbirths
      Neonatal, postneonatal and infant mortality rates are estimates per 1,000 live births
**   Figures for live births are a 10 percent sample coded for father's occupation
*** Inside Marriage and outside marriage/Joint registration including cases where father's occupation was not stated
†   Includes cases where father's occupation was not stated

Table 20 1995 Series DH3 no.28

Table 20 - *continued*

Mother's age	Marital status Social class	Numbers						Rates*				
		Births		Deaths								
		Live births**	Still-births	Early neonatal	Neonatal	Postneo-natal	Infant	Still-birth	Peri-natal	Neo-natal	Postneo-natal	Infant
40 & over	All***	1,064	118	43	55	17	72	11.0	15.0	5.2	*1.6*	6.8
	Inside marriage											
	All†	840	88	32	39	15	54	*10.4*	*14.1*	*4.6*	*1.8*	*6.4*
	I	124	8	5	5	1	6	*6.4*	*10.4*	*4.0*	*0.8*	*4.8*
	II	323	21	12	15	7	22	*6.5*	*10.2*	*4.6*	*2.2*	*6.8*
	IIIN	97	8	3	3	1	4	*8.2*	*11.2*	*3.1*	*1.0*	*4.1*
	IIIM	169	26	6	8	1	9	*15.2*	*18.6*	*4.7*	*0.6*	*5.3*
	IV	71	11	3	3	2	5	*15.3*	*19.4*	*4.2*	*2.8*	*7.0*
	V	34	6	2	4	1	5	*17.3*	*23.1*	*11.8*	*2.9*	*14.7*
	Other	22	8	1	1	2	3	*35.1*	*39.5*	*4.5*	*9.1*	*13.6*
	Outside Marriage Joint registration											
	All†	224	30	11	16	2	18	13.2	18.1	7.1	0.9	8.0
	I	23	2	3	3	1	4	*8.6*	*21.6*	*13.0*	*4.3*	*17.4*
	II	62	3	2	4	-	4	*4.8*	*8.0*	*6.5*	-	*6.5*
	IIIN	20	-	-	-	-	-	-	-	-	-	-
	IIIM	74	16	4	6	-	6	*21.2*	*26.5*	*8.1*	-	*8.1*
	IV	21	1	2	2	-	2	*4.7*	*14.2*	*9.5*	-	*9.5*
	V	15	3	-	1	-	1	*19.6*	*19.6*	*6.7*	-	*6.7*
	Other	9	5	-	-	1	1	*52.6*	*52.6*	-	*11.1*	*11.1*

* Stillbirths and perinatal mortality rates are estimates per 1,000 live and stillbirths
Neonatal, postneonatal and infant mortality rates are estimates per 1,000 live births
** Figures for live births are a 10 percent sample coded for father's occupation
*** Inside Marriage and outside marriage/Joint registration including cases where father's occupation was not stated
† Includes cases where father's occupation was not stated

Table 21 Live births**, stillbirths and infant deaths   **England and Wales**
Mother's country of birth by father's social class (based on occupation at death registration)
Inside marriage and outside marriage/joint registration
Numbers and rates*, 1995

Mother's country of birth	Marital status Social class	Numbers						Rates*				
		Births		Deaths								
		Live births**	Still-births	Early neonatal	Neonatal	Postneo-natal	Infant	Still-birth	Peri-natal	Neo-natal	Postneo-natal	Infant
All	**All****	**59,962**	**3,250**	**1,938**	**2,473**	**1,062**	**3,535**	**5.4**	**8.6**	**4.1**	**1.8**	**5.9**
	Inside marriage All****	42,921	2,224	1,262	1,596	655	2,251	5.2	8.1	3.7	1.5	5.2
	I	4,051	171	97	124	47	171	4.2	6.6	3.1	1.2	4.2
	II	12,150	517	332	406	141	547	4.2	7.0	3.3	1.2	4.5
	IIIN	4,828	240	139	171	69	240	4.9	7.8	3.5	1.4	5.0
	IIIM	12,504	606	349	465	193	658	4.8	7.6	3.7	1.5	5.3
	IV	5,467	369	210	250	105	355	6.7	10.5	4.6	1.9	6.5
	V	1,799	154	65	91	47	138	8.5	12.1	5.1	2.6	7.7
	Other	2,122	167	63	79	43	122	7.8	10.8	3.7	2.0	5.7
	Outside marriage joint registration All****	17,041	1,026	676	877	407	1,284	6.0	9.9	5.1	2.4	7.5
	I	493	27	16	21	14	35	5.4	8.7	4.3	2.8	7.1
	II	2,615	109	87	120	39	159	4.2	7.5	4.6	1.5	6.1
	IIIN	1,285	71	44	54	26	80	5.5	8.9	4.2	2.0	6.2
	IIIM	6,727	413	239	315	140	455	6.1	9.6	4.7	2.1	6.8
	IV	3,277	203	142	179	72	251	6.2	10.5	5.5	2.2	7.7
	V	1,626	118	84	106	46	152	7.2	12.3	6.5	2.8	9.3
	Other	1,018	85	57	71	56	127	8.3	13.8	7.0	5.5	12.5
United Kingdom	**All****	**52,147**	**2,667**	**1,644**	**2,113**	**870**	**2,983**	**5.1**	**8.2**	**4.1**	**1.7**	**5.7**
	Inside marriage All****	36,041	1,709	1,008	1,283	494	1,777	4.7	7.5	3.6	1.4	4.9
	I	3,217	133	72	93	28	121	4.1	6.3	2.9	0.9	3.8
	II	10,332	402	274	339	113	452	3.9	6.5	3.3	1.1	4.4
	IIIN	4,048	181	116	143	48	191	4.5	7.3	3.5	1.2	4.7
	IIIM	10,936	494	302	400	157	557	4.5	7.2	3.7	1.4	5.1
	IV	4,615	285	161	193	86	279	6.1	9.6	4.2	1.9	6.0
	V	1,561	125	44	65	35	100	7.9	10.7	4.2	2.2	6.4
	Other	1,332	89	34	42	20	62	6.6	9.2	3.2	1.5	4.7
	Outside marriage joint registration All****	16,106	958	636	830	376	1,206	5.9	9.8	5.2	2.3	7.5
	I	446	22	15	20	12	32	4.9	8.3	4.5	2.7	7.2
	II	2,409	102	80	113	35	148	4.2	7.5	4.7	1.5	6.1
	IIIN	1,188	70	41	51	22	73	5.9	9.3	4.3	1.9	6.1
	IIIM	6,446	392	227	301	131	432	6.0	9.5	4.7	2.0	6.7
	IV	3,157	189	136	171	69	240	6.0	10.2	5.4	2.2	7.6
	V	1,565	113	77	98	45	143	7.2	12.1	6.3	2.9	9.1
	Other	895	70	53	65	50	115	7.8	13.6	7.3	5.6	12.8
Irish Republic	**All****	**501**	**32**	**10**	**14**	**7**	**21**	**6.3**	**8.3**	**2.8**	**1.4**	**4.2**
	Inside marriage All****	380	23	5	8	3	11	6.0	7.3	2.1	0.8	2.9
	I	64	1	-	-	-	-	1.6	1.6	-	-	-
	II	106	7	-	-	3	3	6.6	6.6	-	2.8	2.8
	IIIN	46	2	1	1	-	1	4.3	6.5	2.2	-	2.2
	IIIM	102	5	-	1	-	1	4.9	4.9	1.0	-	1.0
	IV	30	1	2	2	-	2	3.3	10.0	6.7	-	6.7
	V	17	5	-	2	-	2	28.6	28.6	11.8	-	11.8
	Other	15	2	2	2	-	2	13.2	26.3	13.3	-	13.3
	Outside marriage joint registration All****	121	9	5	6	4	10	7.4	11.5	5.0	3.3	8.3
	I	4	-	1	1	-	1	-	25.0	25.0	-	25.0
	II	21	2	-	-	1	1	9.4	9.4	-	4.8	4.8
	IIIN	8	-	-	-	-	-	-	-	-	-	-
	IIIM	54	6	1	1	2	3	11.0	12.8	1.9	3.7	5.6
	IV	14	1	-	1	1	2	7.1	7.1	7.1	7.1	14.3
	V	11	-	3	3	-	3	-	27.3	27.3	-	27.3
	Other	9	-	-	-	-	-	-	-	-	-	-

*   Stillbirths and perinatal mortality rates are estimates per 1,000 live and stillbirths
      Neonatal, postneonatal and infant mortality rates are estimates per 1,000 live births
**   Figures for live births are a 10 percent sample coded for father's occupation
***   Inside marriage and outside marriage/joint registration including cases where father's occupation was not stated
**** Includes cases where father's occupation was not stated

Table 21 1995 Series DH3 no.28

Table 21 - *continued*

Mother's country of birth	Marital status Social class	Numbers						Rates*				
		Births		Deaths				Still-birth	Peri-natal	Neo-natal	Postneo-natal	Infant
		Live births**	Still-births	Early neonatal	Neonatal	Postneo-natal	Infant					
Rest of European Union	All***	718	48	11	16	21	37	6.6	8.2	2.2	2.9	5.2
	Inside marriage All****	520	38	6	11	14	25	7.3	8.4	2.1	2.7	4.8
	I	83	-	-	2	-	2	-	-	2.4	-	2.4
	II	189	13	4	6	1	7	6.8	8.9	3.2	0.5	3.7
	IIIN	42	4	-	1	5	6	9.4	9.4	2.4	11.9	14.3
	IIIM	106	10	2	2	3	5	9.3	11.2	1.9	2.8	4.7
	IV	48	6	-	-	2	2	12.3	12.3	-	4.2	4.2
	V	16	-	-	-	1	1	-	-	-	6.3	6.3
	Other	36	5	-	-	2	2	13.7	13.7	-	5.6	5.6
	Outside marriage joint registration All****	198	10	5	5	7	12	5.0	7.5	2.5	3.5	6.1
	I	10	1	-	-	1	1	9.9	9.9	-	10.0	10.0
	II	39	2	1	1	1	2	5.1	7.7	2.6	2.6	5.1
	IIIN	17	-	-	-	1	1	-	-	-	5.9	5.9
	IIIM	70	3	1	1	1	2	4.3	5.7	1.4	1.4	2.9
	IV	30	2	2	2	-	2	6.6	13.2	6.7	-	6.7
	V	17	1	1	1	-	1	5.8	11.7	5.9	-	5.9
	Other	15	1	-	-	2	2	6.6	6.6	-	13.3	13.3
Australia Canada, New Zealand	All***	304	19	7	12	7	19	6.2	8.5	3.9	2.3	6.3
	Inside marriage All****	238	17	5	9	5	14	7.1	9.2	3.8	2.1	5.9
	I	47	2	-	1	1	2	4.2	4.2	2.1	2.1	4.3
	II	98	7	3	5	1	6	7.1	10.1	5.1	1.0	6.1
	IIIN	25	2	-	-	-	-	7.9	7.9	-	-	-
	IIIM	37	2	2	2	-	2	5.4	10.8	5.4	-	5.4
	IV	11	3	-	1	1	2	26.5	26.5	9.1	9.1	18.2
	V	4	-	-	-	1	1	-	-	-	25.0	25.0
	Other	16	1	-	-	1	1	6.2	6.2	-	6.3	6.3
	Outside marriage joint registration All****	66	2	2	3	2	5	3.0	6.0	4.5	3.0	7.6
	I	6	-	-	-	-	-	-	-	-	-	-
	II	17	-	-	-	-	-	-	-	-	-	-
	IIIN	9	1	-	-	-	-	11.0	11.0	-	-	-
	IIIM	16	1	-	-	1	1	6.2	6.2	-	6.3	6.3
	IV	13	-	2	3	-	3	-	15.4	23.1	-	23.1
	V	4	-	-	-	-	-	-	-	-	-	-
	Other	1	-	-	-	1	1	-	-	-	100.0	100.0
New Commonwealth††	All***	4,524	385	202	240	131	371	8.4	12.9	5.3	2.9	8.2
	Inside marriage All****	4,153	351	181	216	116	332	8.4	12.7	5.2	2.8	8.0
	I	408	29	14	16	13	29	7.1	10.5	3.9	3.2	7.1
	II	966	63	36	39	18	57	6.5	10.2	4.0	1.9	5.9
	IIIN	536	44	20	22	14	36	8.1	11.8	4.1	2.6	6.7
	IIIM	1,063	88	38	52	32	84	8.2	11.8	4.9	3.0	7.9
	IV	649	67	39	45	14	59	10.2	16.2	6.9	2.2	9.1
	V	173	22	20	23	8	31	12.6	24.0	13.3	4.6	17.9
	Other	358	38	13	18	15	33	10.5	14.1	5.0	4.2	9.2
	Outside marriage joint registration All****	371	34	21	24	15	39	9.1	14.7	6.5	4.0	10.5
	I	19	3	-	-	-	-	15.5	15.5	-	-	-
	II	79	3	5	5	2	7	3.8	10.1	6.3	2.5	8.9
	IIIN	51	-	3	3	3	6	-	5.9	5.9	5.9	11.8
	IIIM	102	9	8	10	5	15	8.7	16.5	9.8	4.9	14.7
	IV	45	7	2	2	2	4	15.3	19.7	4.4	4.4	8.9
	V	20	1	1	1	1	2	19.6	24.5	5.0	5.0	10.0
	Other	55	8	2	3	1	4	14.3	17.9	5.5	1.8	7.3

* Stillbirths and perinatal mortality rates are estimates per 1,000 live and stillbirths
Neonatal, postneonatal and infant mortality rates are estimates per 1,000 livebirths
** Figures for live births are a 10 percent sample coded for father's occupation
*** Inside marriage and outside marriage/joint registration including cases where father's occupation was not stated
**** Includes cases where father's occupation was not stated
†† A full list of countries included in the New Commonwealth is provided in the introduction

Table 21 - *continued*

Mother's country of birth	Marital status Social class	Numbers						Rates*				
		Births		Deaths								
		Live births**	Still-births	Early neonatal	Neonatal	Postneo-natal	Infant	Still-birth	Peri-natal	Neo-natal	Postneo-natal	Infant
Bangladesh	All***	655	62	18	22	16	38	9.4	12.1	3.4	*2.4*	5.8
	Inside marriage All****	652	62	18	22	16	38	9.4	12.2	3.4	*2.5*	*5.8*
	I	11	-	-	-	1	1	-	-	-	*9.1*	*9.1*
	II	85	9	4	4	1	5	*10.5*	*15.1*	*4.7*	*1.2*	*5.9*
	IIIN	74	6	-	-	1	1	*8.0*	*8.0*	-	*1.4*	*1.4*
	IIIM	241	20	7	9	5	14	*8.2*	*11.1*	*3.7*	*2.1*	*5.8*
	IV	168	21	3	5	4	9	*12.3*	*14.1*	*3.0*	*2.4*	*5.4*
	V	25	1	1	1	2	3	*4.0*	*8.0*	*4.0*	*8.0*	*12.0*
	Other	48	5	3	3	2	5	*10.3*	*16.5*	*6.3*	*4.2*	*10.4*
	Outside marriage joint registration All****	3	-	-	-	-	-	-	-	-	-	-
	I	-	-	-	-	-	-	-	-	-	-	-
	II	-	-	-	-	-	-	-	-	-	-	-
	IIIN	1	-	-	-	-	-	-	-	-	-	-
	IIIM	-	-	-	-	-	-	-	-	-	-	-
	IV	2	-	-	-	-	-	-	-	-	-	-
	V	-	-	-	-	-	-	-	-	-	-	-
	Other	-	-	-	-	-	-	-	-	-	-	-
India	All***	633	44	28	30	19	49	6.9	11.3	4.7	*3.0*	7.7
	Inside marriage All****	617	44	28	30	19	49	7.1	11.6	4.9	*3.1*	7.9
	I	72	1	3	4	4	8	*1.4*	*5.5*	*5.6*	*5.6*	*11.1*
	II	176	8	4	4	3	7	*4.5*	*6.8*	*2.3*	*1.7*	*4.0*
	IIIN	89	6	5	5	-	5	*6.7*	*12.3*	*5.6*	-	*5.6*
	IIIM	130	13	3	4	5	9	*9.9*	*12.2*	*3.1*	*3.8*	*6.9*
	IV	96	14	10	10	3	13	*14.4*	*24.6*	*10.4*	*3.1*	*13.5*
	V	23	-	3	3	2	5	-	*13.0*	*13.0*	*8.7*	*21.7*
	Other	31	2	-	-	1	1	*6.4*	*6.4*	-	*3.2*	*3.2*
	Outside marriage joint registration All****	16	-	-	-	-	-	-	-	-	-	-
	I	1	-	-	-	-	-	-	-	-	-	-
	II	4	-	-	-	-	-	-	-	-	-	-
	IIIN	2	-	-	-	-	-	-	-	-	-	-
	IIIM	5	-	-	-	-	-	-	-	-	-	-
	IV	2	-	-	-	-	-	-	-	-	-	-
	V	1	-	-	-	-	-	-	-	-	-	-
	Other	1	-	-	-	-	-	-	-	-	-	-
Pakistan	All***	1,237	133	73	85	53	138	10.6	16.5	6.9	4.3	11.2
	Inside marriage All****	1,222	130	73	85	53	138	10.5	16.4	7.0	4.3	11.3
	I	48	7	2	3	3	6	*14.4*	*18.5*	*6.3*	*6.3*	*12.5*
	II	179	19	15	15	10	25	*10.5*	*18.8*	*8.4*	*5.6*	*14.0*
	IIIN	152	14	7	7	6	13	*9.1*	*13.7*	*4.6*	*3.9*	*8.6*
	IIIM	378	37	18	23	17	40	*9.7*	*14.4*	*6.1*	*4.5*	*10.6*
	IV	239	22	14	16	7	23	*9.1*	*14.9*	*6.7*	*2.9*	*9.6*
	V	98	16	12	15	2	17	*16.1*	*28.1*	*15.3*	*2.0*	*17.3*
	Other	128	15	5	6	7	13	*11.6*	*15.4*	*4.7*	*5.5*	*10.2*
	Outside marriage joint registration All****	15	3	-	-	-	-	*19.6*	*19.6*	-	-	-
	I	-	-	-	-	-	-	-	-	-	-	-
	II	5	-	-	-	-	-	-	-	-	-	-
	IIIN	2	-	-	-	-	-	-	-	-	-	-
	IIIM	4	-	-	-	-	-	-	-	-	-	-
	IV	3	1	-	-	-	-	*32.3*	*32.3*	-	-	-
	V	-	2	-	-	-	-	*1000.0*	*1000.0*	-	-	-
	Other	1	-	-	-	-	-	-	-	-	-	-

* Stillbirths and perinatal mortality rates are estimates per 1,000 live and stillbirths
 Neonatal, postneonatal and infant mortality rates are estimates per 1,000 livebirths
** Figures for live births are a 10 percent sample coded for father's occupation
*** Inside marriage and outside marriage/joint registration including cases where father's occupation was not stated
**** Includes cases where father's occupation was not stated

Table 21 1995 Series DH3 no.28

Table 21 - *continued*

Mother's country of birth	Marital status Social class	Numbers						Rates*				
		Births		Deaths				Still-birth	Peri-natal	Neo-natal	Postneo-natal	Infant
		Live births**	Still-births	Early neonatal	Neonatal	Postneo-natal	Infant					
East Africa	All***	489	36	11	14	10	24	7.3	9.5	2.9	2.0	4.9
	Inside marriage All****	453	36	8	11	10	21	7.9	9.6	2.4	2.2	4.6
	I	75	4	1	1	2	3	5.3	6.6	1.3	2.7	4.0
	II	162	11	1	2	3	5	6.7	7.4	1.2	1.9	3.1
	IIIN	57	6	-	1	3	4	10.4	10.4	1.8	5.3	7.0
	IIIM	80	6	2	3	1	4	7.4	9.9	3.8	1.3	5.0
	IV	47	4	2	2	-	2	8.4	12.7	4.3	-	4.3
	V	8	-	1	1	-	1	-	12.5	12.5	-	12.5
	Other	24	5	-	-	1	1	20.4	20.4	-	4.2	4.2
	Outside marriage joint registration All****	36	-	3	3	-	3	-	8.3	8.3	-	8.3
	I	2	-	-	-	-	-	-	-	-	-	-
	II	4	-	1	1	-	1	-	25.0	25.0	-	25.0
	IIIN	8	-	-	-	-	-	-	-	-	-	-
	IIIM	7	-	-	-	-	-	-	-	-	-	-
	IV	3	-	-	-	-	-	-	-	-	-	-
	V	3	-	-	-	-	-	-	-	-	-	-
	Other	9	-	2	2	-	2	-	22.2	22.2	-	22.2
Caribbean	All***	250	20	20	22	7	29	7.9	15.9	8.8	2.8	11.6
	Inside marriage All****	154	12	13	14	4	18	7.7	16.1	9.1	2.6	11.7
	I	20	2	2	2	-	2	9.9	19.8	10.0	-	10.0
	II	41	1	3	3	-	3	2.4	9.7	7.3	-	7.3
	IIIN	14	5	-	-	1	1	34.5	34.5	-	7.1	7.1
	IIIM	47	2	3	4	1	5	4.2	10.6	8.5	2.1	10.6
	IV	22	1	4	4	-	4	4.5	22.6	18.2	-	18.2
	V	1	-	1	1	1	2	-	100.0	100.0	100.0	200.0
	Other	9	1	-	-	1	1	11.0	11.0	-	11.1	11.1
	Outside marriage joint registration All****	96	8	7	8	3	11	8.3	15.5	8.3	3.1	11.5
	I	4	-	-	-	-	-	-	-	-	-	-
	II	21	-	1	1	1	2	-	4.8	4.8	4.8	9.5
	IIIN	11	-	1	1	-	1	-	9.1	9.1	-	9.1
	IIIM	39	4	5	6	2	8	10.2	22.8	15.4	5.1	20.5
	IV	8	2	-	-	-	-	24.4	24.4	-	-	-
	V	5	1	-	-	-	-	19.6	19.6	-	-	-
	Other	8	1	-	-	-	-	12.3	12.3	-	-	-
Other†	All***	1,768	99	64	78	26	104	5.6	9.2	4.4	1.5	5.9
	Inside marriage All****	1,589	86	57	69	23	92	5.4	9.0	4.3	1.4	5.8
	I	232	6	11	12	5	17	2.6	7.3	5.2	2.2	7.3
	II	459	25	15	17	5	22	5.4	8.7	3.7	1.1	4.8
	IIIN	131	7	2	4	2	6	5.3	6.8	3.1	1.5	4.6
	IIIM	260	7	5	8	1	9	2.7	4.6	3.1	0.4	3.5
	IV	114	7	8	9	2	11	6.1	13.1	7.9	1.8	9.6
	V	28	2	1	1	2	3	7.1	10.6	3.6	7.1	10.7
	Other	365	32	14	17	5	22	8.7	12.5	4.7	1.4	6.0
	Outside marriage joint registration All****	179	13	7	9	3	12	7.2	11.1	5.0	1.7	6.7
	I	8	1	-	-	1	1	12.3	12.3	-	12.5	12.5
	II	50	-	1	1	-	1	-	2.0	2.0	-	2.0
	IIIN	12	-	-	-	-	-	-	-	-	-	-
	IIIM	39	2	2	2	-	2	5.1	10.2	5.1	-	5.1
	IV	18	4	-	-	-	-	21.7	21.7	-	-	-
	V	9	-	2	3	-	3	-	22.2	33.3	-	33.3
	Other	43	6	2	3	2	5	13.8	18.3	7.0	4.7	11.6

* Stillbirths and perinatal mortality rates are estimates per 1,000 live and stillbirths
Neonatal, postneonatal and infant mortality rates are estimates per 1,000 livebirths
** Figures for live births are a 10 percent sample coded for father's occupation
*** Inside marriage and outside marriage/joint registration including cases where father's occupation was not stated
**** Includes cases where father's occupation was not stated
† Including cases where no country of birth was stated

Table 22 Live births, stillbirths and infant deaths
Place of delivery by birthweight
Numbers and rates*, 1995

England and Wales

Place of delivery	Birthweight (grams)	Numbers						Rates*				
		Births		Deaths				Still-birth	Peri-natal	Neo-natal	Postneo-natal	Infant
		Live births	Still-births	Early neonatal	Neonatal	Postneo-natal	Infant					
All	**All**	**648,001**	**3,597**	**2,084**	**2,669**	**1,244**	**3,913**	**5.5**	**8.7**	**4.1**	**1.9**	**6.0**
	<2500	47,324	2,426	1,425	1,789	488	2,277	48.8	77.4	37.8	10.3	48.1
	<1500	7,583	1,625	1,154	1,425	255	1,680	176.5	301.8	187.9	33.6	221.5
	<1000	2,879	1,119	941	1,124	168	1,292	279.9	515.3	390.4	58.4	448.8
	1000-1499	4,704	506	213	301	87	388	97.1	138.0	64.0	18.5	82.5
	1500-1999	9,679	399	134	167	91	258	39.6	52.9	17.3	9.4	26.7
	2000-2499	30,062	402	137	197	142	339	13.2	17.7	6.6	4.7	11.3
	2500-2999	109,436	429	150	217	238	455	3.9	5.3	2.0	2.2	4.2
	3000-3499	234,752	376	191	267	298	565	1.6	2.4	1.1	1.3	2.4
	3500-3999	185,122	198	128	179	147	326	1.1	1.8	1.0	0.8	1.8
	4000 & over	69,150	93	131	153	54	207	1.3	3.2	2.2	0.8	3.0
	not stated	2,217	75	59	64	19	83	32.7	58.5	28.9	8.6	37.4
In hospital	**All**	**634,922**	**3,541**	**2,035**	**2,608**	**1,224**	**3,832**	**5.5**	**8.7**	**4.1**	**1.9**	**6.0**
	<2500	46,931	2,383	1,393	1,751	484	2,235	48.3	76.6	37.3	10.3	47.6
	<1500	7,515	1,598	1,128	1,394	252	1,646	175.4	299.1	185.5	33.5	219.0
	<1000	2,842	1,100	919	1,098	165	1,263	279.0	512.2	386.3	58.1	444.4
	1000-1499	4,673	498	209	296	87	383	96.3	136.7	63.3	18.6	82.0
	1500-1999	9,618	389	134	166	91	257	38.9	52.3	17.3	9.5	26.7
	2000-2499	29,798	396	131	191	141	332	13.1	17.5	6.4	4.7	11.1
	2500-2999	107,953	424	149	215	233	448	3.9	5.3	2.0	2.2	4.1
	3000-3499	230,190	374	189	264	292	556	1.6	2.4	1.1	1.3	2.4
	3500-3999	180,644	198	121	169	145	314	1.1	1.8	0.9	0.8	1.7
	4000 & over	67,228	92	127	148	53	201	1.4	3.3	2.2	0.8	3.0
	not stated	1,976	70	56	61	17	78	34.2	61.6	30.9	*8.6*	39.5
At home	**All**	**12,472**	**41**	**42**	**50**	**19**	**69**	**3.3**	**6.6**	**4.0**	*1.5*	**5.5**
	<2500	326	30	27	30	4	34	*84.3*	*160.1*	*92.0*	*12.3*	*104.3*
	<1500	54	19	21	23	3	26	*260.3*	*547.9*	*425.9*	*55.6*	*481.5*
	<1000	31	14	18	20	3	23	*311.1*	*711.1*	*645.2*	*96.8*	*741.9*
	1000-1499	23	5	3	3	-	3	*178.6*	*285.7*	*130.4*	-	*130.4*
	1500-1999	43	6	-	1	-	1	*122.4*	*122.4*	*23.3*	-	*23.3*
	2000-2499	229	5	6	6	1	7	*21.4*	*47.0*	*26.2*	*4.4*	*30.6*
	2500-2999	1,371	5	1	2	4	6	*3.6*	*4.4*	*1.5*	*2.9*	*4.4*
	3000-3499	4,341	2	2	3	6	9	*0.5*	*0.9*	*0.7*	*1.4*	*2.1*
	3500-3999	4,328	-	6	9	2	11	-	*1.4*	*2.1*	*0.5*	*2.5*
	4000 & over	1,879	1	3	3	1	4	*0.5*	*2.1*	*1.6*	*0.5*	*2.1*
	not stated	227	3	3	3	2	5	*13.0*	*26.1*	*13.2*	*8.8*	*22.0*
Elsewhere	**All**	**607**	**15**	**7**	**11**	**1**	**12**	*24.1*	*35.4*	*18.1*	*1.6*	*19.8*
	<2500	67	13	5	8	-	8	*162.5*	*225.0*	*119.4*	-	*119.4*
	<1500	14	8	5	8	-	8	*363.6*	*590.9*	*571.4*	-	*571.4*
	<1000	6	5	4	6	-	6	*454.5*	*818.2*	*1000.0*	-	*1000.0*
	1000-1499	8	3	1	2	-	2	*272.7*	*363.6*	*250.0*	-	*250.0*
	1500-1999	18	4	-	-	-	-	*181.8*	*181.8*	-	-	-
	2000-2499	35	1	-	-	-	-	*27.8*	*27.8*	-	-	-
	2500-2999	112	-	-	-	1	1	-	-	-	*8.9*	*8.9*
	3000-3499	221	-	-	-	-	-	-	-	-	-	-
	3500-3999	150	-	1	1	-	1	-	*6.7*	*6.7*	-	*6.7*
	4000 & over	43	-	1	2	-	2	-	*23.3*	*46.5*	-	*46.5*
	not stated	14	2	-	-	-	-	*125.0*	*125.0*	-	-	-

* Stillbirths and perinatal deaths per 1,000 live and stillbirths
   Neonatal, postneonatal and infant deaths per 1,000 live births

Table 23 1995 Series DH3 no.28

England and Wales

Table 23 Live births, stillbirths and infant deaths
Place of delivery by mother's age
Numbers and rates*, 1995

Place of delivery	Mother's age	Numbers						Rates*				
		Births		Deaths								
		Live births	Still-births	Early neonatal	Neonatal	Postneo-natal	Infant	Still-birth	Peri-natal	Neo-natal	Postneo-natal	Infant
All	All	**648,001**	**3,597**	**2,084**	**2,669**	**1,244**	**3,913**	**5.5**	**8.7**	**4.1**	**1.9**	**6.0**
	<20	41,926	292	183	232	179	411	6.9	11.3	5.5	4.3	9.8
	20-24	130,729	728	486	613	333	946	5.5	9.2	4.7	2.5	7.2
	25-29	217,356	1,076	647	833	340	1,173	4.9	7.9	3.8	1.6	5.4
	30-34	181,140	932	496	641	241	882	5.1	7.8	3.5	1.3	4.9
	35-39	65,520	443	225	290	129	419	6.7	10.1	4.4	2.0	6.4
	40 & over	11,330	126	47	60	22	82	11.0	15.1	5.3	1.9	7.2
In hospital	All	**634,922**	**3,541**	**2,035**	**2,608**	**1,224**	**3,832**	**5.5**	**8.7**	**4.1**	**1.9**	**6.0**
	<20	41,631	285	171	216	176	392	6.8	10.9	5.2	4.2	9.4
	20-24	129,112	711	479	606	330	936	5.5	9.2	4.7	2.6	7.2
	25-29	213,231	1,063	632	815	335	1,150	5.0	7.9	3.8	1.6	5.4
	30-34	176,318	924	487	629	233	862	5.2	8.0	3.6	1.3	4.9
	35-39	63,581	435	220	283	128	411	6.8	10.2	4.5	2.0	6.5
	40 & over	11,049	123	46	59	22	81	11.0	15.1	5.3	2.0	7.3
At home	All	**12,472**	**41**	**42**	**50**	**19**	**69**	**3.3**	**6.6**	**4.0**	*1.5*	**5.5**
	<20	245	3	11	14	3	17	*12.1*	*56.5*	*57.1*	*12.2*	*69.4*
	20-24	1,445	12	7	7	3	10	*8.2*	*13.0*	*4.8*	*2.1*	*6.9*
	25-29	3,939	8	14	16	5	21	*2.0*	*5.6*	*4.1*	*1.3*	*5.3*
	30-34	4,675	8	5	6	7	13	*1.7*	*2.8*	*1.3*	*1.5*	*2.8*
	35-39	1,893	7	4	6	1	7	*3.7*	*5.8*	*3.2*	*0.5*	*3.7*
	40 & over	275	3	1	1	-	1	*10.8*	*14.4*	*3.6*	-	*3.6*
Elsewhere	All	**607**	**15**	**7**	**11**	**1**	**12**	*24.1*	*35.4*	*18.1*	*1.6*	*19.8*
	<20	50	4	1	2	-	2	*74.1*	*92.6*	*40.0*	-	*40.0*
	20-24	172	5	-	-	-	-	*28.2*	*28.2*	-	-	-
	25-29	186	5	1	2	-	2	*26.2*	*31.4*	*10.8*	-	*10.8*
	30-34	147	-	4	6	1	7	-	*27.2*	*40.8*	*6.8*	*47.6*
	35-39	46	1	1	1	-	1	*21.3*	*42.6*	*21.7*	-	*21.7*
	40 & over	6	-	-	-	-	-	-	-	-	-	-

* Stillbirths and perinatal deaths per 1,000 live and stillbirths
  Neonatal, postneonatal and infant deaths per 1,000 live births

Table 24 Live births, stillbirths and infant deaths
Place of delivery by parity (inside marriage), marital status and type of registration
Numbers and rates*, 1995   **England and Wales**

Place of delivery	Marital Status Social class	Numbers						Rates*				
		Births		Deaths								
		Live births	Still-births	Early neonatal	Neonatal	Postneo-natal	Infant	Still-birth	Peri-natal	Neo-natal	Postneo-natal	Infant
All	All	648,001	3,597	2,084	2,669	1,244	3,913	5.5	8.7	4.1	1.9	6.0
	Inside marriage											
	All	428,099	2,224	1,262	1,596	655	2,251	5.2	8.1	3.7	1.5	5.3
	0	166,798	584	573	701	224	925	3.5	6.9	4.2	1.3	5.5
	1	157,692	806	367	466	218	684	5.1	7.4	3.0	1.4	4.3
	2	67,233	423	184	248	121	369	6.3	9.0	3.7	1.8	5.5
	3 and over	36,376	411	138	181	92	273	11.2	14.9	5.0	2.5	7.5
	Outside marriage											
	All	219,902	1,373	822	1,073	589	1,662	6.2	9.9	4.9	2.7	7.6
	Joint regn/ same address	127,800	729	462	607	280	887	5.7	9.3	4.7	2.2	6.9
	Joint regn/ different address	44,175	297	214	270	127	397	6.7	11.5	6.1	2.9	9.0
	Sole registration	47,927	347	146	196	182	378	7.2	10.2	4.1	3.8	7.9
In hospital	All	634,922	3,541	2,035	2,608	1,224	3,832	5.5	8.7	4.1	1.9	6.0
	Inside marriage											
	All	419,115	2,203	1,238	1,569	648	2,217	5.2	8.2	3.7	1.5	5.3
	0	165,784	581	561	689	222	911	3.5	6.9	4.2	1.3	5.5
	1	153,806	802	360	459	215	674	5.2	7.5	3.0	1.4	4.4
	2	64,598	417	182	244	120	364	6.4	9.2	3.8	1.9	5.6
	3 and over	34,927	403	135	177	91	268	11.4	15.2	5.1	2.6	7.7
	Outside marriage											
	All	215,807	1,338	797	1,039	576	1,615	6.2	9.8	4.8	2.7	7.5
	Joint regn/ same address	125,196	714	454	594	271	865	5.7	9.3	4.7	2.2	6.9
	Joint regn/ different address	43,588	292	210	266	125	391	6.7	11.4	6.1	2.9	9.0
	Sole registration	47,023	332	133	179	180	359	7.0	9.8	3.8	3.8	7.6
At home	All	12,472	41	42	50	19	69	3.3	6.6	4.0	*1.5*	5.5
	Inside marriage											
	All	8,703	17	22	24	7	31	*1.9*	4.5	2.8	0.8	3.6
	0	984	3	10	10	2	12	*3.0*	*13.2*	*10.2*	*2.0*	*12.2*
	1	3,740	3	7	7	3	10	*0.8*	*2.7*	*1.9*	*0.8*	*2.7*
	2	2,573	3	2	4	1	5	*1.2*	*1.9*	*1.6*	*0.4*	*1.9*
	3 and over	1,406	8	3	3	1	4	*5.7*	*7.8*	*2.1*	*0.7*	*2.8*
	Outside marriage											
	All	3,769	24	20	26	12	38	6.3	11.6	6.9	*3.2*	10.1
	Joint regn/ same address	2,463	11	7	11	9	20	*4.4*	*7.3*	*4.5*	*3.7*	8.1
	Joint regn/ different address	517	3	4	4	1	5	*5.8*	*13.5*	*7.7*	*1.9*	*9.7*
	Sole registration	789	10	9	11	2	13	*12.5*	*23.8*	*13.9*	*2.5*	*16.5*
Elsewhere	All	607	15	7	11	1	12	*24.1*	*35.4*	*18.1*	*1.6*	*19.8*
	Inside marriage											
	All	281	4	2	3	-	3	*14.0*	*21.1*	*10.7*	-	*10.7*
	0	30	-	2	2	-	2	-	*66.7*	*66.7*	-	*66.7*
	1	146	1	-	-	-	-	*6.8*	*6.8*	-	-	-
	2	62	3	-	-	-	-	*46.2*	*46.2*	-	-	-
	3 and over	43	-	-	1	-	1	-	-	*23.3*	-	*23.3*
	Outside marriage											
	All	326	11	5	8	1	9	*32.6*	*47.5*	*24.5*	*3.1*	*27.6*
	Joint regn/ same address	141	4	1	2	-	2	*27.6*	*34.5*	*14.2*	-	*14.2*
	Joint regn/ different address	70	2	-	-	1	1	*27.8*	*27.8*	-	*14.3*	*14.3*
	Sole registration	115	5	4	6	-	6	*41.7*	*75.0*	*52.2*	-	*52.2*

* Stillbirths and perinatal deaths per 1,000 live and stillbirths
   Neonatal, postneonatal and infant deaths per 1,000 live births

Table 25 1995 Series DH3 no.28

Table 25 **Live births**, stillbirths and infant deaths**
Place of delivery by father's social class(based on occupation at death registration)
Inside marriage and outside marriage/joint registration
Numbers and rates*, 1995

England and Wales

Place of delivery	Marital status Social class	Numbers						Rates*				
		Births		Deaths								
		Live births**	Still-births	Early neonatal	Neonatal	Postneo-natal	Infant	Still-birth	Peri-natal	Neo-natal	Postneo-natal	Infant
All	**All*****	**59,962**	**3,250**	**1,938**	**2,473**	**1,062**	**3,535**	**5.4**	**8.6**	**4.1**	**1.8**	**5.9**
	Inside marriage											
	All†	**42,921**	**2,224**	**1,262**	**1,596**	**655**	**2,251**	**5.2**	**8.1**	**3.7**	**1.5**	**5.2**
	I	4,051	171	97	124	47	171	4.2	6.6	3.1	1.2	4.2
	II	12,150	517	332	406	141	547	4.2	7.0	3.3	1.2	4.5
	IIIN	4,828	240	139	171	69	240	4.9	7.8	3.5	1.4	5.0
	IIIM	12,504	606	349	465	193	658	4.8	7.6	3.7	1.5	5.3
	IV	5,467	369	210	250	105	355	6.7	10.5	4.6	1.9	6.5
	V	1,799	154	65	91	47	138	8.5	12.1	5.1	2.6	7.7
	Other	2,122	167	63	79	43	122	7.8	10.8	3.7	2.0	5.7
	Outside marriage joint registration											
	All†	**17,041**	**1,026**	**676**	**877**	**407**	**1,284**	**6.0**	**9.9**	**5.1**	**2.4**	**7.5**
	I	493	27	16	21	14	35	5.4	8.7	4.3	2.8	7.1
	II	2,615	109	87	120	39	159	4.2	7.5	4.6	1.5	6.1
	IIIN	1,285	71	44	54	26	80	5.5	8.9	4.2	2.0	6.2
	IIIM	6,727	413	239	315	140	455	6.1	9.6	4.7	2.1	6.8
	IV	3,277	203	142	179	72	251	6.2	10.5	5.5	2.2	7.7
	V	1,626	118	84	106	46	152	7.2	12.3	6.5	2.8	9.3
	Other	1,018	85	57	71	56	127	8.3	13.8	7.0	5.5	12.5
In hospital	**All*****	**58,734**	**3,209**	**1,902**	**2,429**	**1,044**	**3,473**	**5.4**	**8.7**	**4.1**	**1.8**	**5.9**
	Inside marriage											
	All†	**41,999**	**2,203**	**1,238**	**1,569**	**648**	**2,217**	**5.2**	**8.2**	**3.7**	**1.5**	**5.3**
	I	3,934	170	96	123	47	170	4.3	6.7	3.1	1.2	4.3
	II	11,848	514	328	401	141	542	4.3	7.1	3.4	1.2	4.6
	IIIN	4,741	238	139	170	68	238	5.0	7.9	3.6	1.4	5.0
	IIIM	12,249	601	339	454	190	644	4.9	7.6	3.7	1.6	5.3
	IV	5,375	366	204	244	105	349	6.8	10.5	4.5	2.0	6.5
	V	1,775	151	63	89	46	135	8.4	12.0	5.0	2.6	7.6
	Other	2,077	163	62	78	41	119	7.8	10.7	3.8	2.0	5.7
	Outside marriage joint registration											
	All†	**16,735**	**1,006**	**664**	**860**	**396**	**1,256**	**6.0**	**9.9**	**5.1**	**2.4**	**7.5**
	I	476	26	15	20	13	33	5.4	8.6	4.2	2.7	6.9
	II	2,535	109	84	116	38	154	4.3	7.6	4.6	1.5	6.1
	IIIN	1,266	71	44	53	25	78	5.6	9.0	4.2	2.0	6.2
	IIIM	6,631	406	237	311	135	446	6.1	9.6	4.7	2.0	6.7
	IV	3,237	198	140	177	70	247	6.1	10.4	5.5	2.2	7.6
	V	1,596	113	83	105	45	150	7.0	12.2	6.6	2.8	9.4
	Other	994	83	55	68	56	124	8.3	13.8	6.8	5.6	12.5
At home	**All*****	**1,187**	**31**	**33**	**39**	**17**	**56**	**2.6**	**5.4**	**3.3**	*1.4*	**4.7**
	Inside marriage											
	All†	**903**	**17**	**22**	**24**	**7**	**31**	*1.9*	*4.3*	*2.7*	*0.8*	*3.4*
	I	113	1	-	-	-	-	*0.9*	*0.9*	-	-	-
	II	301	3	4	5	-	5	*1.0*	*2.3*	*1.7*	-	*1.7*
	IIIN	87	2	-	1	1	2	*2.3*	*2.3*	*1.1*	*1.1*	*2.3*
	IIIM	247	4	10	10	3	13	*1.6*	*5.7*	*4.0*	*1.2*	*5.3*
	IV	87	2	6	6	-	6	*2.3*	*9.2*	*6.9*	-	*6.9*
	V	24	2	1	1	1	2	*8.3*	*12.4*	*4.2*	*4.2*	*8.3*
	Other	44	3	1	1	2	3	*6.8*	*9.0*	*2.3*	*4.5*	*6.8*
	Outside marriage joint registration											
	All†	**284**	**14**	**11**	**15**	**10**	**25**	*4.9*	*8.8*	*5.3*	*3.5*	*8.8*
	I	17	1	-	-	1	1	*5.8*	*5.8*	-	*5.9*	*5.9*
	II	77	-	3	4	1	5	-	*3.9*	*5.2*	*1.3*	*6.5*
	IIIN	18	-	-	1	1	2	-	-	*5.6*	*5.6*	*11.1*
	IIIM	84	6	2	3	5	8	*7.1*	*9.5*	*3.6*	*6.0*	*9.5*
	IV	39	2	2	2	2	4	*5.1*	*10.2*	*5.1*	*5.1*	*10.3*
	V	27	4	1	1	-	1	*14.6*	*18.2*	*3.7*	-	*3.7*
	Other	22	1	2	3	-	3	*4.5*	*13.6*	*13.6*	-	*13.6*

*   Stillbirths and perinatal mortality rates are estimates per 1,000 live and stillbirths
     Neonatal, postneonatal and infant mortality rates are estimates per 1,000 live births
**   Figures for live births are a 10 percent sample coded for father's occupation
*** Inside marriage and outside marriage/joint registration including cases where father's occupation was not stated
†   Includes cases where father's occupation was not stated

Table 25 - *continued*

Place of delivery	Marital status Social class	Numbers						Rates*				
		Births		Deaths								
		Live births**	Still-births	Early neonatal	Neonatal	Postneo-natal	Infant	Still-birth	Peri-natal	Neo-natal	Postneo-natal	Infant
Elsewhere	**All***	**41**	**10**	**3**	**5**	**1**	**6**	*23.8*	*31.0*	*12.2*	*2.4*	*14.6*
	Inside marriage											
	All†	19	4	2	3	-	3	*20.6*	*30.9*	*15.8*	-	*15.8*
	I	4	-	1	1	-	1	-	*25.0*	*25.0*	-	*25.0*
	II	1	-	-	-	-	-	-	-	-	-	-
	IIIN	-	-	-	-	-	-	-	-	-	-	-
	IIIM	8	1	-	1	-	1	*12.3*	*12.3*	*12.5*	-	*12.5*
	IV	5	1	-	-	-	-	*19.6*	*19.6*	-	-	-
	V	-	1	1	1	-	1	*1000.0*	-	-	-	-
	Other	1	1	-	-	-	-	*90.9*	*90.9*	-	-	-
	Outside marriage joint registration											
	All†	22	6	1	2	1	3	*26.5*	*31.0*	*9.1*	*4.5*	*13.6*
	I	-	-	1	1	-	1	-	-	-	-	-
	II	3	-	-	-	-	-	-	-	-	-	-
	IIIN	1	-	-	-	-	-	-	-	-	-	-
	IIIM	12	1	-	1	-	1	*8.3*	*8.3*	*8.3*	-	*8.3*
	IV	1	3	-	-	-	-	*230.8*	*230.8*	-	-	-
	V	3	1	-	-	1	1	*32.3*	*32.3*	-	*33.3*	*33.3*
	Other	2	1	-	-	-	-	*47.6*	*47.6*	-	-	-

*   Stillbirths and perinatal mortality rates are estimates per 1,000 live and stillbirths
        Neonatal, postneonatal and infant mortality rates are estimates per 1,000 live births
**   Figures for live births are a 10 percent sample coded for father's occupation
*** Inside marriage and outside marriage/joint registration including cases where father's occupation was not stated
†   Includes cases where father's occupation was not stated

Table 26 Live births, stillbirths and infant deaths
   Month of birth in 1994
   Numbers and rates*   **England and Wales**

Note: Babies in this table were born in 1994 but may have died in either 1994 or 1995

Year of birth	Month of birth	Numbers						Rates*				
		Births		Deaths								
		Live births	Stillbirths	Early neonatal	Neonatal	Postneo-natal	Infant	Stillbirth	Perinatal	Neonatal	Postneo-natal	Infant
1994	**All**	**664,256**	**3,816**	**2,144**	**2,730**	**1,259**	**3,989**	**5.7**	**8.9**	**4.1**	**1.9**	**6.0**
	January	55,318	322	191	245	89	334	5.8	9.2	4.4	1.6	6.0
	February	50,975	314	178	215	97	312	6.1	9.6	4.2	1.9	6.1
	March	57,836	350	189	235	96	331	6.0	9.3	4.1	1.7	5.7
	April	55,400	308	194	243	111	354	5.5	9.0	4.4	2.0	6.4
	May	58,056	314	174	218	102	320	5.4	8.4	3.8	1.8	5.5
	June	57,064	305	190	243	108	351	5.3	8.6	4.3	1.9	6.2
	July	57,263	336	163	208	109	317	5.8	8.7	3.6	1.9	5.5
	August	55,470	332	159	227	113	340	5.9	8.8	4.1	2.0	6.1
	September	56,052	284	173	217	110	327	5.0	8.1	3.9	2.0	5.8
	October	55,444	324	159	219	97	316	5.8	8.7	3.9	1.7	5.7
	November	52,230	337	188	231	103	334	6.4	10.0	4.4	2.0	6.4
	December	53,148	290	186	229	124	353	5.4	8.9	4.3	2.3	6.6

* Stillbirth and perinatal mortality rates per 1,000 live and stillbirths
   Neonatal, postneonatal and infant mortality rates per 1,000 live births

Table 27 Live births, stillbirths and infant deaths
   Babies born in 1994 : singleton and multiple births
   Numbers and rates*   **England and Wales**

Note: Babies in this table were born in 1994 but may have died in 1994 or in 1995

Plurality	Numbers						Rates*				
	Births		Deaths								
	Live births	Stillbirths	Early neonatal	Neonatal	Postneo-natal	Infant	Stillbirth	Perinatal	Neonatal	Postneo-natal	Infant
All births	**664,256**	**3,816**	**2,144**	**2,730**	**1,259**	**3,989**	**5.7**	**8.9**	**4.1**	**1.9**	**6.0**
Singletons	646,887	3,468	1,748	2,267	1,177	3,444	5.3	8.0	3.5	1.8	5.3
All multiple births	17,369	348	396	463	82	545	19.6	42.0	26.7	4.7	31.4
Twins	16,577	325	357	420	74	494	19.2	40.4	25.3	4.5	29.8
Triplets	763	20	31	34	8	42	25.5	65.1	44.6	10.5	55.0
Higher multiple births	29	3	8	9	-	9	93.8	343.8	310.3	-	310.3

*Stillbirths and perinatal mortality rates per 1,000 live and stillbirths
   Neonatal, postneonatal and infant mortality rates per 1,000 live births

Table 28 Live births, stillbirths and infant deaths
   Babies born in 1994 : plurality by birthweight
   Numbers and rates*

England and Wales

Note: Babies in this table were born in 1994 but may have died in 1994 or in 1995

Plurality delivery	Birthweight (grams)	Numbers						Rates*				
		Births		Deaths								
		Livebirths	Stillbirths	Early neonatal	Neonatal	Postneo-natal	Infant	Stillbirth	Perinatal	Neonatal	Postneo-natal	Infant
Singletons	All	**646,887**	**3,468**	**1,748**	**2,267**	**1,177**	**3,444**	**5.3**	**8.0**	**3.5**	**1.8**	**5.3**
	<2500	36,262	2,175	1,044	1,329	384	1,713	56.6	83.7	36.6	10.6	47.2
	<1500	5,659	1,440	836	1,040	193	1,233	202.8	320.6	183.8	34.1	217.9
	<1000	2,289	1,028	644	789	115	904	309.9	504.1	344.7	50.2	394.9
	1000-1499	3,370	412	192	251	78	329	108.9	159.7	74.5	23.1	97.6
	1500-1999	6,753	356	110	146	74	220	50.1	65.6	21.6	11.0	32.6
	2000-2499	23,850	379	98	143	117	260	15.6	19.7	6.0	4.9	10.9
	2500-2999	101,605	427	140	200	245	445	4.2	5.6	2.0	2.4	4.4
	3000-3499	232,156	395	150	239	304	543	1.7	2.3	1.0	1.3	2.3
	3500-3999	188,649	214	102	138	155	293	1.1	1.7	0.7	0.8	1.6
	4000 & over	71,896	125	63	83	58	141	1.7	2.6	1.2	0.8	2.0
	not stated	16,319	132	249	278	31	309	8.0	23.2	17.0	1.9	18.9
All multiple births	All	**17,369**	**348**	**396**	**463**	**82**	**545**	**19.6**	**42.0**	**26.7**	**4.7**	**31.4**
	<2500	8,919	305	321	377	61	438	33.1	67.9	42.3	6.8	49.1
	<1500	1,625	228	285	332	41	373	123.0	276.8	204.3	25.2	229.5
	<1000	566	167	235	264	33	297	227.8	548.4	466.4	58.3	524.7
	1000-1499	1,059	61	50	68	8	76	54.5	99.1	64.2	*7.6*	71.8
	1500-1999	2,392	40	19	22	11	33	16.4	24.3	9.2	*4.6*	13.8
	2000-2499	4,902	37	17	23	9	32	7.5	10.9	4.7	*1.8*	6.5
	2500-2999	5,504	17	10	14	10	24	3.1	4.9	*2.5*	*1.8*	4.4
	3000-3499	2,094	8	6	6	8	14	*3.8*	*6.7*	*2.9*	*3.8*	*6.7*
	3500-3999	271	-	4	4	-	4	-	*14.8*	*14.8*	-	*14.8*
	4000 & over	24	-	6	7	-	7	-	*250.0*	*291.7*	-	*291.7*
	not stated	557	18	49	55	3	58	*31.3*	116.5	98.7	*5.4*	104.1

* Stillbirths and perinatal mortality rates per 1,000 live and stillbirths
  Neonatal, postneonatal and infant mortality rates per 1,000 live births

Table 29 Live births, stillbirths and infant deaths
   Babies born in 1994 : plurality by mother's age
   Numbers and rates*

England and Wales

Note: Babies in this table were born in 1994 but may have died in 1994 or in 1995

Plurality	Mother's age	Numbers						Rates*				
		Births		Deaths								
		Live births	Stillbirths	Early neonatal	Neonatal	Postneo-natal	Infant	Stillbirth	Perinatal	Neonatal	Postneo-natal	Infant
Singletons	All	**646,887**	**3,468**	**1,748**	**2,267**	**1,177**	**3,444**	**5.3**	**8.0**	**3.5**	**1.8**	**5.3**
	<20	41,469	274	163	206	174	380	6.6	10.5	5.0	4.2	9.2
	20-24	137,601	783	414	541	364	905	5.7	8.6	3.9	2.6	6.6
	25-29	223,267	1,099	517	692	338	1,030	4.9	7.2	3.1	1.5	4.6
	30-34	173,642	823	430	541	202	743	4.7	7.2	3.1	1.2	4.3
	35-39	60,507	377	192	241	84	325	6.2	9.3	4.0	1.4	5.4
	40 & over	10,401	112	32	46	15	61	10.7	13.7	4.4	*1.4*	5.9
All multiple births	All	**17,369**	**348**	**396**	**463**	**82**	**545**	**19.6**	**42.0**	**26.7**	**4.7**	**31.4**
	<20	537	18	30	37	7	44	*32.4*	86.5	68.9	*13.0*	81.9
	20-24	2,486	60	63	75	16	91	23.6	48.3	30.2	*6.4*	36.6
	25-29	5,636	97	119	135	27	162	16.9	37.7	24.0	4.8	28.7
	30-34	5,863	105	137	157	21	178	17.6	40.5	26.8	3.6	30.4
	35-39	2,532	57	44	56	11	67	22.0	39.0	22.1	*4.3*	26.5
	40 & over	315	11	3	3	-	3	*33.7*	*42.9*	*9.5*	-	*9.5*

*Stillbirths and perinatal mortality rates per 1,000 live and stillbirths
  Neonatal, postneonatal and infant mortality rates per 1,000 live births

Table 30 1994 Series DH3 no.28

Table 30 Live births, stillbirths and infant deaths
  Babies born in 1994: plurality by mother's country of birth
  Numbers and rates *

Note: Babies in this table were born in 1994 but may have died in 1994 or in 1995

Plurality	Country of birth	Numbers						Rates*				
		Births		Deaths								
		Live births	Still-births	Early neonatal	Neonatal	Postneo-natal	Infant	Stillbirth	Perinatal	Neonatal	Postneo-natal	Infant
Singletons	**All**	**646,887**	**3,468**	**1,748**	**2,267**	**1,177**	**3,444**	**5.3**	**8.0**	**3.5**	**1.8**	**5.3**
	United Kingdom	566,892	2,892	1,469	1,907	977	2,884	5.1	7.7	3.4	1.7	5.1
	Irish Republic	5,177	37	15	17	11	28	7.1	10.0	3.3	2.1	5.4
	Rest of European Union	7,633	38	17	25	18	43	5.0	7.2	3.3	2.4	5.6
	Australia, Canada, New Zealand	3,142	12	7	7	5	12	3.8	6.0	2.2	1.6	3.8
	New Commonwealth***	47,141	389	189	245	142	387	8.2	12.2	5.2	3.0	8.2
	Bangladesh	6,160	48	14	22	15	37	7.7	10.0	3.6	2.4	6.0
	India	6,871	40	22	26	15	41	5.8	9.0	3.8	2.2	6.0
	Pakistan	12,506	124	67	83	54	137	9.8	15.1	6.6	4.3	11.0
	East Africa	5,443	44	13	19	10	29	8.0	10.4	3.5	1.8	5.3
	Caribbean	2,975	30	20	23	12	35	10.0	16.6	7.7	4.0	11.8
	Other**	16,902	100	51	66	24	90	5.9	8.9	3.9	1.4	5.3
All multiple births	**All**	**17,369**	**348**	**396**	**463**	**82**	**545**	**19.6**	**42.0**	**26.7**	**4.7**	**31.4**
	United Kingdom	15,263	309	361	427	71	498	19.8	43.0	28.0	4.7	32.6
	Irish Republic	146	7	1	1	1	2	45.8	52.3	6.8	6.8	13.7
	Rest of European Union	201	5	6	6	3	9	24.3	53.4	29.9	14.9	44.8
	Australia, Canada, New Zealand	99	2	-	-	-	-	19.8	19.8	-	-	-
	New Commonwealth***	1,160	19	20	20	4	24	16.1	33.1	17.2	3.4	20.7
	Bangladesh	95	1	5	5	1	6	10.4	62.5	52.6	10.5	63.2
	India	158	5	-	-	-	-	30.7	30.7	-	-	-
	Pakistan	274	2	2	2	1	3	7.2	14.5	7.3	3.6	10.9
	East Africa	202	2	4	4	-	4	9.8	29.4	19.8	-	19.8
	Caribbean	96	2	3	3	-	3	20.4	51.0	31.3	-	31.3
	Other**	500	6	8	9	3	12	11.9	27.7	18.0	6.0	24.0

*   Stillbirths and perinatal mortality rates per 1,000 live and stillbirths
      Neonatal, postneonatal and infant mortality rates per 1,000 live births
**   Including cases where no country of birth was stated
***   A full list of countries included in the New Commonwealth is provided in the introduction

Table 31 Live births, stillbirths and infant deaths
   Babies born in 1994: plurality by parity (inside marriage), marital status and type of registration
   Numbers and rates *

England and Wales

Note: Babies in this table were born in 1994 but may have died in 1994 or in 1995

Plurality	Marital status Parity/type of registration	Numbers						Rates*				
		Births		Deaths								
		Live births	Still-births	Early neonatal	Neonatal	Postneo-natal	Infant	Stillbirth	Perinatal	Neonatal	Postneo-natal	Infant
Singletons	**All**	**646,887**	**3,468**	**1,748**	**2,267**	**1,177**	**3,444**	**5.3**	**8.0**	**3.5**	**1.8**	**5.3**
	Inside marriage											
	All	436,277	2,136	1,095	1,414	613	2,027	4.9	7.4	3.2	1.4	4.6
	0	168,877	978	468	616	224	840	5.8	8.5	3.6	1.3	5.0
	1	161,788	550	347	445	195	640	3.4	5.5	2.8	1.2	4.0
	2	68,439	309	153	196	102	298	4.5	6.7	2.9	1.5	4.4
	3 & over	37,173	299	127	157	92	249	8.0	11.4	4.2	2.5	6.7
	Outside marriage											
	All	210,610	1,332	653	853	564	1,417	6.3	9.4	4.1	2.7	6.7
	Joint regn/same address	121,002	689	362	474	247	721	5.7	8.6	3.9	2.0	6.0
	Joint regn/difft address	41,625	263	146	198	127	325	6.3	9.8	4.8	3.1	7.8
	Sole registration	47,983	380	145	181	190	371	7.9	10.9	3.8	4.0	7.7
All multiple births	**All**	**17,369**	**348**	**396**	**463**	**82**	**545**	**19.6**	**42.0**	**26.7**	**4.7**	**31.4**
	Inside marriage											
	All	12,560	225	265	308	47	355	17.6	38.3	24.5	3.7	28.3
	0	5,598	114	147	173	28	201	20.0	45.7	30.9	5.0	35.9
	1	4,047	59	67	75	11	86	14.4	30.7	18.5	2.7	21.3
	2	1,863	33	36	42	4	46	17.4	36.4	22.5	2.1	24.7
	3 & over	1,052	19	15	18	4	22	17.7	31.7	17.1	3.8	20.9
	Outside marriage											
	All	4,809	123	131	155	35	190	24.9	51.5	32.2	7.3	39.5
	Joint regn/same address	2,856	65	70	79	22	101	22.3	46.2	27.7	7.7	35.4
	Joint regn/difft address	913	41	36	46	5	51	43.0	80.7	50.4	5.5	55.9
	Sole registration	1,040	17	25	30	8	38	16.1	39.7	28.8	7.7	36.5

*Stillbirths and perinatal mortality rates per 1,000 live and stillbirths
 Neonatal, postneonatal and infant mortality rates per 1,000 live births

Table 32 Live births**, stillbirths and infant deaths
    Babies born in 1994: plurality by father's social class (based on occupation at death registration)
    Numbers and rates *   **England and Wales**

Note: Babies in this table were born in 1994 but may have died in 1994 or in 1995

Plurality	Marital status Social class	Numbers						Rates*				
		Births		Deaths								
		Live births**	Still-births	Early neonatal	Neonatal	Postneo-natal	Infant	Stillbirth	Perinatal	Neonatal	Postneo-natal	Infant
Singletons	**All*****	**59,930**	**3,088**	**1,603**	**2,086**	**987**	**3,073**	**5.1**	**7.8**	**3.5**	**1.6**	**5.1**
	Inside marriage											
	All†	43,824	2,136	1,095	1,414	613	2,027	4.9	7.3	3.2	1.4	4.6
	I	4,052	155	80	105	43	148	3.8	5.8	2.6	1.1	3.7
	II	12,117	515	265	328	119	447	4.2	6.4	2.7	1.0	3.7
	IIIN	4,949	243	117	149	60	209	4.9	7.2	3.0	1.2	4.2
	IIIM	13,159	643	320	427	174	601	4.9	7.3	3.2	1.3	4.6
	IV	5,584	318	178	225	109	334	5.7	8.8	4.0	2.0	6.0
	V	1,808	134	50	66	47	113	7.4	10.1	3.7	2.6	6.3
	Other	2,155	128	77	105	54	159	5.9	9.5	4.9	2.5	7.4
	Outside marriage joint registration											
	All†	16,106	952	508	672	374	1,046	5.9	9.0	4.2	2.3	6.5
	I	452	26	8	12	7	19	5.7	7.5	2.7	1.5	4.2
	II	2,424	115	71	94	28	122	4.7	7.6	3.9	1.2	5.0
	IIIN	1,208	75	45	60	19	79	6.2	9.9	5.0	1.6	6.5
	IIIM	6,410	362	182	246	140	386	5.6	8.4	3.8	2.2	6.0
	IV	2,995	176	95	116	60	176	5.8	9.0	3.9	2.0	5.9
	V	1,704	109	56	75	48	123	6.4	9.6	4.4	2.8	7.2
	Other	913	89	45	60	58	118	9.7	14.5	6.6	6.4	12.9
All multiple births	**All*****	**1,622**	**331**	**371**	**433**	**74**	**507**	**20.0**	**42.4**	**26.7**	**4.6**	**31.3**
	Inside marriage											
	All†	1,242	225	265	308	47	355	17.8	38.8	24.8	3.8	28.6
	I	123	23	23	28	7	35	18.4	36.7	22.8	5.7	28.5
	II	368	70	76	84	16	100	18.7	38.9	22.8	4.3	27.2
	IIIN	119	25	30	37	4	41	20.6	45.3	31.1	3.4	34.5
	IIIM	383	67	84	99	14	113	17.2	38.7	25.8	3.7	29.5
	IV	142	25	32	37	-	37	17.3	39.4	26.1	-	26.1
	V	52	10	9	11	2	13	_18.9_	_35.8_	_21.2_	_3.8_	_25.0_
	Other	55	5	11	12	4	16	_9.0_	_28.8_	_21.8_	_7.3_	_29.1_
	Outside marriage joint registration											
	All†	380	106	106	125	27	152	27.1	54.3	32.9	7.1	40.0
	I	16	3	1	1	-	1	_18.4_	_24.5_	_6.3_	-	_6.3_
	II	61	15	11	12	3	15	24.0	41.6	_19.7_	_4.9_	_24.6_
	IIIN	21	3	7	9	6	15	_14.1_	_46.9_	_42.9_	_28.6_	_71.4_
	IIIM	160	35	47	59	10	69	21.4	50.2	36.9	6.3	43.1
	IV	64	17	13	16	6	22	25.9	45.7	25.0	9.4	34.4
	V	35	17	13	13	-	13	_46.3_	_81.7_	_37.1_	-	_37.1_
	Other	23	16	14	14	1	15	_65.0_	_122.0_	_60.9_	_4.3_	_65.2_

*   Stillbirths and perinatal mortality rates are estimates per 1,000 live and stillbirths.
     Neonatal, postneonatal and infant mortality rates are estimates per 1,000 live births.
**   Figures for live births are a 10 percent sample coded for father's occupation
*** Inside marriage and outside marriage/joint registration including cases where father's occupation was not stated
†   Includes cases where father's occupation was not stated

Table 33 Live births, stillbirths and infant deaths
  Babies born in 1994 : plurality by ONS cause groups
  Numbers and rates*, 1994

England and Wales

Note: Babies in this table were born in 1994 but may have died in 1994 or in 1995

Plurality	Cause groups	Numbers						Rates*				
		Births		Deaths								
		Live births	Still-births	Early neonatal	Neonatal	Postneo-natal	Infant	Still-birth	Peri-natal	Neo-natal	Postneo-natal	Infant
Singletons	**All causes**	**646,887**	**3,468**	**1,748**	**2,267**	**1,177**	**3,444**	**5.3**	**8.0**	**3.5**	**1.8**	**5.3**
	Congenital anomalies	-	324	479	658	295	953	0.5	1.2	1.0	0.5	1.5
	Antepartum infections	-	12	12	14	5	19	0.0	0.0	0.0	0.0	0.0
	Immaturity related conditions	-	93	887	1,070	93	1,163	0.1	1.5	1.7	0.1	1.8
	Asphyxia, anoxia or trauma (intrapartum)	-	173	266	315	8	323	0.3	0.7	0.5	0.0	0.5
	External conditions	-	-	2	7	69	76	-	0.0	0.0	0.1	0.1
	Infections	-	15	30	81	178	259	0.0	0.1	0.1	0.3	0.4
	Other specific conditions	-	110	15	19	41	60	0.2	0.2	0.0	0.1	0.1
	Asphyxia, anoxia or trauma (antepartum)	-	1,119	-	-	-	-	1.7	1.7	-	-	-
	Remaining antepartum deaths	-	1,568	-	-	-	-	2.4	2.4	-	-	-
	Sudden infant deaths	-	-	11	39	319	358	-	0.0	0.1	0.5	0.6
	Other conditions	-	54	46	64	169	233	0.1	0.2	0.1	0.3	0.4
All multiple births	**All causes**	**17,369**	**348**	**396**	**463**	**82**	**545**	**19.6**	**42.0**	**26.7**	**4.7**	**31.4**
	Congenital anomalies	-	37	61	74	12	86	2.1	5.6	4.3	0.7	5.0
	Antepartum infections	-	1	1	2	-	2	0.1	0.1	0.1	-	0.1
	Immaturity related conditions	-	15	286	319	15	334	0.9	17.3	18.4	0.9	19.2
	Asphyxia, anoxia or trauma (intrapartum)	-	18	25	30	1	31	1.0	2.5	1.7	0.1	1.8
	External conditions	-	-	-	-	2	2	-	-	-	0.1	0.1
	Infections	-	1	6	14	17	31	0.1	0.4	0.8	1.0	1.8
	Other specific conditions	-	16	4	6	1	7	0.9	1.2	0.3	0.1	0.4
	Asphyxia, anoxia or trauma (antepartum)	-	85	-	-	-	-	4.9	4.9	-	-	-
	Remaining antepartum deaths	-	169	-	-	-	-	9.6	9.6	-	-	-
	Sudden infant deaths	-	-	-	2	18	20	-	-	0.1	1.0	1.2
	Other conditions	-	6	13	16	16	32	0.3	1.1	0.9	0.9	1.8

*Stillbirths and perinatal mortality rates per 1,000 live and stillbirths
 Neonatal, postneonatal and infant mortality rates per 1,000 live births

Appendix A   Certificate used in the current system for certifying stillbirths.

MEDICAL CERTIFICATE OF STILL-BIRTH

(Births and Deaths Registration Act 1953, S 11(1), as amended by the Population (Statistics) Act 1960)
(Form prescribed by the Registration of Births, Deaths and Marriages Regulations (Amendment) (No. 2) Regulations 1985)

SB 000000

To be given only in respect of a child which has issued forth from its mother after the 24th week of pregnancy and which did not at any time after being completely expelled from its mother breathe or show any other signs of life.

Registered at
Entry No.

*I was present at the still-birth of a $\frac{*male}{*female}$ child born

*I have examined the body of a $\frac{*male}{*female}$ child which I am informed and believe was born

on .... day of .... 19 .... to ....
(NAME OF MOTHER)

at ....
(PLACE OF BIRTH)

†{ 1 The certified cause of death has been confirmed by post-mortem.
2 Post-mortem information may be available later.
3 Post-mortem not being held.

Weight of fetus .... grams
Estimated duration of pregnancy
State (a) the number of weeks of delivery ....
(b) When the child died
(i) before labour*
(ii) during labour*
(iii) not known*

*Strike out the words which do not apply.
†Ring appropriate digit.

CAUSE OF DEATH

a. Main diseases or conditions in fetus ....

b. Other diseases or conditions in fetus ....

c. Main maternal diseases or conditions affecting fetus ....

d. Other maternal diseases or conditions affecting fetus ....

e. Other relevant causes ....

I hereby certify that (i) the child was not born alive, and
(ii) to the best of my knowledge and belief the cause of death and the estimated duration of pregnancy of the mother were as stated above.

Signature .... Date ....

Qualification as registered by General Medical Council, or }
Registered No. as Registered Midwife. } ....

Address ....

For still-births in hospital: please give the name of the consultant responsible for the care of the mother ....

THIS IS NOT AN AUTHORITY FOR BURIAL OR CREMATION [SEE OVER]

Appendix B Certificate used in the current system for certifying deaths within the first 28 days of life.

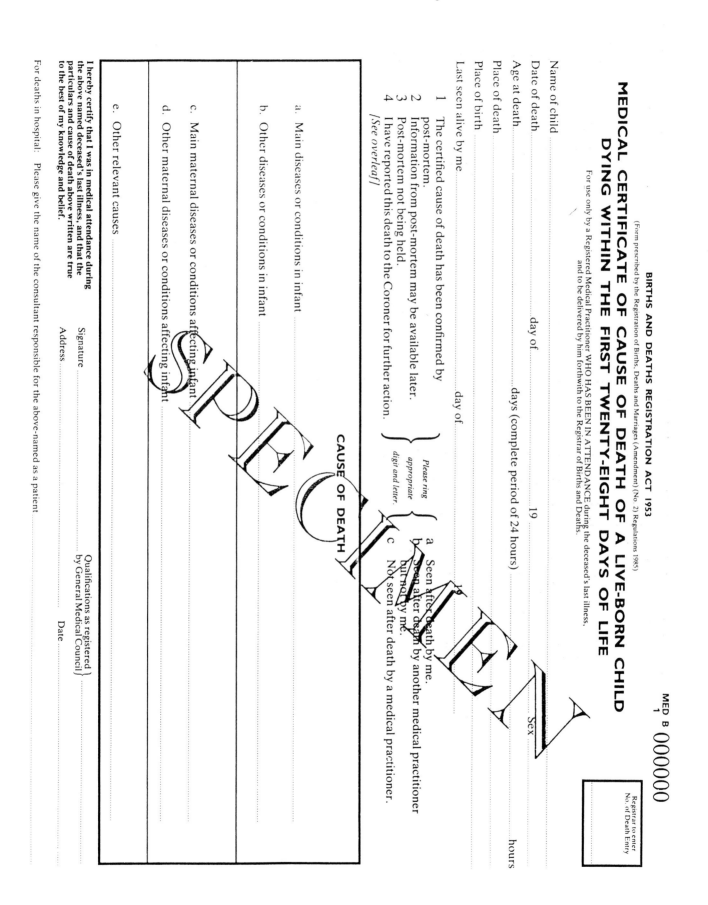

MED B 000000

Registrar to enter No. of Death Entry

BIRTHS AND DEATHS REGISTRATION ACT 1953

(Form prescribed by the Registration of Births, Deaths and Marriages (Amendment) (No. 2) Regulations 1985)

MEDICAL CERTIFICATE OF CAUSE OF DEATH OF A LIVE-BORN CHILD DYING WITHIN THE FIRST TWENTY-EIGHT DAYS OF LIFE

For use only by a Registered Medical Practitioner WHO HAS BEEN IN ATTENDANCE during the deceased's last illness, and to be delivered by him forthwith to the Registrar of Births and Deaths.

Name of child

Date of death .... day of 19

Age at death .... days (complete period of 24 hours)

Place of death

Place of birth .... Sex ....

Last seen alive by me .... day of .... 19 .... hours

1 The certified cause of death has been confirmed by post-mortem.
2 Information from post-mortem may be available later.
3 Post-mortem not being held.
4 I have reported this death to the Coroner for further action.
[See overleaf]

Please ring appropriate digit and letter.

a Seen after death by me.
b Seen after death by another medical practitioner but not by me.
c Not seen after death by a medical practitioner.

CAUSE OF DEATH

a. Main diseases or conditions in infant

b. Other diseases or conditions in infant

c. Main maternal diseases or conditions affecting infant

d. Other maternal diseases or conditions affecting infant

e. Other relevant causes

I hereby certify that I was in medical attendance during the above named deceased's last illness, and that the particulars and cause of death above written are true to the best of my knowledge and belief.

Signature .... Qualifications as registered } by General Medical Council }

Address ....

Date ....

For deaths in hospital: Please give the name of the consultant responsible for the above-named as a patient ....

SPECIMEN

Appendix C Certificate used in the current system for certifying deaths at ages 28 days and over.

Registrar to enter
No. of Death Entry

BIRTHS AND DEATHS REGISTRATION ACT 1953
(Form prescribed by the Registration of Births, Deaths and Marriages (Amendment) Regulations 1985)

MEDICAL CERTIFICATE OF CAUSE OF DEATH

For use only by a Registered Medical Practitioner WHO HAS BEEN IN ATTENDANCE during the deceased's last illness, and to be delivered by him forthwith to the Registrar of Births and Deaths.

Name of deceased ....

Date of death as stated to me .... day of .... 19...... Age as stated to me ....

Place of death ....

Last seen alive by me .... day of .... 19......

1 The certified cause of death takes account of information obtained from post-mortem.

2 Information from post-mortem may be available later.

3 Post-mortem not being held.

4 I have reported this death to the Coroner for further action.

[See overleaf]

Please ring appropriate digit(s) and letter.

a Seen after death by me.

b Seen after death by another medical practitioner but not by me.

c Not seen after death by a medical practitioner.

CAUSE OF DEATH

The condition thought to be the 'Underlying Cause of Death' should appear in the lowest completed line of Part I.

I(a) Disease or condition directly leading to death† ....

(b) Other disease or condition, if any, leading to I(a) ....

(c) Other disease or condition, if any, leading to I(b) ....

II Other significant conditions CONTRIBUTING TO THE DEATH but not related to the disease or condition causing it. ....

These particulars not to be entered in death register

Approximate interval between onset and death

The death might have been due to or contributed to by the employment followed at some time by the deceased.

☐ Please tick where applicable

†This does not mean the mode of dying, such as heart failure, asphyxia, asthenia, etc: it means the disease, injury, or complication which caused death.

I hereby certify that I was in medical attendance during the above named deceased's last illness, and that the particulars and cause of death above written are true to the best of my knowledge and belief.

Signature ....

Residence ....

Qualifications as registered by General Medical Council }...............

Date ....

For deaths in hospital: Please give the name of the consultant responsible for the above-named as a patient ....

Appendix D   Draft entry form used in the current system for registering stillbirths.

STILL-BIRTH

FORM 308

DRAFT OF PARTICULARS OF STILL-BIRTH TO BE REGISTERED

| Reg. Dist. | District & SD. Nos. | | | District & SD. Nos. |
| Sub Dist. | Date of registration | Entry No. | | Date of registration | Entry No. |

CHILD

1. Date and place of birth
   (date) ....

2. Cause of Stillbirth
   a ....
   b ....
   c ....
   d ....
   e ....

   3. Sex

Certified by

FATHER

4. Name and surname

5. Place of birth

6. Occupation

MOTHER

7. Name and surname

8. Place of birth

9. (a) Maiden surname
   (b) Surname at marriage if different from maiden surname

10. Usual address (if different from place of child's birth)

INFORMANT

11. Name and surname (if not the mother or father)

12. Qualification

13. Usual address (if different from that in 10 above)

L (i)
K (ii) (iii)
N *Post Mortem YES NO
(iv) ME 2 4 6
Z

grams   weeks

Y
*Before Labour   During Labour   Not Known
1   a   b   c   (vi)

U (v)
a
b
c
d
e

M
G(a) Father (vii) (viii)
H(a)* 1 2 3 4 5
See cover for Employment Status codes
G(b) Mother (ixa) (ixb)
H(b)* 1 2 3 4 5
See cover for Employment Status codes
POSTCODE

X Is this birth one of twins, triplets, etc *YES NO
If YES, complete (a) and (b)
*(a) Total number of births at this maternity 1 2 3 4 5 6

Edit Control

CONFIDENTIAL PARTICULARS

The particulars below, required under the Population(Statistics) Acts, will not be entered in the register. This information will be confidential and used only for the preparation of statistics by the Registrar General.

1. Where the father's name is entered in register:
   Father's date of birth
   DAY MONTH YEAR

2. In all cases:
   Mother's date of birth
   DAY MONTH YEAR

3. Where the child is of legitimate birth:
   (i) Date of marriage
   DAY MONTH YEAR

   (ii) Has the mother been married more than once? *YES NO

   (iii) Mother's previous children (excluding birth or births now being registered) by her former husband and any former husband
   (a) Number born alive (including any who have died)
   (b) Number still-born

(x)
Live births _____
(a) Entry No. of births
Still-births _____
(b) Entry No. of births
(xi)

Signature of registrar

SPm158 12/86

*Ring as appropriate

123

Appendix E   Draft entry form used in the current system for registering deaths.

A draft death registration form marked SPECIMEN (FORM 310). The form is printed sideways on the page and contains the following sections:

DRAFT OF PARTICULARS OF DEATH TO BE REGISTERED

Reg Dist. / Sub Dist. — District & SD Nos. — Date of registration — Entry No.

1. Date and place of death   (date)
2. Name and surname
3. Sex
4. Maiden surname of woman who has married
5. Date and place of birth   (date)
6. Occupation and usual address
7. (a) Name and surname of informant   (b) Qualification   (c) Usual address
8. Cause of death
   Ia
   b
   c
   II
   Certified by

O National Health Service medical card collected?
   * YES   NO
   If NO, NHS No.
   Signature of registrar

SPT(T)62 5/85

DEATH — CONFIDENTIAL PARTICULARS

District & SD Nos. — Date of registration — Entry No.

These particulars which are required under the Population (Statistics) Acts will not be entered in the register. This information will be confidential and used only for the preparation of statistics by the Registrar General.

POSTCODE

At date of death the deceased was *
Single 1
Married 2
Widowed 3
Divorced 4
Not known 5

(If married insert date of birth of spouse) — Day Month Year

R — Last seen alive — Day Month Year
S — * Seen or Not Seen after death   a b c
T — * Referred to Coroner by   1 Doctor   2 Registrar
B — SD   * Enq   YES   NO   1 ME   2

* Ring as appropriate   † If deceased is under 16 years of age   Employment

FORM 310

124

Appendix F ONS classification of neonatal deaths and associated ICD codes

Group	Description	ICD codes
1	Congenital anomalies	Main or other infant conditions: 270-273, 277, 279.0, 279.2-.9, 282, 284.0, 286.0-.4, 287.3, 288.1-.2, 330, 335.0, 343, 348.0, 359.0-.3, 424.0-.3, 425.0, 425.1, 425.3-.4, 426, 571.4-.9, 655.1, 740.0-743.9, 745.0-746.9, 747.1-749.2, 750.1-751.9, 752.4, 752.6-753.9, 754.3, 754.8, 755.2-757.3, 757.8-759.9, 774.0, 777.0
2	Antepartum infections	Main or other infant conditions: 090, 279.1, 762.7, 770.0, 771.0-.2 Main or other maternal conditions: 655.3
3	Immaturity related conditions	Main infant conditions: 761.0, 761.1, 761.8, 765.0, 765.1, 769.0, 770.2, 770.4-.5, 770.7-.8, 772.1, 774.2, 774.7, 776.6, 777.5, 779.6 Main or other maternal conditions: 655.3, 761.0-.1, 761.8, 765.0, 765.1, 769.0, 770.2, 770.4, 770.5, 770.7, 770.8, 772.1, 774.2, 774.7, 776.6, 777.5, 779.6
4	Asphyxia, anoxia, or trauma	Main or other infant conditions: 760.0, 761.6-.7, 762.0-.2, 762.4-.6, 763, 764, 766-768, 770.1, 772.2, 779.0-.2 Main or other maternal conditions: 641, 642, 760.0, 761.6, 761.7, 762.0-.2, 762.4-.6, 763, 764, 766-768, 770.1, 772.2, 779.0-.2
5	External conditions	Main infant conditions: 260-263, 507, 778.1-.3, 779.3, 800-999
6	Infections	Main or other infant conditions: 001-088.0, 091-139.0, 254.1, 320-326.0, 382, 420-422, 460.0-466.1, 475-476.1, 480-491, 494.0, 510-511, 513.0-.1, 540-542.0, 567, 590, 599.0, 771.3-.8
7	Other specific conditions	Main or other infant conditions: 254.1-.9, 255, 283, 286.7, 762.8-.9, 772.0, 772.3-.9, 773.0-.5, 774.1, 774.3-.6, 775, 776.0-.5, 776.7-.9, 777.1-.4, 777.6-.9, 778.0, 778.4-.9, 779.4-.5 Main or other maternal conditions: 140-253, 254.1-.9, 255, 283, 286.7, 331, 423, 427, 441, 442, 493, 556-558, 760.2, 760.5-.6, 762.3, 762.8-.9, 772.0, 772.3-.9, 773.0-.5, 774.0, 774.1, 774.3-.6, 775, 776.0-.5, 776.7-.9, 777.1-.4, 777.6-.9, 778.0, 778.4-.9, 779.4-.5, 785.5
8	Sudden infant deaths	Main or other infant conditions: 798.1, 798.2, 798.9, 799.1
9	Other conditions	all other codes

Appendix G Tables 4, 5 and 6, Injury and Poisoning, 1993 and 1994

The injury and poisoning sections from these tables were incomplete in the 1993/1994 volume, and so are printed in full here.

Table 4   Stillbirths and neonatal deaths   **England and Wales**
Main and other fetal/infant causes by sex
Numbers of mentions, 1993

ICD number	Cause of Death		Stillbirths		Deaths 0-6 Days		1 week		2 weeks		3 weeks		All neonatal deaths	
			Boys	Girls	Boys	Girls	Boy	Girls	Boys	Girls	Boys	Girls	Boys	Girls
	All babies		2,078	1,788	1,239	939	215	141	88	75	61	38	1,603	1,193
	All main fetal/infant mentions		1,209	1,020	1,502	1,143	293	184	109	91	78	49	1,982	1,467
	All other fetal/infant mentions		392	350	1,018	772	253	158	106	93	65	36	1,442	1,059
800-999	XVII Injury and poisoning	Main	-	1	5	12	1	1	-	1	1	-	7	14
		Other	-	-	4	4	-	-	-	1	-	-	4	5
850-854	Intracranial injury, excluding those with skull fracture	Main	-	-	-	3	-	-	-	1	1	-	1	4
		Other	-	-	-	-	-	-	-	-	-	-	-	-
853	Other and unspecified intracranial haemorrhage following injury	Main	-	-	-	1	-	-	-	-	-	-	-	1
		Other	-	-	-	-	-	-	-	-	-	-	-	-
854	Intracranial injury of other and unspecified nature	Main	-	-	-	2	-	-	-	1	1	-	1	3
		Other	-	-	-	-	-	-	-	-	-	-	-	-
860-869	Internal injury of chest, abdomen and pelvis	Main	-	-	-	1	-	-	-	-	-	-	-	1
		Other	-	-	1	-	-	-	-	-	-	-	1	-
860	Traumatic pneumothorax and haemothorax	Main	-	-	-	-	-	-	-	-	-	-	-	-
		Other	-	-	1	-	-	-	-	-	-	-	1	-
860.2	Haemothorax without mention of open wound into thorax	Main	-	-	-	-	-	-	-	-	-	-	-	-
		Other	-	-	1	-	-	-	-	-	-	-	1	-
864	Injury to liver	Main	-	-	-	1	-	-	-	-	-	-	-	1
		Other	-	-	-	-	-	-	-	-	-	-	-	-
870-897	Open wound	Main	-	-	1	-	-	-	-	-	-	-	1	-
		Other	-	-	-	-	-	-	-	-	-	-	-	-
870-879	Open wound of head, neck and trunk	Main	-	-	1	-	-	-	-	-	-	-	1	-
		Other	-	-	-	-	-	-	-	-	-	-	-	-
878	Open wound of genital organs (external), including traumatic amputation	Main	-	-	1	-	-	-	-	-	-	-	1	-
		Other	-	-	-	-	-	-	-	-	-	-	-	-
878.9	Other and unspecified parts, complicated	Main	-	-	1	-	-	-	-	-	-	-	1	-
		Other	-	-	-	-	-	-	-	-	-	-	-	-
900-904	Injury to blood vessels	Main	-	-	-	2	-	-	-	-	-	-	-	2
		Other	-	-	-	1	-	-	-	-	-	-	-	1
904	Injury to blood vessels of lower extremity and unspecified sites	Main	-	-	-	2	-	-	-	-	-	-	-	2
		Other	-	-	-	1	-	-	-	-	-	-	-	1
904.0	Common femoral artery	Main	-	-	-	2	-	-	-	-	-	-	-	2
		Other	-	-	-	1	-	-	-	-	-	-	-	1
910-919	Superficial injury	Main	-	-	-	-	-	-	-	-	-	-	-	-
		Other	-	-	1	1	-	-	-	-	-	-	1	1
911	Superficial injury of trunk	Main	-	-	-	-	-	-	-	-	-	-	-	-
		Other	-	-	1	-	-	-	-	-	-	-	1	-
913	Superficial injury of elbow, forearm and wrist	Main	-	-	-	-	-	-	-	-	-	-	-	-
		Other	-	-	-	1	-	-	-	-	-	-	-	1
913.9	Other and unspecified superficial injury, infected	Main	-	-	-	-	-	-	-	-	-	-	-	-
		Other	-	-	-	1	-	-	-	-	-	-	-	1
930-939	Effects of foreign body entering through orifice	Main	-	-	1	2	1	-	-	-	-	-	2	2
		Other	-	-	-	-	-	-	-	-	-	-	-	-
933	Foreign body in pharynx and larynx	Main	-	-	1	2	1	-	-	-	-	-	2	2
		Other	-	-	-	-	-	-	-	-	-	-	-	-
960-979	Poisoning by drugs, medicaments and biological substances	Main	-	-	-	-	-	-	-	-	-	-	-	-
		Other	-	-	-	-	-	-	-	1	-	-	-	1

Table 4 - *continued*

ICD number	Cause of Death		Stillbirths		Deaths 0-6 Days		1 week		2 weeks		3 weeks		All neonatal deaths	
			Boys	Girls	Boys	Girls	Boys	Girls	Boys	Girls	Boys	Girls	**Boys**	**Girls**
967	Poisoning by sedatives and hypnotics	Main	-	-	-	-	-	-	-	-	-	-	-	-
		Other	-	-	-	-	-	-	-	1	-	-	-	1
967.9	Unspecified	Main	-	-	-	-	-	-	-	-	-	-	-	-
		Other	-	-	-	-	-	-	-	1	-	-	-	1
990-995	Other and unspecified effects of external causes	Main	-	1	3	4	-	1	-	-	-	-	3	5
		Other	-	-	-	2	-	-	-	-	-	-	-	2
994	Effects of other external causes	Main	-	1	3	4	-	1	-	-	-	-	3	5
		Other	-	-	-	2	-	-	-	-	-	-	-	2
994.1	Drowning and nonfatal submersion	Main	-	-	-	1	-	-	-	-	-	-	-	1
		Other	-	-	-	-	-	-	-	-	-	-	-	-
994.7	Asphyxiation and strangulation	Main	-	-	-	1	-	1	-	-	-	-	-	2
		Other	-	-	-	-	-	-	-	-	-	-	-	-
994.9	Other	Main	-	1	3	2	-	-	-	-	-	-	3	2
		Other	-	-	-	2	-	-	-	-	-	-	-	2
996-999	Complications of surgical and medical care not elsewhere classified	Main	-	-	-	-	-	-	-	-	-	-	-	-
		Other	-	-	2	-	-	-	-	-	-	-	2	-
998	Other complications of procedures, not elsewhere classified	Main	-	-	-	-	-	-	-	-	-	-	-	-
		Other	-	-	2	-	-	-	-	-	-	-	2	-
998.2	Accidental puncture or laceration during a procedure	Main	-	-	-	-	-	-	-	-	-	-	-	-
		Other	-	-	2	-	-	-	-	-	-	-	2	-
E800-E999	**XVII External causes of injury and poisoning**	**Main**	-	1	3	2	2	-	-	-	3	-	**8**	**2**
		Other	-	1	8	4	3	1	6	2	4	-	**21**	**7**
E800-E848	Transport accidents	Main	-	-	-	-	-	-	-	-	-	-	-	-
		Other	-	1	-	-	-	-	-	-	-	-	-	-
E810-E819	Motor vehicle traffic accidents	Main	-	-	-	-	-	-	-	-	-	-	-	-
		Other	-	1	-	-	-	-	-	-	-	-	-	-
E819	Motor vehicle traffic accident of unspecified nature	Main	-	-	-	-	-	-	-	-	-	-	-	-
		Other	-	1	-	-	-	-	-	-	-	-	-	-
E870-E879	Misadventures during medical care, abnormal reactions, late complications	Main	-	-	-	-	2	-	-	-	2	-	**4**	-
		Other	-	-	8	2	3	-	6	2	4	-	**21**	**4**
E878,E879	Surgical and medical procedures as the cause of abnormal reaction of patient or later complication, without mention of misadventure at the time of procedure	Main	-	-	-	-	2	-	-	-	2	-	**4**	-
		Other	-	-	8	2	3	-	6	2	4	-	**21**	**4**
E878	Surgical operation and other surgical procedures as the cause of abnormal reaction of patient, or of later complication, without mention of misadventure at the time of operation	Main	-	-	-	-	2	-	-	-	2	-	**4**	-
		Other	-	-	7	1	3	-	6	2	4	-	**20**	**3**
E879	Other procedures, without mention of misadventure at the time of procedure, as the cause of abnormal reaction of patient, or of later complication	Main	-	-	-	-	-	-	-	-	-	-	-	-
		Other	-	-	1	1	-	-	-	-	-	-	**1**	**1**

Table 4 - *continued*

ICD number	Cause of Death		Stillbirths Boys	Stillbirths Girls	0-6 Days Boys	0-6 Days Girls	1 week Boy	1 week Girls	2 weeks Boys	2 weeks Girls	3 weeks Boys	3 weeks Girls	All neonatal deaths Boys	All neonatal deaths Girls
E900-E929	Other accidents, including late effects	Main	-	1	3	1	-	-	-	-	-	-	3	1
		Other	-	-	-	1	-	1	-	-	-	-	-	2
E900-E909	Accidents due to natural and environmental factors	Main	-	1	3	-	-	-	-	-	-	-	3	-
		Other	-	-	-	1	-	-	-	-	-	-	-	1
E904	Hunger, thirst, exposure, neglect	Main	-	1	3	-	-	-	-	-	-	-	3	-
		Other	-	-	-	1	-	-	-	-	-	-	-	1
E912	Inhalation and ingestion of other object causing obstruction of respiratory tract or suffocation	Main	-	-	-	1	-	-	-	-	-	-	-	1
		Other	-	-	-	-	-	-	-	-	-	-	-	-
E913	Accidental mechanical suffocation	Main	-	-	-	-	-	-	-	-	-	-	-	-
		Other	-	-	-	-	-	1	-	-	-	-	-	1
E960-E969	Homicide and injury purposely inflicted by other persons	Main	-	-	-	-	-	-	-	-	1	-	1	-
		Other	-	-	-	1	-	-	-	-	-	-	-	1
E967	Child battering and other maltreatment	Main	-	-	-	-	-	-	-	-	1	-	1	-
		Other	-	-	-	1	-	-	-	-	-	-	-	1
E970-E999	Other violence	Main	-	-	-	1	-	-	-	-	-	-	-	1
		Other	-	-	-	-	-	-	-	-	-	-	-	-
E980-E989	Injury undetermined whether accidentally or purposely inflicted	Main	-	-	-	1	-	-	-	-	-	-	-	1
		Other	-	-	-	-	-	-	-	-	-	-	-	-
E988	Injury by other and unspecified means, undetermined, accidentally or purposely inflicted	Main	-	-	-	1	-	-	-	-	-	-	-	1
		Other	-	-	-	-	-	-	-	-	-	-	-	-
Other main fetal/infant conditions			-	-	-	-	-	-	-	-	-	-	-	-
Other other fetal/infant conditions			-	-	-	1	-	-	-	-	-	1	-	2

Table 5 Stillbirths and neonatal deaths
Main and other maternal causes by sex
Numbers of mentions, 1993

ICD number	Cause of Death		Stillbirths		Deaths								All neonatal deaths	
					0-6 Days		1 week		2 weeks		3 weeks			
			Boys	Girls	Boys	Girls	Boys	Girls	Boys	Girls	Boys	Girls	Boys	Girls
	All babies		2,078	1,788	1,239	939	215	141	88	75	61	38	1,603	1,193
	All main maternal mentions		625	479	491	361	73	43	24	18	21	5	609	427
	All other maternal mentions		145	124	150	113	25	19	7	3	4	2	186	137
800-999	**XVII Injury and poisoning**	**Main**	5	7	-	3	-	-	-	-	1	-	1	3
		Other	3	1	2	1	-	2	-	-	-	-	2	3
800-829	Fractures	Main	1	-	-	1	-	-	-	-	-	-	-	1
		Other	-	-	-	-	-	-	-	-	-	-	-	-
800-804	Fracture of skull	Main	-	-	-	1	-	-	-	-	-	-	-	1
		Other	-	-	-	-	-	-	-	-	-	-	-	-
800	Fracture of vault of skull	Main	-	-	-	1	-	-	-	-	-	-	-	1
		Other	-	-	-	-	-	-	-	-	-	-	-	-
820-829	Fracture of lower limb	Main	1	-	-	-	-	-	-	-	-	-	-	-
		Other	-	-	-	-	-	-	-	-	-	-	-	-
829	Fracture of unspecified bones	Main	1	-	-	-	-	-	-	-	-	-	-	-
		Other	-	-	-	-	-	-	-	-	-	-	-	-
850-854	Intracranial injury, excluding those with skull fracture	Main	-	-	-	1	-	-	-	-	-	-	-	1
		Other	1	-	-	-	-	-	-	-	-	-	-	-
852	Subarachnoid, subdural and extradural haemorrhage, following injury	Main	-	-	-	1	-	-	-	-	-	-	-	1
		Other												
854	Intracranial injury of other and unspecified nature	Main	-	-	-	-	-	-	-	-	-	-	-	-
		Other	1	-	-	-	-	-	-	-	-	-	-	-
860-869	Internal injury of chest, abdomen and pelvis	Main	1	2	-	-	-	-	-	-	-	-	-	-
		Other	-	-	-	-	-	-	-	-	-	-	-	-
864	Injury to liver	Main	-	1	-	-	-	-	-	-	-	-	-	-
		Other	-	-	-	-	-	-	-	-	-	-	-	-
865	Injury to spleen	Main	-	1	-	-	-	-	-	-	-	-	-	-
		Other	-	-	-	-	-	-	-	-	-	-	-	-
867	Injury to pelvic organs	Main	1	-	-	-	-	-	-	-	-	-	-	-
		Other	-	-	-	-	-	-	-	-	-	-	-	-
870-897	Open wound	Main	1	-	-	-	-	-	-	-	-	-	-	-
		Other	-	-	-	-	-	-	-	-	-	-	-	-
870-879	Open wound of head, neck and trunk	Main	1	-	-	-	-	-	-	-	-	-	-	-
		Other	-	-	-	-	-	-	-	-	-	-	-	-
879	Open wound of other and unspecified sites, except limbs	Main	1	-	-	-	-	-	-	-	-	-	-	-
		Other	-	-	-	-	-	-	-	-	-	-	-	-
879.2	Abdominal wall, anterior, without mention of complication	Main	1	-	-	-	-	-	-	-	-	-	-	-
		Other	-	-	-	-	-	-	-	-	-	-	-	-
958-959	Certain traumatic complications and unspecified injuries	Main	-	-	-	-	-	-	-	-	1	-	1	-
		Other	-	-	-	-	-	-	-	-	-	-	-	-
959	Injury, other and unspecified	Main	-	-	-	-	-	-	-	-	1	-	1	-
		Other	-	-	-	-	-	-	-	-	-	-	-	-
959.9	Unspecified site	Main	-	-	-	-	-	-	-	-	1	-	1	-
		Other	-	-	-	-	-	-	-	-	-	-	-	-

Table 5 - *continued*

ICD number	Cause of Death		Stillbirths		Deaths 0-6 Days		1 week		2 weeks		3 weeks		All neonatal deaths	
			Boys	Girls	Boys	Girls	Boys	Girls	Boys	Girls	Boys	Girls	Boys	Girls
960-979	Poisoning by drugs, medicaments and biological substances	Main	1	5	-	1	-	-	-	-	-	-	-	1
		Other	2	1	2	1	-	2	-	-	-	-	2	3
962	Poisoning by hormones and synthetic substitutes	Main	-	-	-	-	-	-	-	-	-	-	-	-
		Other	-	1	-	-	-	1	-	-	-	-	-	1
962.0	Adrenal cortical steroids	Main	-	-	-	-	-	-	-	-	-	-	-	-
		Other	-	-	-	-	-	1	-	-	-	-	-	1
962.2	Ovarian hormones and synthetic substitutes	Main	-	-	-	-	-	-	-	-	-	-	-	-
		Other	-	1	-	-	-	-	-	-	-	-	-	-
963	Poisoning by primarily systemic agents	Main	-	2	-	-	-	-	-	-	-	-	-	-
		Other	-	-	-	-	-	-	-	-	-	-	-	-
963.1	Antineoplastic and immunosuppressive drugs	Main	-	2	-	-	-	-	-	-	-	-	-	-
		Other	-	-	-	-	-	-	-	-	-	-	-	-
964	Poisoning by agents primarily affecting blood constituents	Main	1	1	-	1	-	-	-	-	-	-	-	1
		Other	-	-	1	-	-	-	-	-	-	-	1	-
964.2	Anticoagulants	Main	1	1	-	1	-	-	-	-	-	-	-	1
		Other	-	-	1	-	-	-	-	-	-	-	1	-
966	Poisoning by anticonvulsants and anti-Parkinsonism drugs	Main	-	-	-	-	-	-	-	-	-	-	-	-
		Other	1	-	-	1	-	1	-	-	-	-	-	2
966.3	Other and unspecified anticonvulsants	Main	-	-	-	-	-	-	-	-	-	-	-	-
		Other	1	-	-	1	-	1	-	-	-	-	-	2
972	Poisoning by agents primarily affecting the cardiovascular system	Main	-	2	-	-	-	-	-	-	-	-	-	-
		Other	-	-	-	-	-	-	-	-	-	-	-	-
972.6	Other antihypertensive agents	Main	-	2	-	-	-	-	-	-	-	-	-	-
		Other	-	-	-	-	-	-	-	-	-	-	-	-
977	Poisoning by other and unspecified drugs and medicaments	Main	-	-	-	-	-	-	-	-	-	-	-	-
		Other	1	-	1	-	-	-	-	-	-	-	1	-
977.9	Unspecified drug or medicament	Main	-	-	-	-	-	-	-	-	-	-	-	-
		Other	1	-	1	-	-	-	-	-	-	-	1	-
996-999	Complications of surgical and medical care not elsewhere classified	Main	1	-	-	-	-	-	-	-	-	-	-	-
		Other	-	-	-	-	-	-	-	-	-	-	-	-
999	Complications of medical care, not elsewhere classified	Main	1	-	-	-	-	-	-	-	-	-	-	-
		Other	-	-	-	-	-	-	-	-	-	-	-	-
999.1	Air embolism	Main	1	-	-	-	-	-	-	-	-	-	-	-
		Other	-	-	-	-	-	-	-	-	-	-	-	-
E800-E999	**XVII External causes of injury and poisoning**	**Main**	1	4	-	4	-	-	-	-	1	-	1	4
		Other	2	3	-	-	-	-	-	-	-	-	-	-
E800-E848	Transport accidents	Main	1	2	-	-	-	-	-	-	1	-	1	-
		Other	-	1	-	-	-	-	-	-	-	-	-	-
E810-E819	Motor vehicle traffic accidents	Main	1	2	-	-	-	-	-	-	1	-	1	-
		Other	-	1	-	-	-	-	-	-	-	-	-	-
E812	Other motor vehicle traffic accident involving collision with another motor vehicle	Main	-	-	-	-	-	-	-	-	1	-	1	-
		Other	-	-	-	-	-	-	-	-	-	-	-	-
E819	Motor vehicle traffic accident of unspecified nature	Main	1	2	-	-	-	-	-	-	-	-	-	-
		Other	-	1	-	-	-	-	-	-	-	-	-	-

Table 5 - *continued*

ICD number	Cause of Death		Stillbirths		Deaths 0-6 Days		1 week		2 weeks		3 weeks		All neonatal deaths	
			Boys	Girls	Boys	Girls	Boys	Girls	Boys	Girls	Boys	Girls	**Boys**	**Girls**
E870-E879	Misadventures during medical care, abnormal reac tions, late complications	Main	-	**2**	-	4	-	-	-	-	-	-	-	**4**
		Other	1	**2**	-	-	-	-	-	-	-	-	-	-
E878,E879	Surgical and medical procedures as the cause of abnormal reaction of patient or later complication, without mention of misadventure at the time of procedure	Main	-	**2**	-	4	-	-	-	-	-	-	-	**4**
		Other	1	**2**	-	-	-	-	-	-	-	-	-	-
E878	Surgical operation and other surgical procedures as the cause of abnormal reaction of patient, or of later complication, without mention of misadventure at the time of operation	Main	-	**2**	-	2	-	-	-	-	-	-	-	**2**
		Other	1	**2**	-	-	-	-	-	-	-	-	-	-
E879	Other procedures, without mention of misadventure at the time of procedure, as the cause of abnormal reaction of patient, or of later complication	Main	-	-	-	2	-	-	-	-	-	-	-	**2**
		Other	-	-	-	-	-	-	-	-	-	-	-	-
E880-E888	Accidental falls	Main	-	-	-	-	-	-	-	-	-	-	-	-
		Other	1	-	-	-	-	-	-	-	-	-	-	-
E884	Other fall from one level to another	Main	-	-	-	-	-	-	-	-	-	-	-	-
		Other	1	-	-	-	-	-	-	-	-	-	-	-
	Other main maternal conditions		-	-	-	-	-	-	-	-	-	1	-	1
	Other other maternal conditions		-	-	-	-	-	-	-	-	-	-	-	-

Table 6 Postneonatal and childhood deaths
Underlying cause of death by sex
Numbers, 1993

ICD number	Cause of Death	Age at death															
		All ages		Months						Years							
		28 days to 15 years		1-5		6-11		1-11		1-4		5-9		10-14		1-15	
		Boys	Girls	Boys	Girls	Boys	Girls	Boys	Girls	Boys	Girls	Boys	Girls	Boys	Girls	Boys	Girls
	All causes	2,039	1,516	594	455	216	181	810	636	510	374	276	194	340	246	1,229	880
800-999	**XVII Injury and poisoning**	421	236	25	13	14	20	39	33	132	69	82	45	121	66	382	203
800-829	Fractures	75	38	4	-	1	2	5	2	13	11	18	10	29	13	70	36
800-804	Fracture of skull	55	31	4	-	-	2	4	2	8	9	14	8	23	10	51	29
800	Fracture of vault of skull	-	1	-	-	-	-	-	-	-	-	-	-	-	1	-	1
801	Fracture of base of skull	7	3	-	-	-	-	-	-	1	-	3	1	3	-	7	3
803	Other and unqualified skull fractures	47	26	4	-	-	2	4	2	7	9	11	7	20	8	43	24
804	Multiple fractures involving skull or face with other bones	1	1	-	-	-	-	-	-	-	-	-	-	-	1	1	1
805-809	Fracture of neck and trunk	20	7	-	-	1	-	1	-	5	2	4	2	6	3	19	7
805	Fracture of vertebral column without mention of spinal cord lesion	14	7	-	-	-	-	-	-	4	2	3	2	5	3	14	7
806	Fracture of vertebral column with spinal cord lesion	2	-	-	-	-	-	-	-	1	-	1	-	-	-	2	-
807	Fracture of rib(s), sternum, larynx and trachea	3	-	-	-	1	-	1	-	-	-	-	-	1	-	2	-
808	Fracture of pelvis	1	-	-	-	-	-	-	-	-	-	-	-	-	-	1	-
830-839	Dislocation	2	-	-	-	-	-	-	-	-	-	-	-	1	-	2	-
839	Other, multiple and ill-defined dislocations	2	-	-	-	-	-	-	-	-	-	-	-	1	-	2	-
840-848	Sprains and strains of joints and adjacent muscles	1	-	-	-	-	-	-	-	-	-	-	-	-	-	1	-
847	Sprains and strains of other and unspecified parts of back	1	-	-	-	-	-	-	-	-	-	-	-	-	-	1	-
850-854	Intracranial injury, excluding those with skull fracture	89	58	7	6	4	4	11	10	23	13	23	10	24	21	78	48
851	Cerebral laceration and contusion	10	7	-	-	1	-	1	-	3	1	2	-	4	5	9	7
852	Subarachnoid, subdural and extradural haemorrhage, following injury	14	6	3	4	2	-	5	4	3	1	2	1	3	-	9	2
853	Other and unspecified intracranial haemorrhage following injury	3	1	-	-	-	-	-	-	1	1	1	-	-	-	3	1
854	Intracranial injury of other and unspecified nature	62	44	4	2	1	4	5	6	16	10	18	9	17	16	57	38
860-869	Internal injury of chest, abdomen and pelvis	50	34	1	-	1	-	2	-	10	5	14	9	13	10	48	34
860	Traumatic pneumothorax and haemothorax	2	2	-	-	-	-	-	-	-	1	-	-	1	1	2	2
861	Injury to heart and lung	4	2	-	-	-	-	-	-	-	-	-	1	4	1	4	2
862	Injury to other and unspecified intrathoracic organs	6	4	-	-	1	-	1	-	-	2	1	-	2	2	5	4

Table 6 - *continued*

ICD number	Cause of Death	All ages 28 days to 15 years Boys	Girls	Months 1-5 Boys	Girls	6-11 Boys	Girls	1-11 Boys	Girls	Years 1-4 Boys	Girls	5-9 Boys	Girls	10-14 Boys	Girls	1-15 Boys	Girls
864	Injury to liver	-	1	-	-	-	-	-	-	-	-	-	-	-	1	-	1
865	Injury to spleen	-	1	-	-	-	-	-	-	-	-	-	1	-	-	-	1
868	Injury to other intraabdominal organs	1	1	-	-	-	-	-	-	1	1	-	-	-	-	1	1
869	Internal injury to unspecified or ill-defined organs	37	23	1	-	-	-	1	-	9	1	13	7	6	5	36	23
870-897	Open wound	3	2	-	-	-	1	-	1	1	-	-	1	1	-	3	1
870-879	Open wound of head, neck and trunk	3	1	-	-	-	1	-	1	1	-	-	-	1	-	3	-
873	Other open wound of head	2	1	-	-	-	1	-	1	1	-	-	-	-	-	2	-
875	Open wound of chest (wall)	1	-	-	-	-	-	-	-	-	-	-	-	1	-	1	-
890-897	Open wound of lower limb	-	1	-	-	-	-	-	-	-	-	-	1	-	-	-	1
890	Open wound of hip and thigh	-	1	-	-	-	-	-	-	-	-	-	1	-	-	-	1
930-939	Effects of foreign body entering through orifice	19	12	4	5	3	3	7	8	9	2	1	-	2	1	12	4
933	Foreign body in pharynx and larynx	18	11	4	5	3	2	7	7	8	2	1	-	2	1	11	4
934	Foreign body in trachea, bronchus and lung	1	-	-	-	-	-	-	-	1	-	-	-	-	-	1	-
938	Foreign body in digestive system, unspecified	-	1	-	-	-	1	-	1	-	-	-	-	-	-	-	-
940-949	Burns	14	4	1	-	1	1	2	1	8	3	4	-	-	-	12	3
946	Burns of multiple specified sites	1	-	1	-	-	-	1	-	-	-	-	-	-	-	-	-
948	Burns classified according to extent of body surface involved	1	-	-	-	-	-	-	-	1	-	-	-	-	-	1	-
948.9	90% or more	1	-	-	-	-	-	-	-	1	-	-	-	-	-	1	-
949	Burn, unspecified	12	4	-	-	1	1	1	1	7	3	4	-	-	-	11	3
949.0	Unspecified degree	2	2	-	-	-	1	-	1	1	1	1	-	-	-	2	1
950-957	Injury to nerves and spinal cord	5	-	2	-	-	-	2	-	1	-	-	-	1	-	3	-
952	Spinal cord lesion without evidence of spinal bone injury	4	-	2	-	-	-	2	-	1	-	-	-	1	-	2	-
954	Injury to other nerve(s) of trunk excluding shoulder and pelvic girdles	1	-	-	-	-	-	-	-	-	-	-	-	-	-	1	-
958-959	Certain traumatic complications and unspecified injuries	10	4	1	1	-	1	1	2	3	-	2	1	2	-	9	2
959	Injury, other and unspecified	10	4	1	1	-	1	1	2	3	-	2	1	2	-	9	2
959.0	Face and neck	1	-	-	-	-	-	-	-	-	-	1	-	-	-	1	-
959.8	Other specified sites, including multiple	5	-	1	-	-	-	1	-	1	-	-	-	2	-	4	-
959.9	Unspecified site	4	4	-	1	-	1	-	2	2	-	1	1	-	-	4	2
960-979	Poisoning by drugs, medicaments and biological substances	7	14	1	-	-	-	1	-	1	3	1	-	3	9	6	14

Table 6 - *continued*

ICD number	Cause of Death	Age at death															
		All ages 28 days to 15 years		Months						Years							
				1-5		6-11		1-11		1-4		5-9		10-14		1-15	
		Boys	Girls	Boys	Girls	Boys	Girls	Boys	Girls	Boys	Girls	Boys	Girls	Boys	Girls	Boys	Girls
961	Poisoning by other anti-infectives	-	2	-	-	-	-	-	-	-	-	-	-	-	2	-	2
961.4	Antimalarials and drugs acting on other blood protozoa	-	2	-	-	-	-	-	-	-	-	-	-	-	2	-	2
965	Poisoning by analgesics, antipyretics and antirheumatics	2	3	-	-	-	-	-	-	-	2	-	-	1	1	2	3
965.0	Opiates and related narcotics	2	2	-	-	-	-	-	-	-	2	-	-	1	-	2	2
965.7	Other non-narcotic analgesics	-	1	-	-	-	-	-	-	-	-	-	-	-	1	-	1
966	Poisoning by anticonvulsants and anti-Parkinsonism drugs	1	-	1	-	-	-	1	-	-	-	-	-	-	-	-	-
966.3	Other and unspecified anticonvulsants	1	-	1	-	-	-	1	-	-	-	-	-	-	-	-	-
968	Poisoning by other central nervous system depressants	1	-	-	-	-	-	-	-	-	-	1	-	-	-	1	-
968.5	Surface and infiltration anaesthetics	1	-	-	-	-	-	-	-	-	-	1	-	-	-	1	-
969	Poisoning by psychotropic agents	2	3	-	-	-	-	-	-	1	1	-	-	1	2	2	3
969.0	Antidepressants	2	3	-	-	-	-	-	-	1	1	-	-	1	2	2	3
972	Poisoning by agents primarily affecting the cardiovascular system	1	3	-	-	-	-	-	-	-	-	-	-	1	2	1	3
972.0	Cardiac rhythm regulators	1	3	-	-	-	-	-	-	-	-	-	-	1	2	1	3
977	Poisoning by other and unspecified drugs and medicaments	-	3	-	-	-	-	-	-	-	-	-	-	-	2	-	3
977.9	Unspecified drug or medicament	-	3	-	-	-	-	-	-	-	-	-	-	-	2	-	3
980-989	Toxic effects of substances chiefly nonmedicinal as to source	46	23	-	-	1	2	1	2	28	8	8	9	9	3	45	21
982	Toxic effect of solvents other than petroleum-based	-	1	-	-	-	-	-	-	-	1	-	-	-	-	-	1
982.8	Other	-	1	-	-	-	-	-	-	-	1	-	-	-	-	-	1
983	Toxic effect of corrosive aromatics, acids and caustic alkalis	1	-	-	-	-	-	-	-	-	-	-	-	1	-	1	-
983.0	Corrosive aromatics	1	-	-	-	-	-	-	-	-	-	-	-	1	-	1	-
986	Toxic effect of carbon monoxide	10	5	-	-	1	-	1	-	6	1	-	2	3	1	9	5
987	Toxic effect of other gases, fumes or vapours	35	17	-	-	-	2	-	2	22	6	8	7	5	2	35	15
987.8	Other	35	17	-	-	-	2	-	2	22	6	8	7	5	2	35	15
990-995	Other and unspecified effects of external causes	95	44	2	1	2	6	4	7	33	23	11	4	36	8	91	37
991	Effects of reduced temperature	1	-	-	-	-	-	-	-	-	-	-	-	-	-	1	-
991.6	Hypothermia	1	-	-	-	-	-	-	-	-	-	-	-	-	-	1	-
994	Effects of other external causes	93	44	2	1	2	6	4	7	32	23	11	4	36	8	89	37
994.0	Effects of lightning	1	-	-	-	-	-	-	-	-	-	-	-	1	-	1	-
994.1	Drowning and nonfatal submersion	38	15	-	-	-	4	-	4	21	8	7	3	6	-	38	11
994.7	Asphyxiation and strangulation	49	28	2	1	2	2	4	3	11	15	3	1	26	8	45	25

Table 6 - *continued*

ICD number	Cause of Death	All ages 28 days to 15 years		Months 1-5		6-11		1-11		Years 1-4		5-9		10-14		1-15	
		Boys	Girls	Boys	Girls	Boys	Girls	Boys	Girls	Boys	Girls	Boys	Girls	Boys	Girls	Boys	Girls
994.8	Electrocution and nonfatal effects of electric current	5	1	-	-	-	-	-	-	-	-	1	-	3	-	5	1
995	Certain adverse effects not elsewhere classified	1	-	-	-	-	-	-	-	1	-	-	-	-	-	1	-
995.5	Child maltreatment syndrome	1	-	-	-	-	-	-	-	1	-	-	-	-	-	1	-
996-999	Complications of surgical and medical care not elsewhere classified	5	3	2	-	1	-	3	-	2	1	-	1	-	1	2	3
996	Complications peculiar to certain specified procedures	1	-	1	-	-	-	1		-		-		-		-	-
996.1	Mechanical complication of other vascular device, implant and graft	1	-	1	-	-	-	1		-		-		-		-	-
997	Complications affecting specified body systems, not elsewhere classified	1	1	1	-	-	-	1		-		-		-	1	-	1
997.0	Central nervous system complications	1	1	1	-	-	-	1		-		-		-	1	-	1
998	Other complications of procedures, not elsewhere classified	3	2	-	-	1	-	1	-	2	1	-	1	-	-	2	2
998.1	Haemorrhage or haematoma complicating a procedure	1	1	-	-	-	-	-	-	1	-	-	1	-	-	1	1
998.2	Accidental puncture or laceration during a procedure	2	1	-	-	1	-	1	-	1	1	-	-	-	-	1	1
E800-E999	**XVII External causes of injury and poisoning**	**421**	**236**	**25**	**13**	**14**	**20**	**39**	**33**	**132**	**69**	**82**	**45**	**121**	**66**	**382**	**203**
E800-E848	Transport accidents	173	105	4	-	2	1	6	1	31	19	50	27	59	43	167	104
E800-E807	Railway accidents	3	-	-	-	-	-	-	-	-	-	-	-	1	-	3	-
E805	Hit by rolling stock	3	-	-	-	-	-	-	-	-	-	-	-	1	-	3	-
E805.2	Pedestrian	3	-	-	-	-	-	-	-	-	-	-	-	1	-	3	-
E810-E819	Motor vehicle traffic accidents	165	101	4	-	2	1	6	1	30	18	50	25	55	43	159	100
E812	Other motor vehicle traffic accident involving collision with another motor vehicle	20	24	4	-	1	1	5	1	2	4	5	1	4	14	15	23
E812.0	Driver of motor vehicle other than motorcycle	1	-	-	-	-	-	-	-	-	-	-	-	-	-	1	-
E812.1	Passenger in motor vehicle other than motorcycle	17	24	4	-	1	1	5	1	2	4	5	1	3	14	12	23
E812.2	Motorcyclist	1	-	-	-	-	-	-	-	-	-	-	-	1	-	1	-
E812.9	Unspecified person	1	-	-	-	-	-	-	-	-	-	-	-	-	-	1	-
E813	Motor vehicle traffic accident involving collision with other vehicle	21	7	-	-	-	-	-	-	-	-	8	2	12	4	21	7
E813.6	Pedal cyclist	21	7	-	-	-	-	-	-	-	-	8	2	12	4	21	7
E814	Motor vehicle traffic accident involving collision with pedestrian	99	48	-	-	-	-	-	-	22	8	35	17	32	19	99	48
E814.7	Pedestrian	99	48	-	-	-	-	-	-	22	8	35	17	32	19	99	48

Table 6 - *continued*

ICD number	Cause of Death	All ages 28 days to 15 years		Months 1-5		Months 6-11		1-11		Years 1-4		Years 5-9		Years 10-14		Years 1-15	
		Boys	Girls	Boys	Girls	Boys	Girls	Boys	Girls	Boys	Girls	Boys	Girls	Boys	Girls	Boys	Girls
E815	Other motor vehicle traffic accident involving collision on the highway	9	5	-	-	-	-	-	-	1	2	1	-	3	3	9	5
E815.1	Passenger in motor vehicle other than motorcycle	7	5	-	-	-	-	-	-	1	2	1	-	2	3	7	5
E815.2	Motorcyclist	2	-	-	-	-	-	-	-	-	-	-	-	1	-	2	-
E816	Motor vehicle traffic accident due to loss of control, without collision on the highway	4	4	-	-	-	-	-	-	1	-	1	-	1	1	4	4
E816.0	Driver of motor vehicle other than motorcycle	1	1	-	-	-	-	-	-	-	-	-	-	-	1	1	1
E816.1	Passenger in motor vehicle other than motorcycle	3	2	-	-	-	-	-	-	1	-	1	-	1	-	3	2
E816.3	Passenger on motorcycle	-	1	-	-	-	-	-	-	-	-	-	-	-	-	-	1
E818	Other noncollision motor vehicle traffic accident	1	1	-	-	-	-	-	-	1	1	-	-	-	-	1	1
E818.1	Passenger in motor vehicle other than motorcycle	1	1	-	-	-	-	-	-	1	1	-	-	-	-	1	1
E819	Motor vehicle traffic accident of unspecified nature	11	12	-	-	1	-	1	-	3	3	-	5	3	2	10	12
E819.1	Passenger in motor vehicle other than motorcycle	8	10	-	-	1	-	1	-	3	3	-	3	1	2	7	10
E819.3	Passenger on motorcycle	1	-	-	-	-	-	-	-	-	-	-	-	1	-	1	-
E819.9	Unspecified person	2	2	-	-	-	-	-	-	-	-	-	2	1	-	2	2
E820-E825	Motor vehicle nontraffic accidents	3	1	-	-	-	-	-	-	-	1	-	-	2	-	3	1
E823	Other motor vehicle nontraffic accident involving collision with stationary object	1	-	-	-	-	-	-	-	-	-	-	-	1	-	1	-
E823.2	Motor cyclist	1	-	-	-	-	-	-	-	-	-	-	-	1	-	1	-
E825	Other motor vehicle nontraffic accident of other unspecified nature	2	1	-	-	-	-	-	-	-	1	-	-	1	-	2	1
E825.2	Motor cyclist	1	-	-	-	-	-	-	-	-	-	-	-	1	-	1	-
E825.6	Pedal cyclist	-	1	-	-	-	-	-	-	-	1	-	-	-	-	-	1
E825.9	Unspecified person	1	-	-	-	-	-	-	-	-	-	-	-	-	-	1	-
E826-E829	Other road vehicle accidents	1	2	-	-	-	-	-	-	1	-	-	1	-	-	1	2
E826	Pedal cycle accident	-	1	-	-	-	-	-	-	-	-	-	1	-	-	-	1
E828	Accident involving animal being ridden	-	1	-	-	-	-	-	-	-	-	-	-	-	-	-	1
E828.2	Rider of animal	-	1	-	-	-	-	-	-	-	-	-	-	-	-	-	1
E829	Other road vehicle accidents	1	-	-	-	-	-	-	-	1	-	-	-	-	-	1	-
E829.0	Pedestrian	1	-	-	-	-	-	-	-	1	-	-	-	-	-	1	-
E830-E838	Water transport accidents	1	1	-	-	-	-	-	-	-	-	-	1	1	-	1	1
E830	Accident to watercraft causing submersion	1	-	-	-	-	-	-	-	-	-	-	-	1	-	1	-
E830.0	Occupant of small boat, unpowered	1	-	-	-	-	-	-	-	-	-	-	-	1	-	1	-
E838	Other and unspecified water transport accident	-	1	-	-	-	-	-	-	-	-	-	1	-	-	-	1
E838.3	Occupant of other watercraft - other than crew	-	1	-	-	-	-	-	-	-	-	-	1	-	-	-	1

Table 6 - *continued*

ICD number	Cause of Death	All ages 28 days to 15 years Boys	Girls	Months 1-5 Boys	Girls	6-11 Boys	Girls	1-11 Boys	Girls	Years 1-4 Boys	Girls	5-9 Boys	Girls	10-14 Boys	Girls	1-15 Boys	Girls
E850-E869	Accidental poisoning	10	8	-	-	-	-	-	-	7	1	-	2	2	5	10	8
E850-E858	Accidental poisoning by drugs, medicaments and biologicals	3	5	-	-	-	-	-	-	1	1	-	-	1	4	3	5
E850	Accidental poisoning by analgesics, antipyretics antirheumatics	2	1	-	-	-	-	-	-	-	-	-	-	1	1	2	1
E850.0	Opiates and related narcotics	2	-	-	-	-	-	-	-	-	-	-	-	1	-	2	-
E850.5	Other non-narcotic analgesics	-	1	-	-	-	-	-	-	-	-	-	-	-	1	-	1
E854	Accidental poisoning by other psychotropic agents	1	1	-	-	-	-	-	-	1	1	-	-	-	-	1	1
E854.0	Antidepressants	1	1	-	-	-	-	-	-	1	1	-	-	-	-	1	1
E857	Accidental poisoning by anti-infectives	-	1	-	-	-	-	-	-	-	-	-	-	-	1	-	1
E858	Accidental poisoning by other drugs	-	2	-	-	-	-	-	-	-	-	-	-	-	2	-	2
E858.3	Agents primarily affecting cardiovascular system	-	1	-	-	-	-	-	-	-	-	-	-	-	1	-	1
E858.9	Unspecified	-	1	-	-	-	-	-	-	-	-	-	-	-	1	-	1
E860-E869	Accidental poisoning by other solid and liquid substances, gases and vapours	7	3	-	-	-	-	-	-	6	-	-	2	1	1	7	3
E866	Accidental poisoning by other and unspecified solid and liquid substances	1	-	-	-	-	-	-	-	-	-	-	-	1	-	1	-
E866.8	Other	1	-	-	-	-	-	-	-	-	-	-	-	1	-	1	-
E867	Accidental poisoning by gas distributed by pipeline	2	1	-	-	-	-	-	-	2	-	-	-	-	1	2	1
E868	Accidental poisoning by other utility gas and other carbon monoxide	1	-	-	-	-	-	-	-	1	-	-	-	-	-	1	-
E868.9	Unspecified carbon monoxide	1	-	-	-	-	-	-	-	1	-	-	-	-	-	1	-
E869	Accidental poisoning by other gases and vapours	3	2	-	-	-	-	-	-	3	-	-	2	-	-	3	2
E869.8	Other specified gases and vapours	3	2	-	-	-	-	-	-	3	-	-	2	-	-	3	2
E870-E879	Misadventures during medical care, abnormal reactions, late complications	5	3	2	-	1	-	3	-	2	1	-	1	-	1	2	3
E870-E876	Misadventures to patients during surgical and medical care	4	2	1	-	1	-	2	-	2	1	-	1	-	-	2	2
E870	Accidental cut, puncture, perforation or haemorrhage during medical care	3	2	-	-	1	-	1	-	2	1	-	1	-	-	2	2
E870.0	Surgical operation	2	-	-	-	-	-	-	-	2	-	-	-	-	-	2	-
E870.6	Heart catheterization	-	1	-	-	-	-	-	-	-	1	-	-	-	-	-	1
E870.8	Other	1	1	-	-	1	-	1	-	-	-	-	1	-	-	-	1
E876	Other and unspecified misadventures during medical care	1	-	1	-	-	-	1	-	-	-	-	-	-	-	-	-
E876.3	Endotracheal tube wrongly placed during anaesthetic procedure	1	-	1	-	-	-	1	-	-	-	-	-	-	-	-	-

Table 6 - *continued*

ICD number	Cause of Death	All ages 28 days to 15 years		Months 1-5		Months 6-11		Months 1-11		Years 1-4		Years 5-9		Years 10-14		Years 1-15	
		Boys	Girls	Boys	Girls	Boys	Girls	Boys	Girls	Boys	Girls	Boys	Girls	Boys	Girls	Boys	Girls
E878	Surgical operation and other surgical procedures as the cause of abnormal reaction of patient, or of later complication, without mention of misadventure at the time of operation	1	1	1	-	-	-	1	-	-	-	-	-	-	1	-	1
E878.8	Other	-	1	-	-	-	-	-	-	-	-	-	-	-	1	-	1
E878.9	Unspecified	1	-	1	-	-	-	1	-	-	-	-	-	-	-	-	-
E880-E888	Accidental falls	18	14	1	-	-	2	1	2	6	8	4	2	4	1	17	12
E880	Fall on or from stairs or steps	1	1	-	-	-	-	-	-	1	-	-	1	-	-	1	1
E880.9	Other stairs or steps	1	1	-	-	-	-	-	-	1	-	-	1	-	-	1	1
E882	Fall from or out of building or other structure	6	5	-	-	-	-	-	-	3	5	2	-	-	-	6	5
E883	Fall into hole or other opening in surface	-	1	-	-	-	-	-	-	-	-	-	-	-	-	-	1
E883.9	Fall into other hole or other opening in surface	-	1	-	-	-	-	-	-	-	-	-	-	-	-	-	1
E884	Other fall from one level to another	8	4	1	-	-	1	1	1	2	2	2	-	2	1	7	3
E884.1	Fall from cliff	2	-	-	-	-	-	-	-	-	-	1	-	-	-	2	-
E884.2	Fall from chair or bed	3	2	1	-	-	-	1	-	2	1	-	-	-	1	2	2
E884.9	Other fall from one level to another	3	2	-	-	-	1	-	1	-	1	1	-	2	-	3	1
E887	Fracture, cause unspecified	2	2	-	-	-	1	-	1	-	1	-	-	2	-	2	1
E888	Other and unspecified fall	1	1	-	-	-	-	-	-	-	-	-	1	-	-	1	1
E890-E899	Accidents caused by fire and flames	43	19	-	-	2	3	2	3	26	7	10	7	5	2	41	16
E890	Conflagration in private dwelling	32	15	-	-	1	2	1	2	18	5	9	6	4	2	31	13
E890.1	Fumes from combustion of polyvinylchloride (PVC) and similar material in conflagration	1	-	-	-	-	-	-	-	1	-	-	-	-	-	1	-
E890.2	Other smoke and fumes from conflagration	28	14	-	-	1	2	1	2	15	5	8	5	4	2	27	12
E890.3	Burning caused by conflagration	3	1	-	-	-	-	-	-	2	-	1	1	-	-	3	1
E894	Ignition of highly inflammable material	4	1	-	-	-	-	-	-	3	-	1	1	-	-	4	1
E898	Accident caused by other specified fire and flames	7	3	-	-	1	1	1	1	5	2	-	-	1	-	6	2
E898.1	Other	7	3	-	-	1	1	1	1	5	2	-	-	1	-	6	2
E900-E929	Other accidents, including late effects	103	40	6	6	5	8	11	14	40	15	15	4	28	5	92	26
E900-E909	Accidents due to natural and environmental factors	2	-	-	-	-	-	-	-	-	-	1	-	1	-	2	-
E906	Other injury caused by animals	1	-	-	-	-	-	-	-	-	-	1	-	-	-	1	-
E906.0	Dog bite	1	-	-	-	-	-	-	-	-	-	1	-	-	-	1	-
E907	Lightning	1	-	-	-	-	-	-	-	-	-	-	-	1	-	1	-
E910	Accidental drowning and submersion	35	13	-	-	-	3	-	3	19	7	7	3	6	-	35	10

Table 6 - *continued*

ICD number	Cause of Death	Age at death														
		All ages 28 days to 15 years		Months						Years							
				1-5		6-11		1-11		1-4		5-9		10-14		1-15	
		Boys	Girls	Boys	Girls	Boys	Girls	Boys	Girls	Boys	Girls	Boys	Girls	Boys	Girls	Boys	Girls
E910.2	While engaged in other sport or recreational activity without diving equipment	6	2	-	-	-	-	-	-	1	1	2	1	1	-	6	2
E910.4	In bathtub	2	2	-	-	-	2	-	2	1	-	1	-	-	-	2	-
E910.8	Other	7	2	-	-	-	-	-	-	4	1	2	1	1	-	7	2
E910.9	Unspecified	20	7	-	-	-	1	-	1	13	5	2	1	4	-	20	6
E911	Inhalation and ingestion of food causing obstruction of respiratory tract or suffocation	10	6	2	3	1	1	3	4	5	1	1	-	1	-	7	2
E912	Inhalation and ingestion of other object causing obstruction of respiratory tract or suffocation	8	5	2	2	2	1	4	3	4	1	-	-	-	1	4	2
E913	Accidental mechanical suffocation	21	11	1	1	1	3	2	4	5	4	-	-	11	3	19	7
E913.0	In bed or cradle	2	2	1	-	-	1	1	1	1	1	-	-	-	-	1	1
E913.1	By plastic bag	2	1	-	-	-	-	-	-	1	-	-	-	-	1	2	1
E913.3	By falling earth or other substance	1	-	-	-	-	-	-	-	-	-	-	-	1	-	1	-
E913.8	Other specified means	16	5	-	-	1	1	1	1	3	3	-	-	10	1	15	4
E913.9	Unspecified	-	3	-	1	-	1	-	2	-	-	-	-	-	1	-	1
E916-E928	Other accidents	27	5	1	-	1	-	2	-	7	2	6	1	9	1	25	5
E916	Struck accidentally by falling object	9	-	-	-	-	-	-	-	4	-	4	-	1	-	9	-
E917	Striking against or struck accidentally by objects or persons	4	-	-	-	-	-	-	-	-	-	1	-	2	-	4	-
E917.0	In sports	2	-	-	-	-	-	-	-	-	-	-	-	1	-	2	-
E917.9	Other	2	-	-	-	-	-	-	-	-	-	1	-	1	-	2	-
E918	Caught accidently in or between objects	1	-	-	-	-	-	-	-	-	-	-	-	-	-	1	-
E922	Accident caused by firearm missile	1	-	-	-	-	-	-	-	1	-	-	-	-	-	1	-
E922.8	Other	1	-	-	-	-	-	-	-	1	-	-	-	-	-	1	-
E924	Accident caused by hot substance or object, caustic or corrosive material and steam	1	-	1	-	-	-	1	-	-	-	-	-	-	-	-	-
E924.0	Hot liquids and vapours, including steam	1	-	1	-	-	-	1	-	-	-	-	-	-	-	-	-
E925	Accident caused by electric current	4	1	-	-	-	-	-	-	-	-	1	-	3	-	4	1
E925.0	Domestic wiring and appliances	-	1	-	-	-	-	-	-	-	-	-	-	-	-	-	1
E925.1	Electric power generating plants, distribution stations, transmission lines	1	-	-	-	-	-	-	-	-	-	-	-	1	-	1	-
E925.8	Other	3	-	-	-	-	-	-	-	-	-	1	-	2	-	3	-
E928	Other and unspecified environmental and accidental causes	7	4	-	-	1	-	1	-	2	2	-	1	3	1	6	4
E928.9	Unspecified accidents	7	4	-	-	1	-	1	-	2	2	-	1	3	1	6	4
E938	Other central nervous system depressants	1	-	-	-	-	-	-	-	-	-	1	-	-	-	1	-
E938.5	Surface and infiltration anaesthetics	1	-	-	-	-	-	-	-	-	-	1	-	-	-	1	-

Table 6 - *continued*

ICD number	Cause of Death	All ages 28 days to 15 years Boys	Girls	Months 1-5 Boys	Girls	6-11 Boys	Girls	1-11 Boys	Girls	Years 1-4 Boys	Girls	5-9 Boys	Girls	10-14 Boys	Girls	1-15 Boys	Girls
E950-E959	Suicide and selfinflicted injury	10	4	-	-	-	-	-	-	-	-	-	-	5	2	10	4
E950	Suicide and selfinflicted poisoning by solid or liquid substances	1	2	-	-	-	-	-	-	-	-	-	-	1	1	1	2
E950.3	Tranquillizers and other psychotropic agents	1	1	-	-	-	-	-	-	-	-	-	-	1	1	1	1
E950.5	Unspecified drug or medicament	-	1	-	-	-	-	-	-	-	-	-	-	-	-	-	1
E952	Suicide and selfinflicted poisoning by other gases and vapours	-	1	-	-	-	-	-	-	-	-	-	-	-	-	-	1
E952.0	Motor vehicle exhaust gas	-	1	-	-	-	-	-	-	-	-	-	-	-	-	-	1
E953	Suicide and selfinflicted injury by hanging, strangulation and suffocation	5	1	-	-	-	-	-	-	-	-	-	-	4	1	5	1
E953.0	Hanging	5	1	-	-	-	-	-	-	-	-	-	-	4	1	5	1
E955	Suicide and selfinflicted injury by firearms and explosives	1	-	-	-	-	-	-	-	-	-	-	-	-	-	1	-
E955.4	Other and unspecified firearm	1	-	-	-	-	-	-	-	-	-	-	-	-	-	1	-
E958	Suicide and selfinflicted injury by other and unspecified means	3	-	-	-	-	-	-	-	-	-	-	-	-	-	3	-
E958.0	Jumping or lying before moving object	1	-	-	-	-	-	-	-	-	-	-	-	-	-	1	-
E958.4	Electrocution	1	-	-	-	-	-	-	-	-	-	-	-	-	-	1	-
E958.9	Unspecified means	1	-	-	-	-	-	-	-	-	-	-	-	-	-	1	-
E960-E969	Homicide and injury purposely inflicted by other persons	31	30	9	5	2	4	11	9	14	14	2	2	4	3	20	21
E962	Assault by poisoning	3	1	1	-	-	-	1	-	-	1	-	-	2	-	2	1
E962.0	Drugs and medicaments	1	1	1	-	-	-	1	-	-	1	-	-	-	-	-	1
E962.2	Other gases and vapours	2	-	1	-	-	-	-	-	-	-	-	-	2	-	2	-
E963	Assault by hanging and strangulation	7	9	1	-	1	-	2	-	3	4	2	1	-	3	5	9
E965	Assault by firearms and explosives	3	1	-	-	-	1	-	1	1	-	-	-	2	-	3	-
E965.1	Shotgun	1	-	-	-	-	-	-	-	-	-	-	-	1	-	1	-
E965.4	Other and unspecified firearm	-	1	-	-	-	1	-	1	-	-	-	-	-	-	-	-
E965.8	Other specified explosive	2	-	-	-	-	-	-	-	1	-	-	-	1	-	2	-
E967	Child battering and other maltreatment	4	3	3	1	-	2	3	3	1	-	-	-	-	-	1	-
E967.0	By parent	3	-	2	-	-	-	2	-	1	-	-	-	-	-	1	-
E967.1	By other specified person	1	-	1	-	-	-	1	-	-	-	-	-	-	-	-	-
E967.9	By unspecified person	-	3	-	1	-	2	-	3	-	-	-	-	-	-	-	-
E968	Assault by other and unspecified means	14	16	4	4	1	1	5	5	9	9	-	1	-	-	9	11
E968.0	Fire	3	2	-	-	-	-	-	-	3	1	-	1	-	-	3	2
E968.3	Hot liquid	-	1	-	-	-	-	-	-	-	1	-	1	-	-	-	1
E968.8	Other specified means	2	1	-	-	-	-	-	-	2	1	-	-	-	-	2	1
E968.9	Unspecified means	9	12	4	4	1	1	5	5	4	6	-	-	-	-	4	7
E970-E999	Other violence	27	13	3	2	2	2	5	4	6	4	-	-	14	4	22	9

Table 6 - *continued*

ICD number	Cause of Death	All ages 28 days to 15 years Boys	Girls	Months 1-5 Boys	Girls	6-11 Boys	Girls	1-11 Boys	Girls	Years 1-4 Boys	Girls	5-9 Boys	Girls	10-14 Boys	Girls	1-15 Boys	Girls
E980-E989	Injury undetermined whether accidentally or purposely inflicted	27	13	3	2	2	2	5	4	6	4	-	-	14	4	22	9
E980	Poisoning by solid or liquid substances, undetermined whether accidentally or purposely inflicted	1	6	-	-	-	-	-	-	-	1	-	-	1	4	1	6
E980.0	Analgesics, antipyretics and antirheumatics	-	1	-	-	-	-	-	-	-	1	-	-	-	-	-	1
E980.3	Tranquillizers and other psychotropic agents	-	1	-	-	-	-	-	-	-	-	-	-	-	1	-	1
E980.4	Other specified drugs and medicaments	1	3	-	-	-	-	-	-	-	-	-	-	1	2	1	3
E980.5	Unspecified drug or medicament	-	1	-	-	-	-	-	-	-	-	-	-	-	1	-	1
E983	Hanging, strangulation or suffocation, undetermined whether accidentally or purposely inflicted	11	-	-	-	-	-	-	-	-	-	-	-	10	-	11	-
E983.0	Hanging	11	-	-	-	-	-	-	-	-	-	-	-	10	-	11	-
E984	Submersion(drowning), undetermined whether accidentally or purposely inflicted	3	1	-	-	-	1	-	1	2	-	-	-	-	-	3	-
E988	Injury by other or unspecified means, undetermined whether accidentally or purposely inflicted	12	6	3	2	2	1	5	3	4	3	-	-	3	-	7	3
E988.8	Other specified means	6	4	-	1	1	1	1	2	3	2	-	-	2	-	5	2
E988.9	Unspecified means	6	2	3	1	1	-	4	1	1	1	-	-	1	-	2	1

Table 4 Stillbirths and neonatal deaths
Main and other fetal/infant causes by sex
Numbers of mentions, 1994

ICD number	Cause of Death		Stillbirths		Deaths 0-6 Days		1 week		2 weeks		3 weeks		All neonatal deaths	
			Boys	Girls	Boys	Girls	Boy	Girls	Boys	Girls	Boys	Girls	Boys	Girls
All babies			2,035	1,781	1,279	863	161	147	90	86	64	59	1,594	1,155
All main fetal/infant mentions			1,172	1,020	1,521	1,015	206	202	117	106	96	72	1,940	1,395
All other fetal/infant mentions			383	369	1,120	700	188	163	107	103	77	48	1,492	1,014
800-999	**XVII Injury and poisoning**	Main	-	-	2	1	1	2	2	1	1	1	6	5
		Other	-	-	2	7	-	2	1	3	-	2	3	14
850-854	Intracranial injury, excluding those with skull fracture	Main	-	-	-	-	-	1	1	-	-	-	1	1
		Other	-	-	-	-	-	1	-	-	-	-	-	1
854	Intracranial injury of other and unspecified nature	Main	-	-	-	-	-	1	1	-	-	-	1	1
		Other	-	-	-	-	-	1	-	-	-	-	-	1
870-897	Open wound	Main	-	-	-	-	-	1	-	1	1	-	1	2
		Other	-	-	-	1	-	1	1	3	-	-	1	5
870-879	Open wound of head, neck and trunk	Main	-	-	-	-	-	1	-	1	1	-	1	2
		Other	-	-	-	1	-	1	1	3	-	-	1	5
878	Open wound of genital organs (external), including traumatic amputation	Main	-	-	-	-	-	1	-	1	1	-	1	2
		Other	-	-	-	-	-	1	1	3	-	-	1	4
878.9	Other and unspecified parts, complicated	Main	-	-	-	-	-	1	-	1	1	-	1	2
		Other	-	-	-	-	-	1	1	3	-	-	1	4
879	Open wound of other and unspecified sites, except limbs	Main	-	-	-	-	-	-	-	-	-	-	-	-
		Other	-	-	-	1	-	-	-	-	-	-	-	1
879.8	Open wound(s) (multiple) of unspecified site(s) without mention of complication	Main	-	-	-	-	-	-	-	-	-	-	-	-
		Other	-	-	-	1	-	-	-	-	-	-	-	1
900-904	Injury to blood vessels	Main	-	-	-	-	-	-	-	-	-	-	-	-
		Other	-	-	-	1	-	-	-	-	-	-	-	1
904	Injury to blood vessels of lower extremity and unspecified sites	Main	-	-	-	-	-	-	-	-	-	-	-	-
		Other	-	-	-	1	-	-	-	-	-	-	-	1
904.0	Common femoral artery	Main	-	-	-	-	-	-	-	-	-	-	-	-
		Other	-	-	-	1	-	-	-	-	-	-	-	1
910-919	Superficial injury	Main	-	-	-	-	-	-	-	-	-	-	-	-
		Other	-	-	-	-	-	-	-	-	-	1	-	1
911	Superficial injury of trunk	Main	-	-	-	-	-	-	-	-	-	-	-	-
		Other	-	-	-	-	-	-	-	-	-	1	-	1
930-939	Effects of foreign body entering through orifice	Main	-	-	-	-	-	-	1	-	-	-	1	-
		Other	-	-	-	-	-	-	-	-	-	1	-	1
933	Foreign body in pharynx and larynx	Main	-	-	-	-	-	-	1	-	-	-	1	-
		Other	-	-	-	-	-	-	-	-	-	-	-	-
934	Foreign body in trachea, bronchus and lung	Main	-	-	-	-	-	-	-	-	-	-	-	-
		Other	-	-	-	-	-	-	-	-	-	1	-	1
990-995	Other and unspecified effects of external causes	Main	-	-	2	1	1	-	-	-	-	1	3	2
		Other	-	-	2	4	-	-	-	-	-	-	2	4

Table 4 - *continued*

ICD number	Cause of Death		Stillbirths		Deaths 0-6 Days		1 week		2 weeks		3 weeks		All neonatal deaths	
			Boys	Girls	Boys	Girls	Boys	Girls	Boys	Girls	Boys	Girls	**Boys**	**Girls**
994	Effects of other external causes	Main	-	-	2	1	1	-	-	-	-	1	**3**	**2**
		Other	-	-	2	4	-	-	-	-	-	-	**2**	**4**
994.7	Asphyxiation and strangulation	Main	-	-	-	-	1	-	-	-	-	1	**1**	**1**
		Other	-	-	-	2	-	-	-	-	-	-	**-**	**2**
994.9	Other	Main	-	-	2	1	-	-	-	-	-	-	**2**	**1**
		Other	-	-	2	2	-	-	-	-	-	-	**2**	**2**
996-999	Complications of surgical and medical care not elsewhere classified	Main	-	-	-	-	-	-	-	-	-	-	**-**	**-**
		Other	-	-	-	1	-	-	-	-	-	-	**-**	**1**
998	Other complications of procedures, not elsewhere classified	Main	-	-	-	-	-	-	-	-	-	-	**-**	**-**
		Other	-	-	-	1	-	-	-	-	-	-	**-**	**1**
998.2	Accidental puncture or laceration during a procedure	Main	-	-	-	-	-	-	-	-	-	-	**-**	**-**
		Other	-	-	-	1	-	-	-	-	-	-	**-**	**1**
E800-E999	**XVII External causes of injury and poisoning**	**Main**	-	-	1	1	3	2	1	-	1	2	**6**	**5**
		Other	-	-	4	7	1	2	-	1	1	-	**6**	**10**
E870-E879	Misadventures during medical care, abnormal reactions, late complications	Main	-	-	-	-	2	2	-	-	1	1	**3**	**3**
		Other	-	-	2	4	1	1	-	1	1	-	**4**	**6**
E870-E876	Misadventures to patients during surgical and medical care	Main	-	-	-	-	-	-	-	-	-	-	**-**	**-**
		Other	-	-	-	2	-	-	-	-	-	-	**-**	**2**
E870	Accidental cut, puncture, perforation or haemorrhage during medical care	Main	-	-	-	-	-	-	-	-	-	-	**-**	**-**
		Other	-	-	-	2	-	-	-	-	-	-	**-**	**2**
E878,E879	Surgical and medical procedures as the cause of abnormal reaction of patient or later complication, without mention of misadventure at the time of procedure	Main	-	-	-	-	2	2	-	-	1	1	**3**	**3**
		Other	-	-	2	2	1	1	-	1	1	-	**4**	**4**
E878	Surgical operation and other surgical procedures as the cause of abnormal reaction of patient, or of later complication, without mention of misadventure at the time of operation	Main	-	-	-	-	2	2	-	-	1	1	**3**	**3**
		Other	-	-	2	1	1	1	-	1	1	-	**4**	**3**
E879	Other procedures, without mention of misadventure at the time of procedure, as the cause of abnormal reaction of patient, or of later complication	Main	-	-	-	-	-	-	-	-	-	-	**-**	**-**
		Other	-	-	-	1	-	-	-	-	-	-	**-**	**1**

Table 4 - *continued*

ICD number	Cause of Death		Stillbirths		Deaths 0-6 Days		1 week		2 weeks		3 weeks		All neonatal deaths	
			Boys	Girls	Boys	Girls	Boy	Girls	Boys	Girls	Boys	Girls	Boys	Girls
E880-E888	Accidental falls	Main	-	-	-	-	-	-	-	-	-	-	-	-
		Other	-	-	-	-	-	1	-	-	-	-	-	1
E884	Other fall from one level to another	Main	-	-	-	-	-	-	-	-	-	-	-	-
		Other	-	-	-	-	-	1	-	-	-	-	-	1
E900-E929	Other accidents, including late effects	Main	-	-	1	1	1	-	1	-	-	1	3	2
		Other	-	-	2	3	-	-	-	-	-	-	2	3
E900-E909	Accidents due to natural and environmental factors	Main	-	-	1	1	-	-	-	-	-	-	1	1
		Other	-	-	2	1	-	-	-	-	-	-	2	1
E904	Hunger, thirst, exposure, neglect	Main	-	-	1	1	-	-	-	-	-	-	1	1
		Other	-	-	2	1	-	-	-	-	-	-	2	1
E911	Inhalation and ingestion of food causing obstruction of respiratory tract or suffocation	Main	-	-	-	-	-	-	1	-	-	-	1	-
		Other	-	-	-	-	-	-	-	-	-	-	-	-
E913	Accidental mechanical suffocation	Main	-	-	-	-	1	-	-	-	-	1	1	1
		Other	-	-	-	2	-	-	-	-	-	-	-	2
	Other main fetal/infant conditions		-	-	-	-	-	-	-	-	-	-	-	-
	Other other fetal/infant conditions		-	-	-	1	-	1	-	-	-	-	-	2

Main and other maternal causes by sex
Numbers of mentions, 1994

ICD number	Cause of Death		Stillbirths		Deaths 0-6 Days		1 week		2 weeks		3 weeks		All neonatal deaths	
			Boys	Girls	Boys	Girls	Boys	Girls	Boys	Girls	Boys	Girls	**Boys**	**Girls**
	All babies		**2,035**	**1,781**	**1,279**	**863**	**161**	**147**	**90**	**86**	**64**	**59**	**1,594**	**1,155**
	All main maternal mentions		**564**	**474**	**526**	**292**	**56**	**55**	**19**	**20**	**21**	**13**	**622**	**380**
	All other maternal mentions		**136**	**121**	**146**	**91**	**20**	**14**	**13**	**3**	**4**	**1**	**183**	**109**
800-999	**XVII Injury and poisoning**	**Main**	1	1	1	3	1	-	-	-	-	-	2	3
		Other	-	1	-	1	-	-	-	-	-	-	-	1
870-897	Open wound	Main	-	-	-	2	-	-	-	-	-	-	-	2
		Other	-	-	-	1	-	-	-	-	-	-	-	1
870-879	Open wound of head, neck and trunk	Main	-	-	-	2	-	-	-	-	-	-	-	2
		Other	-	-	-	1	-	-	-	-	-	-	-	1
878	Open wound of genital organs (external), including traumatic amputation	Main	-	-	-	2	-	-	-	-	-	-	-	2
		Other	-	-	-	1	-	-	-	-	-	-	-	1
878.9	Other and unspecified parts, complicated	Main	-	-	-	2	-	-	-	-	-	-	-	2
		Other	-	-	-	1	-	-	-	-	-	-	-	1
960-979	Poisoning by drugs, medicaments and biological substances	Main	1	1	-	1	1	-	-	-	-	-	1	1
		Other	-	1	-	-	-	-	-	-	-	-	-	-
964	Poisoning by agents primarily affecting blood constituents	Main	1	-	-	1	1	-	-	-	-	-	1	1
		Other	-	-	-	-	-	-	-	-	-	-	-	-
964.2	Anticoagulants	Main	1	-	-	1	1	-	-	-	-	-	1	1
		Other	-	-	-	-	-	-	-	-	-	-	-	-
967	Poisoning by sedatives and hypnotics	Main	-	-	-	-	-	-	-	-	-	-	-	-
		Other	-	1	-	-	-	-	-	-	-	-	-	-
967.0	Barbiturates	Main	-	-	-	-	-	-	-	-	-	-	-	-
		Other	-	1	-	-	-	-	-	-	-	-	-	-
977	Poisoning by other and unspecified drugs and medicaments	Main	-	1	-	-	-	-	-	-	-	-	-	-
		Other	-	-	-	-	-	-	-	-	-	-	-	-
977.9	Unspecified drug or medicament	Main	-	1	-	-	-	-	-	-	-	-	-	-
		Other	-	-	-	-	-	-	-	-	-	-	-	-
990-995	Other and unspecified effects of external causes	Main	-	-	1	-	-	-	-	-	-	-	1	-
		Other	-	-	-	-	-	-	-	-	-	-	-	-
995	Certain adverse effects not elsewhere classified	Main	-	-	1	-	-	-	-	-	-	-	1	-
		Other	-	-	-	-	-	-	-	-	-	-	-	-
995.2	Unspecified adverse effect of drug, medicament and biological	Main	-	-	1	-	-	-	-	-	-	-	1	-
		Other	-	-	-	-	-	-	-	-	-	-	-	-
E800-E999	**XVII External causes of injury and poisoning**	**Main**	3	2	1	-	-	-	-	-	-	-	1	-
		Other	2	2	-	-	1	-	-	-	-	-	1	-
E800-E848	Transport accidents	Main	3	-	-	-	-	-	-	-	-	-	-	-
		Other	1	-	-	-	-	-	-	-	-	-	-	-
E810-E819	Motor vehicle traffic accidents	Main	3	-	-	-	-	-	-	-	-	-	-	-
		Other	1	-	-	-	-	-	-	-	-	-	-	-
E819	Motor vehicle traffic accident of unspecified nature	Main	3	-	-	-	-	-	-	-	-	-	-	-
		Other	1	-	-	-	-	-	-	-	-	-	-	-

Table 5 - *continued*

ICD number	Cause of Death		Stillbirths		Deaths 0-6 Days		1 week		2 weeks		3 weeks		All neonatal deaths	
			Boys	Girls	Boys	Girls	Boys	Girls	Boys	Girls	Boys	Girls	Boys	Girls
E870-E879	Misadventures during medical care, abnormal reactions, late complications	Main	-	-	-	-	-	-	-	-	-	-	-	-
		Other	-	1	-	-	1	-	-	-	-	-	1	-
E878,E879	Surgical and medical procedures as the cause of abnormal reaction of patient or later complication, without mention of misadventure at the time of procedure	Main	-	-	-	-	-	-	-	-	-	-	-	-
		Other	-	1	-	-	1	-	-	-	-	-	1	-
E878	Surgical operation and other surgical procedures as the cause of abnormal reaction of patient, or of later complication, without mention of misadventure at the time of operation	Main	-	-	-	-	-	-	-	-	-	-	-	-
		Other	-	1	-	-	1	-	-	-	-	-	1	-
E880-E888	Accidental falls	Main	-	2	-	-	-	-	-	-	-	-	-	-
		Other	1	-	-	-	-	-	-	-	-	-	-	-
E888	Other and unspecified fall	Main	-	2	-	-	-	-	-	-	-	-	-	-
		Other	1	-	-	-	-	-	-	-	-	-	-	-
E938	Other central nervous system depressants	Main	-	-	1	-	-	-	-	-	-	-	1	-
		Other	-	-	-	-	-	-	-	-	-	-	-	-
E960-E969	Homicide and injury purposely inflicted by other persons	Main	-	-	-	-	-	-	-	-	-	-	-	-
		Other	-	1	-	-	-	-	-	-	-	-	-	-
E966	Assault by cutting and piercing instrument	Main	-	-	-	-	-	-	-	-	-	-	-	-
		Other	-	1	-	-	-	-	-	-	-	-	-	-
	Other main maternal conditions		-	-	-	-	-	-	-	-	-	-	-	-
	Other other maternal conditions		-	-	-	-	-	-	-	-	-	-	-	-

Table 6 Postneonatal and childhood deaths
Underlying cause of death by sex
Numbers, 1994

ICD number	Cause of Death	Age at death All ages 28 days to 15 years Boys	Girls	Months 1-5 Boys	Girls	6-11 Boys	Girls	1-11 Boys	Girls	Years 1-4 Boys	Girls	5-9 Boys	Girls	10-14 Boys	Girls	1-15 Boys	Girls
	All causes	1,924	1,396	569	410	212	180	781	590	432	364	278	187	331	204	1,143	806
800-999	**XVII Injury and poisoning**	391	223	21	14	12	16	33	30	98	76	92	40	120	62	358	193
800-829	Fractures	57	38	2	-	1	2	3	2	8	9	15	6	22	16	54	36
800-804	Fracture of skull	50	31	2	-	1	2	3	2	7	8	12	5	19	13	47	29
801	Fracture of base of skull	8	4	-	-	-	-	-	-	1	1	4	-	3	2	8	4
802	Fracture of face bones	-	1	-	-	-	-	-	-	-	-	-	-	-	1	-	1
803	Other and unqualified skull fractures	41	24	2	-	1	2	3	2	6	6	8	5	16	9	38	22
804	Multiple fractures involving skull or face with other bones	1	2	-	-	-	-	-	-	-	1	-	-	-	1	1	2
805-809	Fracture of neck and trunk	4	7	-	-	-	-	-	-	-	1	1	1	3	3	4	7
805	Fracture of vertebral column without mention of spinal cord lesion	4	5	-	-	-	-	-	-	-	1	1	1	3	2	4	5
808	Fracture of pelvis	-	2	-	-	-	-	-	-	-	-	-	-	-	1	-	2
810-819	Fracture of upper limb	1	-	-	-	-	-	-	-	-	-	1	-	-	-	1	-
814	Fracture of carpal bone(s)	1	-	-	-	-	-	-	-	-	-	1	-	-	-	1	-
820-829	Fracture of lower limb	2	-	-	-	-	-	-	-	1	-	1	-	-	-	2	-
820	Fracture of neck of femur	1	-	-	-	-	-	-	-	1	-	-	-	-	-	1	-
828	Multiple fractures involving both lower limbs, lower with upper limb, & lower limb(s) with rib(s) and sternum	1	-	-	-	-	-	-	-	-	-	1	-	-	-	1	-
850-854	Intracranial injury, excluding those with skull fracture	91	60	8	6	4	2	12	8	14	17	26	9	32	22	79	52
850	Concussion	-	1	-	-	-	-	-	-	-	1	-	-	-	-	-	1
851	Cerebral laceration and contusion	10	3	-	-	1	-	1	-	2	1	3	-	4	2	9	3
852	Subarachnoid, subdural and extradural haemorrhage, following injury	8	6	3	-	1	1	4	1	2	3	1	1	1	1	4	5
853	Other and unspecified intracranial haemorrhage following injury	4	1	1	-	-	-	1	-	-	1	1	-	1	-	3	1
854	Intracranial injury of other and unspecified nature	69	49	4	6	2	1	6	7	10	11	21	8	26	19	63	42
854.0	Without mention of open intracranial wound	-	1	-	-	-	-	-	-	-	-	-	-	-	-	-	1
860-869	Internal injury of chest, abdomen and pelvis	73	30	2	1	1	-	3	1	6	9	26	9	25	8	70	29
860	Traumatic pneumothorax and haemothorax	1	-	-	-	-	-	-	-	-	-	1	-	-	-	1	-
861	Injury to heart and lung	4	1	-	-	-	-	-	-	-	1	3	-	-	-	4	1
862	Injury to other and unspecified intrathoracic organs	3	2	-	1	-	-	-	1	1	-	1	-	-	1	3	1
863	Injury to gastrointestinal tract	-	1	-	-	-	-	-	-	-	-	-	-	-	1	-	1
864	Injury to liver	2	-	1	-	-	-	1	-	1	-	-	-	-	-	1	-
867	Injury to pelvic organs	1	-	-	-	-	-	-	-	-	-	-	-	1	-	1	-
868	Injury to other intraabdominal organs	2	-	-	-	-	-	-	-	-	-	1	-	-	-	2	-

Table 6 - *continued*

ICD number	Cause of Death	All ages 28 days to 15 years Boys	Girls	1-5 Boys	Girls	6-11 Boys	Girls	1-11 Boys	Girls	1-4 Boys	Girls	5-9 Boys	Girls	10-14 Boys	Girls	1-15 Boys	Girls
				Months						Years							
869	Internal injury to unspecified or ill-defined organs	60	26	1	-	1	-	2	-	4	8	20	9	24	6	58	26
869.0	Without mention of open wound into cavity	1	-	-	-	-	-	-	-	-	-	-	-	1	-	1	-
870-897	Open wound	3	4	-	-	-	-	-	-	-	1	-	1	2	1	3	4
870-879	Open wound of head, neck and trunk	3	4	-	-	-	-	-	-	-	1	-	1	2	1	3	4
873	Other open wound of head	2	1	-	-	-	-	-	-	-	-	-	-	2	-	2	1
875	Open wound of chest (wall)	1	1	-	-	-	-	-	-	-	-	-	1	-	-	1	1
879	Open wound of other and unspecified sites, except limbs	-	2	-	-	-	-	-	-	-	1	-	-	-	1	-	2
900-904	Injury to blood vessels	2	-	-	-	-	-	-	-	-	-	1	-	1	-	2	-
904	Injury to blood vessels of lower extremity and unspecified sites	2	-	-	-	-	-	-	-	-	-	1	-	1	-	2	-
904.2	Femoral veins	2	-	-	-	-	-	-	-	-	-	1	-	1	-	2	-
905-909	Late effects of injuries, poisonings, toxic effects and other external causes	2	1	-	-	-	-	-	-	1	1	-	-	1	-	2	1
907	Late effects of injuries to the nervous system	1	1	-	-	-	-	-	-	1	1	-	-	-	-	1	1
907.0	Late effect of intracranial injury without mention of skull fracture	1	1	-	-	-	-	-	-	1	1	-	-	-	-	1	1
908	Late effects of other and unspecified injuries	1	-	-	-	-	-	-	-	-	-	-	-	1	-	1	-
908.9	Late effect of unspecified injury	1	-	-	-	-	-	-	-	-	-	-	-	1	-	1	-
930-939	Effects of foreign body entering through orifice	20	13	5	3	2	3	7	6	8	5	3	2	2	-	13	7
933	Foreign body in pharynx and larynx	18	12	4	2	2	3	6	5	7	5	3	2	2	-	12	7
934	Foreign body in trachea, bronchus and lung	2	-	1	-	-	-	1	-	1	-	-	-	-	-	1	-
938	Foreign body in digestive system, unspecified	-	1	-	1	-	-	-	1	-	-	-	-	-	-	-	-
940-949	Burns	11	9	-	-	1	1	1	1	4	5	4	3	2	-	10	8
948	Burns classified according to extent of body surface involved	1	-	-	-	-	-	-	-	-	-	1	-	-	-	1	-
948.5	50-59%	1	-	-	-	-	-	-	-	-	-	1	-	-	-	1	-
949	Burn, unspecified	10	9	-	-	1	1	1	1	4	5	3	3	2	-	9	8
949.0	Unspecified degree	2	1	-	-	-	-	-	-	1	-	1	1	-	-	2	1
950-957	Injury to nerves and spinal cord	2	1	-	-	-	1	-	1	-	-	-	-	2	-	2	-
952	Spinal cord lesion without evidence of spinal bone injury	2	1	-	-	-	1	-	1	-	-	-	-	2	-	2	-
958-959	Certain traumatic complications and unspecified injuries	6	3	-	2	-	-	-	2	2	-	1	-	3	1	6	1
959	Injury, other and unspecified	6	3	-	2	-	-	-	2	2	-	1	-	3	1	6	1

Table 6 - *continued*

ICD number	Cause of Death	All ages 28 days to 15 years		Months 1-5		6-11		1-11		Years 1-4		5-9		10-14		1-15	
		Boys	Girls	Boys	Girls	Boys	Girls	Boys	Girls	Boys	Girls	Boys	Girls	Boys	Girls	Boys	Girls
959.8	Other specified sites, including multiple	3	1	-	-	-	-	-	-	-	-	1	-	2	1	3	1
959.9	Unspecified site	3	2	-	2	-	-	-	2	2	-	-	-	1	-	3	-
960-979	Poisoning by drugs, medicaments and biological substances	7	10	1	-	1	1	2	1	3	2	-	2	-	3	5	9
963	Poisoning by primarily systemic agents	1	-	-	-	-	-	-	-	1	-	-	-	-	-	1	-
963.1	Antineoplastic and immunosuppressive drugs	1	-	-	-	-	-	-	-	1	-	-	-	-	-	1	-
965	Poisoning by analgesics, antipyretics and antirheumatics	3	7	-	-	1	1	1	1	2	2	-	1	-	2	2	6
965.0	Opiates and related narcotics	1	2	-	-	-	1	-	1	1	1	-	-	-	-	1	1
965.4	Aromatic analgesics, not elsewhere classified	2	2	-	-	1	-	1	-	1	1	-	-	-	1	1	2
965.7	Other non-narcotic analgesics	-	3	-	-	-	-	-	-	-	-	-	1	-	1	-	3
969	Poisoning by psychotropic agents	1	2	-	-	-	-	-	-	-	-	-	1	-	1	1	2
969.0	Antidepressants	-	2	-	-	-	-	-	-	-	-	-	1	-	1	-	2
969.7	Psychostimulants	1	-	-	-	-	-	-	-	-	-	-	-	-	-	1	-
972	Poisoning by agents primarily affecting the cardiovascular system	1	-	1	-	-	-	1	-	-	-	-	-	-	-	-	-
972.4	Coronary vasodilators	1	-	1	-	-	-	1	-	-	-	-	-	-	-	-	-
977	Poisoning by other and unspecified drugs and medicaments	1	1	-	-	-	-	-	-	-	-	-	-	-	-	1	1
977.8	Other drugs and medicaments	1	1	-	-	-	-	-	-	-	-	-	-	-	-	1	1
980-989	Toxic effects of substances chiefly nonmedicinal as to source	29	26	-	1	-	-	-	1	21	16	5	5	-	4	29	25
986	Toxic effect of carbon monoxide	12	12	-	-	-	-	-	-	9	7	3	4	-	1	12	12
987	Toxic effect of other gases, fumes or vapours	15	14	-	1	-	-	-	1	12	9	2	1	-	3	15	13
987.1	Other hydrocarbon gas	1	-	-	-	-	-	-	-	-	-	-	-	-	-	1	-
987.8	Other	14	14	-	1	-	-	-	1	12	9	2	1	-	3	14	13
989	Toxic effect of other substances, chiefly nonmedicinal as to source	2	-	-	-	-	-	-	-	-	-	-	-	-	-	2	-
989.0	Hydrocyanic acid and cyanides	1	-	-	-	-	-	-	-	-	-	-	-	-	-	1	-
989.9	Unspecified	1	-	-	-	-	-	-	-	-	-	-	-	-	-	1	-
990-995	Other and unspecified effects of external causes	84	26	3	1	2	5	5	6	28	11	10	3	28	6	79	20
991	Effects of reduced temperature	1	-	1	-	-	-	1	-	-	-	-	-	-	-	-	-
991.6	Hypothermia	1	-	1	-	-	-	1	-	-	-	-	-	-	-	-	-
992	Effects of heat and light	-	1	-	-	-	-	-	-	-	1	-	-	-	-	-	1
992.0	Heat stroke and sunstroke	-	1	-	-	-	-	-	-	-	1	-	-	-	-	-	1
994	Effects of other external causes	83	24	2	1	2	5	4	6	28	9	10	3	28	6	79	18
994.0	Effects of lightning	-	1	-	-	-	-	-	-	-	1	-	-	-	-	-	1
994.1	Drowning and nonfatal submersion	30	10	1	-	1	2	2	2	20	5	4	2	2	1	28	8
994.7	Asphyxiation and strangulation	49	12	1	1	1	3	2	4	6	3	6	1	25	4	47	8
994.8	Electrocution and nonfatal effects of electric current	4	1	-	-	-	-	-	-	-	-	2	-	-	-	1	1	4	1
995	Certain adverse effects not elsewhere classified	-	1	-	-	-	-	-	-	-	1	-	-	-	-	-	1
995.5	Child maltreatment syndrome	-	1	-	-	-	-	-	-	-	1	-	-	-	-	-	1

149

Table 6 - *continued*

ICD number	Cause of Death	All ages 28 days to 15 years		Months 1-5		6-11		1-11		Years 1-4		5-9		10-14		1-15	
		Boys	Girls	Boys	Girls	Boys	Girls	Boys	Girls	Boys	Girls	Boys	Girls	Boys	Girls	Boys	Girls
996-999	Complications of surgical and medical care not elsewhere classified	4	2	-	-	-	1	-	1	3	-	1	-	-	1	4	1
997	Complications affecting specified body systems, not elsewhere classified	2	1	-	-	-	-	-	-	1	-	1	-	-	1	2	1
997.0	Central nervous system complications	1	1	-	-	-	-	-	-	-	-	1	-	-	1	1	1
997.3	Respiratory complications	1	-	-	-	-	-	-	-	1	-	-	-	-	-	1	-
998	Other complications of procedures, not elsewhere classified	2	1	-	-	-	1	-	1	2	-	-	-	-	-	2	-
998.1	Haemorrhage or haematoma complicating a procedure	1	-	-	-	-	-	-	-	1	-	-	-	-	-	1	-
998.2	Accidental puncture or laceration during a procedure	1	1	-	-	-	1	-	1	1	-	-	-	-	-	1	-
E800-E999	**XVII External causes of injury and poisoning**	**391**	**223**	**21**	**14**	**12**	**16**	**33**	**30**	**98**	**76**	**92**	**40**	**120**	**62**	**358**	**193**
E800-E848	Transport accidents	177	100	2	1	1	3	3	4	19	23	58	22	73	41	174	96
E800-E807	Railway accidents	5	-	-	-	-	-	-	-	1	-	1	-	3	-	5	-
E804	Fall in, on or from railway train	1	-	-	-	-	-	-	-	-	-	-	-	1	-	1	-
E804.1	Passenger on railway	1	-	-	-	-	-	-	-	-	-	-	-	1	-	1	-
E805	Hit by rolling stock	4	-	-	-	-	-	-	-	1	-	1	-	2	-	4	-
E805.2	Pedestrian	3	-	-	-	-	-	-	-	-	-	1	-	2	-	3	-
E805.9	Unspecified person	1	-	-	-	-	-	-	-	1	-	-	-	-	-	1	-
E810-E819	Motor vehicle traffic accidents	160	97	2	1	1	3	3	4	17	21	54	22	64	40	157	93
E812	Other motor vehicle traffic accident involving collision with another motor vehicle	24	17	1	1	1	2	2	3	4	5	7	5	8	2	22	14
E812.0	Driver of motor vehicle other than motorcycle	2	1	-	-	-	-	-	-	-	-	-	-	1	1	2	1
E812.1	Passenger in motor vehicle other than motorcycle	19	16	1	1	1	2	2	3	4	5	7	5	5	1	17	13
E812.2	Motorcyclist	2	-	-	-	-	-	-	-	-	-	-	-	1	-	2	-
E812.3	Passenger on motorcycle	1	-	-	-	-	-	-	-	-	-	-	-	1	-	1	-
E813	Motor vehicle traffic accident involving collision with other vehicle	27	7	-	-	-	-	-	-	-	1	9	1	11	5	27	7
E813.6	Pedal cyclist	27	7	-	-	-	-	-	-	-	1	9	1	11	5	27	7
E814	Motor vehicle traffic accident involving collision with pedestrian	85	55	-	-	-	1	-	1	11	15	31	12	35	22	85	54
E814.7	Pedestrian	85	55	-	-	-	1	-	1	11	15	31	12	35	22	85	54
E815	Other motor vehicle traffic accident involving collision on the highway	9	5	-	-	-	-	-	-	-	-	3	2	4	1	9	5
E815.0	Driver of motor vehicle other than motorcycle	1	-	-	-	-	-	-	-	-	-	-	-	-	-	1	-
E815.1	Passenger in motor vehicle other than motorcycle	6	5	-	-	-	-	-	-	-	-	3	2	2	1	6	5
E815.2	Motorcyclist	2	-	-	-	-	-	-	-	-	-	-	-	2	-	2	-
E816	Motor vehicle traffic accident due to loss of control, without collision on the highway	5	3	-	-	-	-	-	-	1	-	1	1	3	2	5	3

Table 6 - *continued*

ICD number	Cause of Death	All ages 28 days to 15 years		Months 1-5		6-11		1-11		Years 1-4		5-9		10-14		1-15	
		Boys	Girls	Boys	Girls	Boys	Girls	Boys	Girls	Boys	Girls	Boys	Girls	Boys	Girls	Boys	Girls
E816.1	Passenger in motor vehicle other than motorcycle	5	3	-	-	-	-	-	-	1	-	1	1	3	2	5	3
E819	Motor vehicle traffic accident of unspecified nature	10	10	1	-	-	-	1	-	1	-	3	1	3	8	9	10
E819.0	Driver of motor vehicle other than motorcycle	1	-	-	-	-	-	-	-	-	-	-	-	-	-	1	-
E819.1	Passenger in motor vehicle other than motorcycle	5	6	-	-	-	-	-	-	-	-	2	1	2	4	5	6
E819.9	Unspecified person	4	4	1	-	-	-	1	-	1	-	1	-	1	4	3	4
E820-E825	Motor vehicle nontraffic accidents	5	2	-	-	-	-	-	-	1	2	1	-	2	-	5	2
E821	Nontraffic accident involving other off-road motor vehicle	3	-	-	-	-	-	-	-	-	-	1	-	2	-	3	-
E821.0	Driver of motor vehicle other than motorcycle	1	-	-	-	-	-	-	-	-	-	1	-	-	-	1	-
E821.2	Motor cyclist	1	-	-	-	-	-	-	-	-	-	-	-	1	-	1	-
E821.9	Unspecified person	1	-	-	-	-	-	-	-	-	-	-	-	1	-	1	-
E822	Other motor vehicle nontraffic accident involving collision with moving object	1	2	-	-	-	-	-	-	1	2	-	-	-	-	1	2
E822.7	Pedestrian	-	2	-	-	-	-	-	-	-	2	-	-	-	-	-	2
E822.8	Other specified person	1	-	-	-	-	-	-	-	1	-	-	-	-	-	1	-
E825	Other motor vehicle nontraffic accident of other unspecified nature	1	-	-	-	-	-	-	-	-	-	-	-	-	-	1	-
E825.8	Other specified person	1	-	-	-	-	-	-	-	-	-	-	-	-	-	1	-
E826-E829	Other road vehicle accidents	5	-	-	-	-	-	-	-	-	-	1	-	3	-	5	-
E826	Pedal cycle accident	5	-	-	-	-	-	-	-	-	-	1	-	3	-	5	-
E826.1	Pedal cyclist	4	-	-	-	-	-	-	-	-	-	1	-	2	-	4	-
E826.2	Rider of animal	1	-	-	-	-	-	-	-	-	-	-	-	1	-	1	-
E830-E838	Water transport accidents	2	1	-	-	-	-	-	-	-	-	1	-	1	1	2	1
E831	Accident to watercraft causing other injury	2	1	-	-	-	-	-	-	-	-	1	-	1	1	2	1
E831.0	Occupant of small boat, unpowered	1	-	-	-	-	-	-	-	-	-	-	-	1	-	1	-
E831.1	Occupant of small boat, powered	-	1	-	-	-	-	-	-	-	-	-	-	-	1	-	1
E831.3	Occupant of other watercraft - other than crew	1	-	-	-	-	-	-	-	-	-	1	-	-	-	1	-
E850-E869	Accidental poisoning	7	6	1	-	1	-	2	-	2	2	-	1	-	1	5	6
E850-E858	Accidental poisoning by drugs, medicaments and biologicals	4	5	1	-	1	-	2	-	-	1	-	1	-	1	2	5
E850	Accidental poisoning by analgesics, antipyretics antirheumatics	1	3	-	-	1	-	1	-	-	1	-	1	-	1	-	3
E850.0	Opiates and related narcotics	-	2	-	-	-	-	-	-	-	1	-	-	-	1	-	2
E850.2	Aromatic analgesics, not elsewhere classified	1	-	-	-	1	-	1	-	-	-	-	-	-	-	-	-
E850.5	Other non-narcotic analgesics	-	1	-	-	-	-	-	-	-	-	-	-	-	1	-	1
E854	Accidental poisoning by other psychotropic agents	1	1	-	-	-	-	-	-	-	-	-	-	-	-	1	1

Table 6 - *continued*

ICD number	Cause of Death	All ages 28 days to 15 years		Months 1-5		6-11		1-11		Years 1-4		5-9		10-14		1-15	
		Boys	Girls	Boys	Girls	Boys	Girls	Boys	Girls	Boys	Girls	Boys	Girls	Boys	Girls	Boys	Girls
E854.0	Antidepressants	-	1	-	-	-	-	-	-	-	-	-	-	-	-	-	1
E854.2	Psychostimulants	1	-	-	-	-	-	-	-	-	-	-	-	-	-	1	-
E858	Accidental poisoning by other drugs	2	1	1	-	-	-	1	-	-	-	-	-	-	-	1	1
E858.3	Agents primarily affecting cardiovascular system	1	-	1	-	-	-	1		-	-	-	-	-	-	-	-
E858.8	Other	1	1	-	-	-	-	-	-	-	-	-	-	-	-	1	1
E860-E869	Accidental poisoning by other solid and liquid substances, gases and vapours	3	1	-	-	-	-	-	-	2	1	-	-	-	-	3	1
E867	Accidental poisoning by gas distributed by pipeline	1	1	-	-	-	-	-	-	1	1	-	-	-	-	1	1
E868	Accidental poisoning by other utility gas and other carbon monoxide	2	-	-	-	-	-	-	-	1	-	-	-	-	-	2	-
E868.9	Unspecified carbon monoxide	2	-	-	-	-	-	-	-	1	-	-	-	-	-	2	-
E870-E879	Misadventures during medical care, abnormal reactions, late complications	4	2	-	-	-	1	-	1	3	-	1	-	-	1	4	1
E870-E876	Misadventures to patients during surgical and medical care	1	1	-	-	-	1	-	1	1	-	-	-	-	-	1	-
E870	Accidental cut, puncture, perforation or haemorrhage during medical care	1	1	-	-	-	1	-	1	1	-	-	-	-	-	1	-
E870.0	Surgical operation	1	1	-	-	-	1	-	1	1	-	-	-	-	-	1	-
E878	Surgical operation and other surgical procedures as the cause of abnormal reaction of patient, or of later complication, without mention of misadventure at the time of operation	3	1	-	-	-	-	-	-	2	-	1	-	-	1	3	1
E878.6	Removal of other organ (partial) (total)	1	-	-	-	-	-	-	-	1	-	-	-	-	-	1	-
E878.8	Other	1	1	-	-	-	-	-	-	-	-	1	-	-	1	1	1
E878.9	Unspecified	1	-	-	-	-	-	-	-	1	-	-	-	-	-	1	-
E880-E888	Accidental falls	17	5	1	1	-	-	1	1	4	3	4	-	5	1	16	4
E880	Fall on or from stairs or steps	4	1	-	-	-	-	-	-	2	1	1	-	-	-	4	1
E880.9	Other stairs or steps	4	1	-	-	-	-	-	-	2	1	1	-	-	-	4	1
E882	Fall from or out of building or other structure	6	1	-	-	-	-	-	-	1	-	2	-	2	1	6	1
E884	Other fall from one level to another	5	2	1	1	-	-	1	1	-	1	1	-	2	-	4	1
E884.9	Other fall from one level to another	5	2	1	1	-	-	1	1	-	1	1	-	2	-	4	1
E887	Fracture, cause unspecified	1	1	-	-	-	-	-	-	1	1	-	-	-	-	1	1
E888	Other and unspecified fall	1	-	-	-	-	-	-	-	-	-	-	-	1	-	1	-
E890-E899	Accidents caused by fire and flames	22	18	-	1	1	1	1	2	15	11	5	2	1	3	21	16
E890	Conflagration in private dwelling	17	12	-	1	1	1	1	2	11	7	4	2	1	1	16	10
E890.2	Other smoke and fumes from conflagration	13	10	-	1	-	-	-	1	10	7	3	1	-	1	13	9
E890.3	Burning caused by conflagration	4	2	-	-	1	1	1	1	1	-	1	1	1	-	3	1

Table 6 - *continued*

ICD number	Cause of Death	All ages 28 days to 15 years		Months 1-5		6-11		1-11		Years 1-4		5-9		10-14		1-15	
		Boys	Girls	Boys	Girls	Boys	Girls	Boys	Girls	Boys	Girls	Boys	Girls	Boys	Girls	Boys	Girls
E894	Ignition of highly inflammable material	-	1	-	-	-	-	-	-	-	-	-	-	-	1	-	1
E898	Accident caused by other specified fire and flames	5	5	-	-	-	-	-	-	4	4	1	-	-	1	5	5
E898.0	Burning bedclothes	-	1	-	-	-	-	-	-	-	1	-	-	-	-	-	1
E898.1	Other	5	4	-	-	-	-	-	-	4	3	1	-	-	1	5	4
E900-E929	Other accidents, including late effects	106	35	8	4	7	5	15	9	42	17	17	6	27	2	91	26
E900-E909	Accidents due to natural and environmental factors	3	3	1	-	1	-	2	-	1	2	-	-	-	1	1	3
E900	Excessive heat	1	1	-	-	-	-	-	-	1	1	-	-	-	-	1	1
E900.0	Due to weather conditions	1	1	-	-	-	-	-	-	1	1	-	-	-	-	1	1
E901	Excessive cold	1	-	1	-	-	-	1	-	-	-	-	-	-	-	-	-
E901.9	Of unspecified origin	1	-	1	-	-	-	1	-	-	-	-	-	-	-	-	-
E906	Other injury caused by animals	1	1	-	-	1	-	1	-	-	-	-	-	-	1	-	1
E906.0	Dog bite	1	-	-	-	1	-	1	-	-	-	-	-	-	-	-	-
E906.8	Other specified injury caused by animal	-	1	-	-	-	-	-	-	-	-	-	-	-	1	-	1
E907	Lightning	-	1	-	-	-	-	-	-	-	1	-	-	-	-	-	1
E910	Accidental drowning and submersion	29	8	-	-	1	1	1	1	20	5	5	2	1	-	28	7
E910.2	While engaged in other sport or recreational activity without diving equipment	4	1	-	-	-	-	-	-	1	1	1	-	1	-	4	1
E910.4	In bathtub	6	1	-	-	1	1	1	1	5	-	-	-	-	-	5	-
E910.8	Other	8	2	-	-	-	-	-	-	6	1	1	1	-	-	8	2
E910.9	Unspecified	11	4	-	-	-	-	-	-	8	3	3	1	-	-	11	4
E911	Inhalation and ingestion of food causing obstruction of respiratory tract or suffocation	13	8	2	1	2	2	4	3	8	3	-	2	1	-	9	5
E912	Inhalation and ingestion of other object causing obstruction of respiratory tract or suffocation	7	5	3	2	-	1	3	3	-	2	3	-	1	-	4	2
E913	Accidental mechanical suffocation	25	2	1	-	1	1	2	1	3	1	3	-	15	-	23	1
E913.0	In bed or cradle	3	2	-	-	1	1	1	1	2	1	-	-	-	-	2	1
E913.1	By plastic bag	1	-	-	-	-	-	-	-	-	-	-	-	-	-	1	-
E913.3	By falling earth or other substance	1	-	-	-	-	-	-	-	-	-	-	-	1	-	1	-
E913.8	Other specified means	19	-	-	-	-	-	-	-	1	-	3	-	14	-	19	-
E913.9	Unspecified	1	-	1	-	-	-	1	-	-	-	-	-	-	-	-	-
E916-E928	Other accidents	27	8	1	1	2	-	3	1	9	3	6	2	8	1	24	7
E916	Struck accidentally by falling object	6	-	-	-	-	-	-	-	2	-	2	-	2	-	6	-
E917	Striking against or struck accidentally by objects or persons	2	-	-	-	1	-	1	-	-	-	1	-	-	-	1	-
E917.9	Other	2	-	-	-	1	-	1	-	-	-	1	-	-	-	1	-
E919	Accidents caused by machinery	2	2	-	-	-	-	-	-	1	1	-	-	1	-	2	2
E919.0	Agricultural machines	-	1	-	-	-	-	-	-	-	1	-	-	-	-	-	1
E919.2	Lifting machines and appliances	1	-	-	-	-	-	-	-	1	-	-	-	-	-	1	-
E919.8	Other	1	1	-	-	-	-	-	-	-	-	-	-	1	-	1	1
E921	Accident caused by explosion of pressure level	1	-	-	-	-	-	-	-	-	-	1	-	-	-	1	-
E921.8	Other	1	-	-	-	-	-	-	-	-	-	1	-	-	-	1	-

Table 6 - *continued*

ICD number	Cause of Death	All ages 28 days to 15 years		Months 1-5		6-11		1-11		Years 1-4		5-9		10-14		1-15	
		Boys	Girls	Boys	Girls	Boys	Girls	Boys	Girls	Boys	Girls	Boys	Girls	Boys	Girls	Boys	Girls
E922	Accident caused by firearm missile	2	-	-	-	-	-	-	-	-	-	-	-	2	-	2	-
E922.1	Shotgun (automatic)	1	-	-	-	-	-	-	-	-	-	-	-	1	-	1	-
E922.8	Other	1	-	-	-	-	-	-	-	-	-	-	-	1	-	1	-
E924	Accident caused by hot substance or object, caustic or corrosive material and steam	3	-	-	-	-	-	-	-	2	-	1	-	-	-	3	-
E924.0	Hot liquids and vapours, including steam	3	-	-	-	-	-	-	-	2	-	1	-	-	-	3	-
E925	Accident caused by electric current	4	1	-	-	-	-	-	-	2	-	-	-	1	1	4	1
E925.0	Domestic wiring and appliances	3	-	-	-	-	-	-	-	2	-	-	-	-	-	3	-
E925.8	Other	1	1	-	-	-	-	-	-	-	-	-	-	1	1	1	1
E928	Other and unspecified environmental and accidental causes	7	5	1	1	1	-	2	1	2	2	1	2	2	-	5	4
E928.8	Other	-	1	-	1	-	-	-	1	-	-	-	-	-	-	-	-
E928.9	Unspecified accidents	7	4	1	-	1	-	2	-	2	2	1	2	2	-	5	4
E929	Late effects of accidental injury	2	1	-	-	-	-	-	-	1	1	-	-	1	-	2	1
E929.0	Late effects of motor vehicle accident	1	1	-	-	-	-	-	-	-	1	-	-	1	-	1	1
E929.9	Late effects of unspecified accident	1	-	-	-	-	-	-	-	1	-	-	-	-	-	1	-
E933	Primarily systemic agents	1	-	-	-	-	-	-	-	1	-	-	-	-	-	1	-
E933.1	Antineoplastic and immunosuppressive drugs	1	-	-	-	-	-	-	-	1	-	-	-	-	-	1	-
E950-E959	Suicide and selfinflicted injury	8	2	-	-	-	-	-	-	-	-	-	-	5	2	8	2
E950	Suicide and selfinflicted poisoning by solid or liquid substances	1	-	-	-	-	-	-	-	-	-	-	-	-	-	1	-
E950.9	Other and unspecified solid and liquid substances	1	-	-	-	-	-	-	-	-	-	-	-	-	-	1	-
E953	Suicide and selfinflicted injury by hanging, strangulation and suffocation	4	1	-	-	-	-	-	-	-	-	-	-	2	1	4	1
E953.0	Hanging	4	1	-	-	-	-	-	-	-	-	-	-	2	1	4	1
E955	Suicide and selfinflicted injury by firearms and explosives	1	-	-	-	-	-	-	-	-	-	-	-	1	-	1	-
E955.1	Shot gun	1	-	-	-	-	-	-	-	-	-	-	-	1	-	1	-
E958	Suicide and selfinflicted injury by other and unspecified means	2	1	-	-	-	-	-	-	-	-	-	-	2	1	2	1
E958.4	Electrocution	1	-	-	-	-	-	-	-	-	-	-	-	1	-	1	-
E958.9	Unspecified means	1	1	-	-	-	-	-	-	-	-	-	-	1	1	1	1
E960-E969	Homicide and injury purposely inflicted by other persons	14	35	1	6	2	4	3	10	5	14	4	6	1	4	11	25
E962	Assault by poisoning	3	5	-	-	-	-	-	-	2	1	1	3	-	1	3	5
E962.0	Drugs and medicaments	-	1	-	-	-	-	-	-	-	-	-	-	-	1	-	1
E962.2	Other gases and vapours	3	4	-	-	-	-	-	-	2	1	1	3	-	-	3	4
E963	Assault by hanging and strangulation	3	6	-	-	-	2	-	2	2	2	1	1	-	1	3	4
E964	Assault by submersion (drowning)	1	-	1	-	-	-	1	-	-	-	-	-	-	-	-	-

154

Table 6 - *continued*

ICD number	Cause of Death	All ages 28 days to 15 years Boys	Girls	Months 1-5 Boys	Girls	6-11 Boys	Girls	1-11 Boys	Girls	Years 1-4 Boys	Girls	5-9 Boys	Girls	10-14 Boys	Girls	1-15 Boys	Girls
E965	Assault by firearms and explosives	-	1	-	-	-	-	-	-	-	-	-	-	-	-	-	1
E965.4	Other and unspecified firearm	-	1	-	-	-	-	-	-	-	-	-	-	-	-	-	1
E966	Assault by cutting and piercing instrument	1	1	-	-	-	-	-	-	-	-	-	1	-	-	1	1
E967	Child battering and other maltreatment	2	4	-	2	1	-	1	2	-	1	1	-	-	1	1	2
E967.9	By unspecified person	2	4	-	2	1	-	1	2	-	1	1	-	-	1	1	2
E968	Assault by other and unspecified means	4	17	-	4	1	2	1	6	1	10	1	1	1	-	3	11
E968.0	Fire	2	8	-	-	-	-	-	-	1	7	1	1	-	-	2	8
E968.8	Other specified means	-	1	-	-	-	-	-	-	-	1	-	-	-	-	-	1
E968.9	Unspecified means	2	8	-	4	1	2	1	6	-	2	-	-	1	-	1	2
E969	Late effects of injury purposely inflicted by other person	-	1	-	-	-	-	-	-	-	-	-	-	-	1	-	1
E970-E999	Other violence	35	20	8	1	-	2	8	3	7	6	3	3	8	7	27	17
E980-E989	Injury undetermined whether accidentally or purposely inflicted	35	20	8	1	-	2	8	3	7	6	3	3	8	7	27	17
E980	Poisoning by solid or liquid substances, undetermined whether accidentally or purposely inflicted	3	3	-	-	-	-	-	-	2	-	-	1	-	1	3	3
E980.0	Analgesics, antipyretics and antirheumatics	2	2	-	-	-	-	-	-	2	-	-	-	-	1	2	2
E980.3	Tranquillizers and other psychotropic agents	-	1	-	-	-	-	-	-	-	-	-	1	-	-	-	1
E980.9	Other and unspecified solid and liquid substances	1	-	-	-	-	-	-	-	-	-	-	-	-	-	1	-
E982	Poisoning by other gases, undetermined whether accidentally or purposely inflicted	-	1	-	-	-	-	-	-	-	1	-	-	-	-	-	1
E982.8	Other specified gases and vapours	-	1	-	-	-	-	-	-	-	1	-	-	-	-	-	1
E983	Hanging, strangulation or suffocation, undetermined whether accidentally or purposely inflicted	12	2	-	-	-	-	-	-	-	-	-	-	8	2	12	2
E983.0	Hanging	11	2	-	-	-	-	-	-	-	-	-	-	8	2	11	2
E983.9	Unspecified means	1	-	-	-	-	-	-	-	-	-	-	-	-	-	1	-
E984	Submersion(drowning), undetermined whether accidentally or purposely inflicted	1	1	-	-	-	1	-	1	-	-	1	-	-	-	1	-
E988	Injury by other or unspecified means, undetermined whether accidentally or purposely inflicted	19	13	8	1	-	1	8	2	5	5	2	2	-	4	11	11
E988.1	Burns, fire	1	1	-	-	-	-	-	-	1	-	-	1	-	-	1	1
E988.8	Other specified means	16	9	6	1	-	1	6	2	4	4	2	1	-	2	10	7
E988.9	Unspecified means	2	3	2	-	-	-	2	-	-	1	-	-	-	2	-	3